BACKGROUND TO
SET AND GROUP THEORY

Other books by D. E. Mansfield

MATHEMATICS: A NEW APPROACH

Pupils' Books 1, 2 & 3
Teachers' Books 1, 2 & 3
(*with D. Thompson*)

❖

Pupils' Books 4 & 5
Teachers' Books 4 & 5
(*with M. Bruckheimer*)

BACKGROUND TO SET AND GROUP THEORY

*Including applications in the
teaching of mathematics*

D. E. MANSFIELD

*Nuffield Mathematics Project
Formerly Head of Mathematics Department
Holloway School*

M. BRUCKHEIMER, Ph.D.

Northampton College of Advanced Technology, London

WITH A FOREWORD BY
W. H. COCKCROFT

Professor of Mathematics, University of Hull

1965
CHATTO AND WINDUS
LONDON

Published by
Chatto & Windus (Educational) Ltd
42 William IV Street
London W.C.2

❖

Clarke, Irwin & Co Ltd
Toronto

Printed in Great Britain by
Butler & Tanner Ltd
Frome and London

CONTENTS

Foreword by Professor W. H. Cockcroft   *page* 6

List of symbols   7

Chapter

  1 Introduction   9

  2 Sets   18

  3 Equivalence Relations   40

  4 Mappings   53

  5 Cardinals   67

  6 Groups   84

  7 Exercises   102

  8 Isomorphisms   119

  9 Matrices   136

 10 Homomorphisms   158

 11 Consequences   180

 12 Geometry   201

 13 Extensions   229

Index   248

FOREWORD

By Professor W. H. Cockcroft

SYLLABUS reform in Great Britain cannot be achieved in our schools without the willing and whole-hearted co-operation of the teaching profession. The willingness of a growing minority of mathematics teachers to consider the new syllabi has already been shown by the demand for the new text-books which have appeared in the last few years. But when, as at present, radical reforms are proposed, it is surely essential for the well-being of our school children that our mathematical teachers should not only be able to see examples of school texts incorporating new material, but that they should be able to find texts written to enable them to make a proper judgement of the mathematical content of these new courses before embarking upon them in the classroom.

D. E. Mansfield already has to his credit the school texts, based on tested classroom material, written in collaboration with D. Thompson: they were, of course, pioneers in this field. With his present co-author, Mansfield now offers a working text for the teacher; again they are among the leaders in attempting to fill an obvious gap.

A word of warning: *This is a working text.* If you wish to proceed, therefore, take out your paper and sharpen your pencils! With your co-operation it could help you towards a position which our system implicitly offers to every teacher—that of the independent professional, designing his or her own syllabus, not dictated to by any outside authority, examining or otherwise.

There are many advanced texts on set theory and group theory, but most are written for the academically committed mathematician. Mansfield and Bruckheimer have not made this assumption about their readers; they have tried always to bear in mind the kind of question which would arise in the mind of the teacher when faced with new ideas. There are hints in plenty for classroom use, but there are also many asides which have been incorporated simply because the authors have tried to approach their advanced material as teachers looking on the subject anew and facing learning difficulties themselves.

The authors offer you the results of their own efforts and thought on this new material. I wish them, and you the reader, every success in this effort.

LIST OF SYMBOLS

$A = B$	A is the same set as B	*page* 20
$A \subset B$	A is properly contained in B	21
$A \subseteq B$	A is contained in B	21
$A \cup B$	union of A and B	22
$A \cap B$	intersection of A and B	24
$\emptyset$	the null (or empty) set	24
$A \neq B$	A is not the same set as B	27
$A \sim B$	set of elements of A which are not elements of B	28
$A \triangle B$	symmetric difference of A and B	29
$(x; 2 < x < 3)$	set notation for set of all real values of x such that $2 < x < 3$	31
o	general binary operation	36
$A \times B$	direct product of A with B	37
$A \triangledown B$	ditto	37
$\triangledown ABC$	set of ordered triples	37
$T:A$	topology for A	38
$(A, T:A)$	topological space	38
$\{a\}$	equivalence class containing a	40
$a \in A$	a is an element of A	41
$a \equiv b(\text{mod } n)$	a is equivalent to b modulo n	45
f	inverse mapping of f	54
(S, o)	set S with binary operation o	63
$a \Rightarrow b$	a implies b	69
$a \Leftrightarrow b$	a implies and is implied by b	69
$n(A)$	cardinal number associated with A	71
$\aleph_0$	aleph 0	76
$\aleph$	aleph	80
$\tilde{a}$	inverse element of a	90
(G, o)	group	91
$\tilde{f}$	inverse mapping of f	101
S_i	section of a braid	116
$\begin{pmatrix} a & b \\ c & d \end{pmatrix}$	2×2 matrix	122
$\begin{pmatrix} x \\ y \end{pmatrix}$	column vector of the point (x, y)	124
M	set of all 2×2 matrices	140

M'	set of invertible 2×2 matrices	143
v	vector	148
O_2	orthogonal group of 2×2 matrices	151
R_1	the set of real numbers x such that $0 \leqslant x \leqslant 1$	153
e_G	neutral element in group G	160
e_H	neutral element in group H	160
gK	left coset of K	167
G/K	factor group of left cosets of K	167
$f \sim g$	path f homotopic to path g	177
P_x	set of closed paths to x	177
P'_x	equivalence classes of closed paths to x	177
D_8	dihedral group of order 8	184, 189
S_2	similarity group of 2×2 matrices	185
$\chi(A)$	chi(A), character of matrix A	191
$\begin{pmatrix} 1 & 2 & \ldots & n \\ x_1 & x_2 & \ldots & x_n \end{pmatrix}$	permutation of n objects	193
P_n	symmetric group of degree n	194
A_n	alternating group of degree n	196
$(G, \mathrm{o}, T{:}G)$	topological group	226
$_0 g$	additive neutral element in a field	231
$_1 g$	multiplicative neutral element in a field	231
$\tilde{g}$	additive inverse of g	231
$\underset{\sim}{g}$	multiplicative inverse of g	231
$^r f$	$f + f + f \ldots$ (to r terms)	237
	$^r f$ notation extended	238
L_g	left translation by g	245
R_g	right translation by g	245

CHAPTER 1

INTRODUCTION

THE Preface to a book is usually skipped by most readers. We think that a book of this sort needs explanation, and have therefore written the explanation, not in the Preface, but in Chapter 1. We need to make it clear to the potential reader what the purpose of this book is, and we also wish to justify it and give a sufficiently broad outline of its contents to allow the reader to see the book as a whole.

Mathematics, at all levels, is changing rapidly, both in content and in approach and attitude. This book has been written for teachers and lecturers who have to cope with the changing teaching situation; nevertheless, it is not a teaching book: it attempts to present the reader with an outline of the changed situation and attitude in a central area of the subject, and to show, implicitly and by results, the justification for the change.

The following quotation from Klein's book, *Geometry: elementary mathematics from an advanced standpoint* (Dover), written nearly sixty years ago, is as significant now as it was then: 'Too often I have had the experience that, while students acquired facility with the formulas, which are so useful in abbreviating long expressions, they often failed to gain familiarity with their *meaning*, and skill in manipulation prevented the student from going into all the details of the subject and so gaining a mastery.'

Skill in manipulation is certainly not enough, although for a long time we have taught as if it were: we want our students to *understand* what they are doing, if only in order that they shall cease from making foolish mistakes, the foolishness of which we have difficulty in getting them to grasp. Such mistakes very often arise from a lack of background in the student (and, perhaps, in the teacher?). This book is an attempt to provide some of that background, for we think that the very word 'understand', italicized above, means 'fit into a pre-existing background of ideas'.

Without some more or less coherent and unified background grasp of the basic ideas of the subject (so far as one knows it), no single part of it can be, in any proper sense, understood, for the part cannot be fitted into the whole. Of course, one does not

9

begin to study a subject with one's background in it fully formed: one builds up the background as one goes along. But it is this very process of building up the appropriate background that we have so neglected in our teaching: we have tended to pile up techniques without bothering to show the relation of one to another, or the relation of each to the basic ideas.

The fact seems to be that the number of important basic ideas in mathematics is very small, while the number of special techniques, each of which unfortunately can be 'drilled' home as a separate entity, is very large. This book is an attempt to explain some of the basic ideas and to indicate, mainly by means of examples and exercises, the relation to them of some of the well-known techniques.

It is this sort of relation which is sometimes loosely referred to by the word 'structure'. This word is freely bandied about nowadays, particularly in descriptions of modernized syllabuses. We prefer to use 'structure' rather precisely, to mean relations between the elements and operations of a set (see, for instance, the passage quoted on page 225, Chapter 12). This definition may well mean very little at present, for the idea of structure in this sense is one of the things so disastrously omitted from our teaching. The best way to grasp its meaning is to undertake a serious and active study (involving the solution and construction of problems and examples) of some particular structure, e.g. groups. To use the word 'structure' as loosely as is sometimes done is to pay lip service to a crucial idea: worse, it leads to the misplaced self-satisfaction sometimes shown by people who use the word in this sense but who teach no worthwhile grasp of structure at all.

It is convenient here to explain the distinction which we make between examples and exercises. Both are printed in smaller type than the main text as are some occasional notes.

The **examples** are lettered in alphabetical sequence throughout each chapter: they are intended to illustrate and illuminate the text and are, on the whole, essential to a proper understanding of the text. The reader is very strongly recommended to do his best to read them, to work them out, or to prove them as appropriate. The results obtained in the examples are sometimes used later in the text. Some, but by no means all, of the examples are of direct use in the teaching situation.

On the other hand, the material of the **exercises** is not usually required in the text (except in a few cases, which are specifically mentioned). The exercises are intended as further illustrations of the text, and, in particular, show some of the possible applications of the text *in the teaching situation*. The reader will not, of course, expect to find in these exercises a comprehensive teaching scheme: what he will find are merely miscellaneous illustrations. For a teaching scheme the reader should go to a teaching text (e.g. *Mathematics: A New Approach*, Books 1, 2 and 3, by Mansfield and Thompson, Books 4 and 5 by Mansfield and Bruckheimer (Chatto and Windus)) or, better, make his own. The exercises are numbered sequentially in each batch.

Since the examples and exercises frequently demonstrate a relation between a well-known technique and the basic ideas of the text, it follows that they will contain techniques and subject matter which have not yet been met in the text (or, in fact, may never be introduced in the text) and some few of them may make considerable demands upon the skill of the reader in these techniques. This should cause no difficulty: the main text is in sequence. It follows also that the examples and exercises are not 'in order of difficulty' (whatever this means).

While on the subject of 'difficulty', we would mention that there is a topological section at the end of each chapter. Topology is a 'difficult' subject in the sense that it is at present lacking in enough elementary examples of anything resembling a rigorous kind. Nevertheless, it is a subject with which one should try to come to grips since it lies at the centre of much modern mathematics. It is another subject whose language is that of 'algebraic' structure: its subject matter is 'topological' structure and there may be an interaction between the two types of structure as we explain at the end of Chapters 12 and 13. The fact that we use algebraic structure in our topological investigations has motivated our choice of topological ideas: as far as possible, we have chosen the topological topic in each chapter to match the ideas dealt with in the main part of that chapter, so that many of the 'easier' topics in topology have been omitted. Because of all this, the topological sections are often quite demanding. For this reason care has been taken to ensure that although the topology depends on the rest of the book, the rest of the book is entirely independent of the topological sections. Nevertheless, we hope that some readers will be encouraged to introduce some of the subject into their courses and that they will invent their own, more appropriate, teaching exercises. Slowly the subject must come within the normal teaching syllabus.

With the possible exception of the topological sections, it is felt that the text should be well within the scope of any teacher of mathematics: if he has not taught at or above G.C.E. O level he may find some of the examples difficult, but he should nevertheless be able to manage enough of them to serve the purpose.

In most chapters, and for most topics, the approach chosen has been that of a loose, intuitive, informal establishment of the background for the ideas to come: once the concepts have had time to form then they are defined precisely and a little formal development is given. We have tried to avoid the unmotivated 'Theorem-Proof' type of exposition as far as possible, for except for the sophisticated this form is not very effective in the teaching situation. We prefer the 'probe and explore, verify and advance' technique, where the results follow, rather than precede, the investigation.

It is perhaps proper to mention here that we have tried to apply the same ideas to such things as the choice of defining properties for particular structures. After all, we have some freedom: we can choose any consistent set of axioms, and we can sometimes incorporate into the axioms some statements which are usually theorems if this makes the structure seem more immediately sensible and effective. The reader should not suppose that the economy and elegance which he finds attractive is necessarily the best approach for pupils.

Lastly, we use the mathematically sinful words 'clearly' and 'obviously' with considerable abandon, for in much of the book no attempt at rigour is made. Worse, we use these words in two quite different senses; sometimes to mean that the statement is intuitively 'self-evident' (and we hope that what this means, if anything, will not be the subject of correspondence!); on other occasions we use the same words to mean that the proof of the statement is trivial.

*   *   *   *   *

We now present a short summary of the main contents of each chapter: we shall indicate the scope and the interconnection between the major topics: no attempt has been made to list all the topics covered; all we try to do is give an overall picture.

The mathematical ideas introduced in Chapters 2, 3 and 4 are the fundamental language in terms of which we create our structure.

Chapter 2. The basic concept is undoubtedly that of a *set*, for without a set of objects we have nothing to discuss. So the chapter begins by introducing the elementary points one can discuss given a set (or sets) of objects, e.g. the *relations* of the *equality* of sets and *inclusion* of one set in another. Then we consider the formation of new sets from given sets, e.g. the *combination operations* of *union* and *intersection* of sets. In introducing these basic definitions we investigate the fundamental properties of relations and combination operations. The brief discussion of the possible properties of a relation prepares the ground for the details of Chapter 3: the corresponding discussion of operations is not specifically mentioned again in a separate chapter, but constant use is made of it throughout the book. There are a large number of elementary 'teaching' exercises and, in fact, the whole chapter can be regarded as basic teaching material. The topological section defines a *topological space* in the terms introduced in the chapter and a few elementary examples are given.

Chapter 3. We are next interested in the problem of *classification* of objects in a set. The word 'same' as applied to objects depends for its use on the purpose to which the objects are being put. 'All monkeys look the same to me': you tell that to a monkey! We introduce the idea of an *equivalence relation* on a set of objects which gives a precise mathematical context to the discussion. It is remarkable how often an equivalence relation is implicit in any particular field of mathematics where the words 'convention' and 'representative' are used: we give a few of the many elementary examples scattered about mathematics, indicating the unification and improvements in definition possible. One may be able to combine the objects of a set (say, the integers under addition) and one may also wish to classify them (say, the integers into two classes, where all even numbers are the 'same' and all odd numbers are the 'same'). Can we induce a 'sensible' combination operation onto the set of classes of equivalent elements (e.g. does 'even + odd' mean anything)? We answer questions of this sort by discussing the *compatibility* of the operation and the relation. The topological section is concerned with the induction of a topology on to a set of equivalence classes.

Chapter 4. Having obtained sets and classification of their contents we now seek relations between sets. This requires the general definition of a *mapping* and its associated concepts. Once again the exercises show how many elementary mathematical examples are properly expressed in the terms introduced. We consider the problem analogous to the one discussed in the second half of Chapter 3: given two sets each with its own operation and a mapping of one to the other, are the operation and mapping compatible? i.e. if we combine two elements in the first set and then map the result of the combination do we get the same result as we would get if we mapped the two elements first and then combined them? If the result is the same we call the mapping a *homomorphism* (in particular, when the mapping is one-one, an *isomorphism*). Again, this idea is implicit in much of our elementary work, e.g. logarithms. We go into more details for these mappings in Chapters 8, 10 and 11 when we have obtained group structure. The topological section gives a fundamental definition of a *continuous* mapping from one topological space to another and the topological definition is compared with that used in real analysis.

Chapter 5. This chapter in a sense is a diversion. We use the concepts of set, equivalence relation and mapping to establish the intuitive idea of *cardinal number*. We establish a characteristic property of an *infinite set*, and show, for instance, that our definition of addition of two cardinal numbers is quite general and need not be restricted to the finite case. The reader can see that the ideas of Chapters 2, 3 and 4 allow us to obtain a high degree of precision in this topic.

Chapter 6. We return to the main line of development. Given a set S and an operation of combination o we consider the problem 'find x if $a \text{ o } x = b$', where a, b and x are members of S, and obtain a structure in which the solution is guaranteed, i.e., we define *group structure*. This is the main algebraic structure to be discussed in the book and the topic is developed slowly by way of examples, and a few general results (such as the uniqueness of the solution) are proved. The topological section, which is quite long, discusses *continuous deformation* as an intuitive notion and compares it with *topological equivalence*. We derive an equivalence relation between topological spaces, *homeomorphism*: we further show that the set of all homeomorphisms of a space onto itself can be given group structure.

Chapter 7. Some sets are born with group structure, some achieve group structure and some have group structure thrust upon them. We are here concerned almost entirely with teaching exercises displaying sets with group structure, and sets which can have group structure imposed upon them. This chapter includes the important teaching exercises in which the natural numbers are *extended*, (i) to form a group under multiplication (*positive rationals*), (ii) to form a group under addition (*integers* or *directed numbers*). The topological section deals with a group associated with *braids*: besides the general algebraic terms we use the intuitive idea of continuous deformation only.

Chapter 8. We return to the idea of isomorphism as a connection between structured sets (first introduced in Chapter 4) with particular reference to *isomorphic groups*. As usual we investigate the particular uses of the various concepts in teaching exercises. *Matrices* are introduced in these exercises and discussed in application in preparation for the formal development in Chapter 9. The topological section is not directly relevant to the chapter, but develops a few simple ideas for later application.

Chapter 9. Having created the excuse, and since we need the ideas later, we devote a chapter to the discussion of matrix algebra. The work is largely confined to 2×2 matrices, but the restriction is only apparent and the methods and definitions are general. The whole chapter, like Chapter 2, is largely a teaching chapter: matrices, for very good reasons, are creeping into school syllabuses. We present the topic from the structural point of view and illustrate our previously established results. Matrix algebra is of great practical importance in many technical fields. The topological section introduced in this chapter is continued in Chapters 10 and 11. We develop a particular topological invariant, the *fundamental homotopy group*. The section here introduces the idea of a *curve* in a topological space, and its continuous deformation. The section in Chapter 10 defines a *path* (a mapping whose image set is a curve), equivalence classes of paths and combination of paths: we show that we thus obtain a group. In Chapter 11 we give examples of groups for some spaces and consider what happens to the group under a mapping from one space onto another. In the discussion we use many of the algebraic concepts previously developed.

Chapter 10. This chapter continues the discussion of Chapter 8 by considering *homomorphic mappings* of structured sets and, in particular, groups. This theory is much richer in the sense that the structures are not the 'same' (as is the case when they are isomorphic) and the relation between them needs a deeper investigation. Given a homomorphism of one group onto another we define an equivalence relation in the first group using a particular subgroup (the *kernel*) which turns the homomorphism into an isomorphism. We then consider the problem from the other side: given any subgroups of a group G do we get an equivalence relation and hence a new group (the *factor group*) which is the homomorphic image of G? The discussion uses the language of Chapters 3 and 4 extensively. The problem of finding the subgroups of a group is simplified by the result of *Lagrange's theorem*, the proof of which is there for the taking.

Chapter 11. Since Chapter 10 carried a greater weight of theory than usual, Chapter 11 is devoted to examples, exercises, applications and extensions of the ideas of Chapter 10. Although much of the material is suitable for pupils and students it is, for convenience, all classified in this chapter as examples. The number of topics covered is large.

Chapter 12. Group structure is central to geometrical studies as explained by Klein. We give a brief outline in this chapter of this approach to geometry which we define as a study of geometrical objects or properties *invariant under groups of transformations*. We describe how one can generalize from one geometry to another and put the matrix theory of Chapter 9 to considerable use. This chapter is again very much a teaching chapter. The topological section (partially anticipating the main text of Chapter 13) considers the interaction between a topology and a group structure, both on one set, leading to the definition of a *topological group*. The topological section of Chapter 13 continues this topic.

Chapter 13. With group structure as the basis, we conclude by surveying some '*higher*' structures. We come to a definition of a *field* by showing that complete double group structure in a single set is impossible if we require a particular interaction between the two operations. Some basic results for fields (and *rings*) are given in the examples and exercises. We also define a *vector space*, a structure arising from the interaction of a field and a group, and again develop a few of the basic results in the examples and exercises. The final paragraph, before the topological section, surveys the situation as it can now be understood.

* * * * *

It is unfortunate that different authors use different notation and symbolism. We explain our choices as we go along and try to justify them. One point needs to be mentioned here: the use of brackets in the 'mathematical' text. (In the ordinary prose we use brackets as parentheses, and for numbering, in any way which is typographically convenient.) Broadly, there are three kinds of bracket: round (); square []; and braces {}. It is common practice to mix the three kinds to indicate priorities: we do not do this. We indicate priority by size and weight of bracket. For example, the various sizes of *square* bracket indicate 'order of performance', e.g. $[\frac{1}{2} - [\frac{7}{8} - \frac{2}{5}]]^2$. *Braces* are reserved for one purpose only, to indicate equivalence classes. *Round* brackets serve several purposes: to indicate the beginning and end of a list of the elements of a set, e.g. (Tom, Jim, Joan); to indicate the image of some element under some mapping, e.g. $f(x)$, and again different sizes indicate order, e.g. $\sinh(\log(x + v(x^2 + 1)))$; to enclose ordered pairs, triples, etc., and in the usual way for coordinates, matrices and permutations.

The number of cross-references is very high; the purpose of such references is often merely to remind the reader of those other topics more or less closely associated with that particular topic being dealt with. The reader in whose mind the associated topics are fresh need not, of course, turn up all the references.

The authors are grateful to Professor W. H. Cockcroft for the corrections and other improvements arising from his scrutiny of the typescript. They are also grateful to Mr F. R. Fraser for the time and care devoted to the diagrams and cartoons.

CHAPTER 2

SETS

OUR object, as we have explained in Chapter 1, is, in part, to present some of the concepts of what is vaguely referred to as 'modern mathematics' or as 'abstract algebra', or described by some other equally misleading phrase. For example, the term 'modern' is purely relative, and only by an abuse of language can subjects be called modern which were first discussed more than a century ago. Again, by the emotive word 'abstract' we certainly do not mean the opposite to concrete, nor do we mean something which exists only as a mental concept. Some of the topics of 'modern abstract mathematics' are less abstract in these senses than the so-called applied mathematics associated with weightless elephants, inextensible strings or similar topics. We would perhaps give a clearer picture by suggesting that that which is abstracted is the essence, the basic substratum, on which and in terms of which much of the rest of mathematics can be built.

One wonders whether the above paragraph has any real meaning for the reader. One would think not, except for those readers who are already familiar with some of the topics which we shall describe. As usual, the preface and introduction are best understood after reading the last chapter in the book. Well, then, what of the beginner for whom this book is intended? Let him throw away any prejudices or preconceived ideas, and let him apply himself to understand the text and then, at the end, he may understand the headings too.

To work then! We must have something about which we can talk, let us suppose then that we have a *set* of objects or elements. What objects? That does not matter so long as we can recognize them when we see them. The people who live next door at the present time form a set, or if you do not like them, you might prefer to think of all the books in your house, or the gobstoppers in the sweetshop on the corner, or what you will. Notice that we must always be able to decide, in theory at least, whether a given object belongs to the set under consideration or not; that is, the set of objects must be well defined.

There are essentially two ways in which we can define the objects of a set: we can either list them all or give a description of the objects. The description must, of course, be complete. We shall be satisfied with an intuitive comprehension of 'complete'; the 'complete' meaning of 'complete' raises logical problems which lie beyond the scope of this book. Thus, if we consider 'the set of all bench seats in Highgate Wood' as a well-described set, then 'the set of all bench seats' is an incomplete description of the first-named set.

In some cases we can define the set in both ways; in other cases only one of the two methods is feasible. For example, all the cars registered in the county of Essex on the first of January 1965 could, in fact, be listed, although the description of the set already given would suffice. On the other hand 'the set of all the stars in the universe' is a sufficient description to enable us to recognize an object of the set, but we defy you to make a complete list. Can you think of an example where a description is impossible, or at least so awkward as to be regarded as pedantic?

NOTE: The idea of a set can also be obtained by using the concept of a defining property as follows. A set of elements is specified by a property which all the elements belonging to the set possess and which is not possessed by elements not belonging to the set. This is very similar to giving a description of the set and presents the same logical difficulties.

All the different words in the third paragraph in this chapter form a set, which to save space we shall denote by P. Some words, such as the word 'set' itself, are repeated but, in general, it proves inconvenient to write a particular word twice when we are only interested in the words as a set of objects (see, however, Exercise 7, page 33). From P we can form *subsets*, i.e. sets, the elements of which are contained in P. In this instance we shall choose to form the six subsets which are made up of all the different words between successive punctuation marks, excluding commas and semi-colons. We label these subsets $p_1, p_2, \ldots, p_6$ respectively. Thus p_3 is the set (what, objects), where the brackets are used to show where the list begins and ends.* We shall use P and its subsets, as far as possible, to illustrate subsequent remarks.

There are quite a number of interesting things that one can do with a set of objects, without being specific about them or any of the properties they may have. Thus, until we say any more about our objects, all results will be valid for every set and everything will be universally applicable.

* Other authors use braces, {}, to indicate where a list of elements of a set begins and ends. We reserve braces for equivalence classes.

It is clearly important, for the sake of economy if nothing else, to be able to decide when two sets, A and B say, are the same. By this term we shall mean that A and B have the same elements, and in such a case we shall write $A = B$. For example,

$$p_3 = (\text{what, objects}) = (\text{objects, what}).$$

Notice that we are only listing the objects: the order in which we list them is immaterial.

We have introduced here the symbol $=$, usually called an equals sign. It is familiar to everyone, and we shall introduce other such signs quite often, perhaps for no better reason than that if we were to invent our own symbols every time, this book would become extraordinarily difficult to read. It is important, therefore, to point out that the reader must be careful not to associate with these symbols any properties to which he is accustomed from his previous use of them. If he bears this in mind, not only will he avoid pitfalls, but he will not make the common and serious mistake of assuming that we are engaged in trivialities which lead nowhere; the ideas with which we deal are simple, commonsensical and untechnical perhaps, but not trivial. It is also important to note that even such a simple sign as the equals sign is in common use with a number of different meanings; in each case, of course, it is usually clear from the context which particular meaning is being attached. The common use is for the expression 'the same as' in some specifically qualified respect. In general, we shall explain the particular contextual use, but we may occasionally forget.

In particular, we note that the symbol as used here has three fundamental properties:

(i)   if $A = B$ then $B = A$,
(ii) $A = A$,
(iii) if $A = B$ and $B = C$, then $A = C$.

These results can be verified by saying in words exactly what each statement means. Thus, the first would read: 'If A has the same elements as B then B has the same elements as A.' The three properties have been given names: the first is called the *symmetric* property, the second *reflexive* and the third *transitive*. It can, of course, be asked why we mention just these three properties, for surely there are others? The answer to this is simply that these three are found to be the essential ones: in normal life not all the properties of a physical object may be relevant, or, alternatively, its further properties may be deducible from those already given. For the moment we shall leave this point and return to a further discussion of these properties later, when their significance should become clear (Chapter 3). If two sets do not contain the same objects, one set may perhaps lie entirely within the other, that is all the elements of A, say, may also appear in B. We described such a situation earlier by saying that A is a subset of B. If A is a *proper subset* of B, i.e. all the elements of A appear in B but B has elements which are not in A, then we write

$$A \subset B$$

and read 'A is properly contained in B'.

If we only know that all the elements in A are in B, but do not know whether or not B contains elements which are not in A, we write $A \subseteq B$, denoting that A may be the same as B, but certainly all the elements in A are also in B.

Since $A \subset B$ and $A \subseteq B$ both express relations between A and B, just as $A = B$ does, we may ask whether our three fundamental properties are also satisfied by these relations of inclusion. The reader may easily convince himself (by replacing $=$ by the appropriate symbol) that for $\subset$ only (iii), the transitive property, is valid, whereas for $\subseteq$ (ii) and (iii) are true and (i), the symmetric property, holds only in the special case when the sets have the same elements.

It is not surprising that these relations do not possess all the fundamental properties, for, as we shall see in Chapter 3, any relation between objects which possesses these three properties is what we shall call an *equivalence relation*. That is, elements which are so related will be lumped together and considered, in some sense at least, as equivalent. Now the relation of inclusion is not in this category; it may be regarded as a relation which emphasizes the difference rather than the similarity between sets, whereas the equality relation is a statement about the 'sameness' of two sets.

Example A. Let A be any set. We can form the set A' of all subsets of A. We shall say that two subsets of A, A_1 and A_2 say, are related if they have one or more elements in common. Is this relation an equivalence relation for the subsets of A?

An example of such a set A' is obtained if we take for A the set p_1 above. Then p'_1 is the set

(to, work, then), (to, work), (to, then), (work, then), (to), (work), (then),

where each pair of brackets contains an element of p'_1. In this example (to, work) and (work, then) are related but not (to, work) and (then). Note that we include p_1 itself among the elements of p_1': it is one of the two *improper* subsets of any set; we shall introduce the second one later (page 24).

The elements of any one of the subsets p_1, p_2, etc., are, of course, elements of the set P. Further, it will be noticed that p_3, for instance, is contained in the combination of p_2 and p_5, that is, the set which contains all the elements in p_2 together with those in p_5. (Note that words like 'a, set, or' occur in both p_2 and p_5, but as we remarked earlier we would not in general write them twice in the combination of p_2 and p_5.) Now this set has no label and to describe it each time is wasteful, so we shall denote it by $p_2 \cup p_5$. Then we can write $p_3 \subset (p_2 \cup p_5)$. There are, of course, reasons other than that of saving space for introducing symbolism. A neat and familiar symbolism enables one to discern the pattern and symmetry of mathematical relations. Although it may be doubtful whether symbolism in itself has caused any major discoveries in mathematics, it is fairly certain that a poor or inadequate notation not only retards progress but it also hinders understanding.

The symbol $\cup$ we have here introduced is usually read as 'cup'. $A \cup B$ is the set of all elements which are either in A or in B or in both. Briefly we call this set the *union* of A and B. The union of two sets is our first operation with sets; a law of combination of two or more sets which gives a new set. In the same way as we investigate any new relations that we come across, so we investigate the operations which we perform to find out which elementary properties they possess. The first property is *commutativity*. Any operation is commutative if the order, in which the elements to be combined are written, is immaterial. Thus, the union of two sets A and B is commutative if

(a) $$A \cup B = B \cup A.$$

This property is seen to hold since the two unions contain the same elements and the order of the elements is immaterial to the equality of the sets. Suppose now that we have three sets A, B and C. The union of all three is that set which contains all the elements which are in A, B or C, or in any combination of two or in all three (without repetitions). If we write this as $A \cup B \cup C$, is this correct and unambiguous? If we introduce square brackets to denote which combination is to be performed first, is

(b) $$[A \cup B] \cup C = A \cup [B \cup C]$$

a true statement? The reader can satisfy himself that (b) is a true statement and agrees with our description by saying each side of the expression in words. We express the truth of (b) by saying that the cup operation is *associative*.

The fact that union satisfies (a) is of obvious utility. Not all operations with which the reader is familiar enjoy this advantage. When we become familiar with an operation the knowledge that the operation does, or does not, possess this property becomes so much a part of us that we find it difficult to believe that it is not obvious to a beginner. A careful analysis of similar properties will help the pupil to avoid errors: it will also help the teacher to appreciate the cause of the pupil's difficulties. The second property (b) allows us to write and manipulate $A \cup B \cup C$ without ambiguity but again it should be noted that not all operations possess it.

Example B. Verify that the operation of subtraction in the set of real numbers is (a) not commutative, (b) not associative. It may be observed that some children are taught that $9 - 5 - 2$ is to be interpreted as $[9 - 5] - 2$. This is certainly not a necessary property of the subtraction operation; it is a purely arbitrary convention and not universally upheld.

It is clear that, by virtue of the associative property, we can extend union to any number of sets and that the expression

$$A \cup B \cup C \cup D \cup \ldots \cup K$$

is quite unambiguous. (This statement demands a proof but we do not give one.) If we return to our example we note that

$$P = p_1 \cup p_2 \cup p_3 \cup p_4 \cup p_5 \cup p_6,$$

but also $\quad P = p_1 \cup p_2 \cup p_4 \cup p_5 \cup p_6.$

This could lead us to speculate about such relations as

$$A \cup B = A \quad \text{or} \quad A \cup B \cup C = A \cup C$$

The first of these relations implies that all the elements which are in A or B are the same as all the elements in A. Thus B can contain no elements which are not in A, that is $B \subseteq A$. In particular, it is possible that $B = A$, i.e. $A \cup A = A$.

Example C. If $A \cup B \cup C = A \cup C$ what general statement can be made about B in terms of the inclusion relation? Write down also some special statements, in terms of inclusion and equality, which satisfy the given equality.

A very common question is, 'What have these things in common?'—and it can also be asked of sets. If we have two sets A and B, have they any objects in common? We shall denote the set of common objects by $A \cap B$, that is, the set of all elements of A that are also in B. In particular we shall employ the symbol $\emptyset$ to denote that A and B have no elements in common by writing $A \cap B = \emptyset$. In order for this last statement to be meaningful we must say that $\emptyset$ is also a set, and that it is a subset common to A and B. Therefore, we shall call $\emptyset$ the *null* or *empty set* and admit it as an improper subset of any set. For instance, $\emptyset$ is the set of all five-storey houses in a road of bungalows. In terms of our original example P and its subsets we have,

$$p_1 \cap p_3 = \emptyset, \quad p_2 \cap p_4 = \text{(we, can, that)}.$$

The symbol $\cap$ is read 'cap' and the set $A \cap B$ is referred to briefly as the *intersection* of A and B. Since the intersection of two sets is a set we should examine this new operation to see whether it is commutative and associative.

Example D. The reader should satisfy himself that this is the case, i.e. that

(a) $A \cap B = B \cap A$,　(b) $A \cap [B \cap C] = [A \cap B] \cap C$.

NOTE: At the end of Example A on page 22 we remarked that any set A has two improper subsets: one is A itself and the other is now seen to be $\emptyset$. It follows that in the list of elements of p_1' in that example we should have included an eighth element $\emptyset$. The set of all subsets of a given set A is called the *power set* of A. We leave the reader to prove, or find elsewhere, the result that if A is a set with a finite number n of elements, the power set of A contains 2^n elements.

NOTE: That we call $\emptyset$ a set should cause no more intuitive difficulty than calling zero a real number. We try to avoid special statements in mathematics. Consider, for instance, the statement in Euclidean geometry that two lines meet in a point unless they are parallel. We shall see in a much later section (in Chapter 12) that this statement can be simplified to 'two lines meet in a point' without the conditional clause. The effect of this simplification is enormous; not only does the geometry become richer in a sense, but its methods achieve a wonderful symmetry. Similarly, here, if we want to write $A \cap B = C$ without occasional qualification we must admit $\emptyset$ as a set.

Example E. $A \cap \emptyset = \emptyset$, $A \cup \emptyset = A$, for any set A.

Now that we have two operations on sets we may ask the further question whether these operations are distributive over each other. We say that $\cap$ is *distributive from the left* over $\cup$ if

(c)　　　　$A \cap [B \cup C] = [A \cap B] \cup [A \cap C],$

and that $\cap$ is *distributive from the right* over $\cup$ if

(d)　　　　$[B \cup C] \cap A = [B \cap A] \cup [C \cap A].$

By interchanging ∩ and ∪ we obtain relations which, if valid, express that ∪ is distributive from the left or from the right over ∩.

NOTE: For example, the operation of multiplication in the set of real numbers is distributive over addition; e.g. 2.[3 + 5] = [2.3] + [2.5] and [3 + 5].2 = [3.2] + [5.2]. But addition is not distributive over multiplication; i.e. 2 + [3.5] ≠ [2 + 3].[2 + 5] and [3.5] + 2 ≠ [3 + 2].[5 + 2].

Example F. Show that if in any set an operation is commutative and left distributive over some other, then it is right distributive.

Example G. Investigate the distributivity of all pairs of the operations, addition, subtraction, multiplication and division in the set of real numbers. Note in particular that division is distributive from the right over addition but not from the left—a very significant teaching point.

As yet we have not examined the validity of the relations (c) and (d). It follows from the first of the two examples above that we need only prove (or disprove) either (c) or (d). But to write out in words an investigation of each side of the relation (c) would become very tedious. A very useful intuitive verification is obtained by representing a set by the interior and boundary of a closed curve. We can then draw diagrams of both sides of any relation and see if they are the same. Such diagrams are known as *Venn diagrams* (introduced by John Venn in 1880). For instance $A \cup B$ and $A \cap B$ are represented by the shaded areas in the figures below.

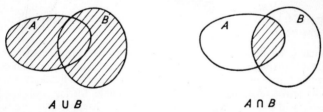

$$A \cup B \qquad\qquad\qquad A \cap B$$

Note that the second figure does not assert that there are necessarily any elements at all in $A \cap B$, for the magnitude of the area enclosed by each curve does not in any way represent the number of elements in the set. Also note that a single set may be represented by the interior of more than one closed curve. For example, if we have two sets A and B, where $A \cap B = \emptyset$, then we may properly define a set C as $C = A \cup B$, although the Venn diagram will then represent the *single* set C as the interior of *two* closed curves, one representing A and the other B. The obvious limitations of this method of verification do not, in general, lead to abuse. On the other hand the advantages of an investigation of this type will be made clear in Example I. We shall first use Venn diagrams to examine the validity of the relation (c). In each figure the region shaded represents the set mentioned below that figure.

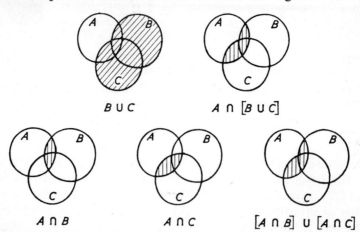

The last figures in each row have the same sections shaded, so we may conjecture that the relation is true. We shall not be interested in the more formal approach to set theory, and for teaching purposes the Venn diagram is attractive and quite sufficient.

Example H. Use Venn diagrams to investigate whether union is distributive over intersection.

Example I. We have been very careful so far to insert brackets which show in which order the operations are to be performed, and yet in each case we have justified their removal. So we shall now consider the brackets in the left-hand side of the relation (c). Would it be justifiable, for instance, to remove the brackets in the expression $A \cap [B \cup C]$? Is this expression the same as $[A \cap B] \cup C$? A consideration of the following diagrams shows that this is not the case.

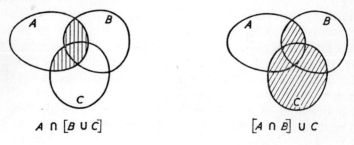

Thus the order in which the operations are performed for arbitrary sets A, B and C is important. If, for instance, we refer to our original example, we have $p_1 \cap [p_2 \cup p_3]$ = (then), whereas $[p_1 \cap p_2] \cup p_3$ = (then, what, objects). The Venn diagram has here been found useful in disproving a suggested result, since one counter example is sufficient to disprove a conjecture. On the other hand, no number of true examples is a proof (unless, of course, there are only a finite number of examples to which the conjecture can apply and these have all been tested).

Writing $\neq$ to mean 'is not the same as', we have, in general,

$$A \cap [B \cup C] \neq [A \cap B] \cup C.$$

But we may ask whether there exist special conditions under which the equality holds. Consider the two diagrams again.

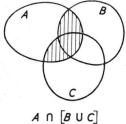

$A \cap [B \cup C]$

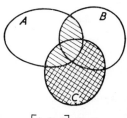

$[A \cap B] \cup C$

It is clear that $A \cap [B \cup C] \subseteq [A \cap B] \cup C$, and it would seem that the equality can only hold if the cross-hatched section is the null set $\emptyset$, i.e. $C \subseteq A$. This condition is in fact not only necessary, as shown here, but also sufficient.

The idea of *necessary* and *sufficient* conditions mentioned in this last example can be stated precisely as follows. A result R is 'necessary' for a result S if the truth of S implies the truth of R. A result R is 'sufficient' for a result S if the truth of R implies the truth of S. If one statement is both necessary and sufficient for another then each implies the other and the two statements are in a sense equivalent. For example, that one is a British subject is a necessary condition for being able to vote in a British parliamentary election, but it is by no means sufficient. Here 'being a British subject' is the statement R and 'being able to vote in an election' is the statement S. The reader is advised to make up simple examples of all three possibilities and analyse them, to clarify the concept which is of fundamental importance in mathematics.

Example J. Consider a set of statements. Let the individual statements be denoted by R, S, ... Let RnS denote that R is necessary for S, RsS that R is sufficient for S, and Rn,sS that R is both necessary and sufficient for S.

Investigate these three relations between statements to see which of (i), (ii) and (iii) on page 20 they satisfy. In particular, show that n,s is an equivalence relation, i.e. that it satisfies all three.

Example K. We are continually trying to press home the idea of examining all new relations and operations. In the last but one example we introduced the new relation $\neq$ between sets. Show that it is symmetric, but not reflexive or transitive.

Example L. There are other laws of combination that we could invent for sets. We introduce a further one which we shall denote by $\sim$. $A \sim B$ is defined to be the set of elements of A which are not in B, that is A 'less' the elements of $A \cap B$, as shown in the figure.

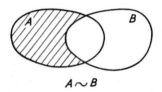

$$A \sim B$$

This combination provides an example of a non-associative operation; verify this. Investigate also other possibilities, such as:

(i) is $\sim$ commutative?

(ii) is $\sim$ left and right-distributive over $\cap$?

(iii) is $\cup$ left and right-distributive over $\sim$? Note here that since $\cup$ is commutative it must be both or neither.

(iv) is $[A \sim B] \cup C = A \sim [B \cup C]$?

Example M. Give examples of $A \sim B$ for sets A and B within your experience.

Example N. If N is the set of natural numbers, E the set of even natural numbers and P the set of prime numbers, we see that

$$E \cup N = P \cup N \quad (= N).$$

The temptation to 'cancel' the N's must be resisted: it does *not* follow that

$$E = P.$$

Similarly, if R is the set of real numbers, I the set of irrational numbers and T the set of transcendental numbers, we have

$$I \cap T = R \cap T \quad (= T)$$

and, again, one must not 'cancel'; it is *not* true that

$$I = R.$$

Also

$$E \sim N = P \sim N \quad (= \emptyset)$$

and, as before, $E \neq P$.

There is an operation on sets which does permit this sort of 'cancelling' procedure: it is the operation called *symmetric difference*. The symmetric difference of two sets, A and B, is defined as the set containing all members of A which are not members of B together with all members of B which are not members of A. This set is written $A \triangle B$ and is indicated by the shaded sections of the Venn diagram below. It is evident that

$$A \triangle B = [A \cup B] \sim [A \cap B] = [A \sim B] \cup [B \sim A].$$

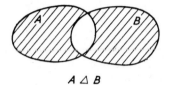

$A \triangle B$

The symmetric difference operation is extremely important and is dealt with more fully in Chapter 6. The reader should discover for himself whether or not the following statements are true. (They are not all true.)

(a) $\triangle$ is commutative.

(b) $\triangle$ is associative.

(c) $\cap$ is distributive (both from the left and right or neither) over $\triangle$.

(d) $\cup$ is distributive over $\triangle$.

(e) If $A \triangle B = A \triangle C$ it follows that $B = C$.

At this point we shall break off the development of what we like to regard as the 'pure' (but not, of course, 'rigorous') theory and give some applications and illustrations from other fields. We wish to re-emphasize that, as with the examples, exercises and notes introduced in small print throughout the text, these applications are not in the logical order of this book, but are introduced from time to time to make the rest palatable and of direct use in a variety of teaching situations. It is the application of general principles to a collection of previously experienced particulars which gives the whole subject interest. One should, therefore, not worry about over-shooting the theory. It should, perhaps, also be pointed out again that the illustrations and applications are not 'in order of difficulty'; such an order, if it exists at all, is intensely individual.

Exercises

Exercises 1 and 2 have been found useful for clarifying pupils' ideas about set notation.

1. Let N be the set of natural numbers 1, 2, 3, 4, . .; let P be the set of prime numbers; let E be the set of even natural numbers. Then some of the following statements are true and some are false. Which is which?

(a) $P \subset N$; (b) $E \subset N$; (c) $E \cup P = N$; (d) $E \cup N = N$; (e) $E \cap N = E$; (f) $E \cap P = \emptyset$.

2. Let R be the set of all real numbers, A the set of algebraic numbers, T the set of transcendental numbers, I the set of irrational numbers, F the set of rational numbers. Then some of the following statements are true and some are false. Which is which?

(a) $I \subset A$; (b) $F \subset A$; (c) $I \cup A = R$; (d) $T \cup A = R$; (e) $I = T$; (f) $F \cup I = A$; (g) $T \cap I = T$; (h) $T \cap F = \emptyset$; (i) $T \cap [I \cap F] = A$.

3. Very simple geometrical examples are particularly effective in introducing set notation to young children. A typical example, concerning a plane figure, follows.

Single points are referred to by single letters, e.g. A. The set of all points on the straight line joining two points, say A and B, is referred to as AB. The set of all points inside, or on the boundaries of, the triangle ABC is referred to as ABC, and so on for any polygon. Note that, for instance, AB means the set of all points on the straight line segment while (E, F) means the set consisting of two isolated points.

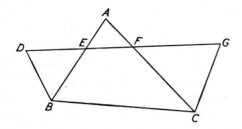

Use the figure given and simplify the following expressions, e.g. the answer to (a) is AB.

(a) $AE \cup EB$; (b) $AE \cap EB$; (c) $DG \cap AB$; (d) $DG \cap AC$; (e) $DG \cap [AB \cup AC]$; (f) $EBCF \cup AEF$; (g) $DG \cap ABC$; (h) $EBCF \cap AEF$; (i) $BC \cap AEF$.

4. A linear inequality in one variable is solvable intuitively, e.g. the solution set of $3 - x > 0$ is evidently $x < 3$. The solution of a factorizable inequality of higher degree can best be demonstrated by intersecting sets on the number line. For example, to solve $[3 - x][x - 2] > 0$ we take

(i)
$$3 - x > 0$$

and

$$x - 2 > 0$$

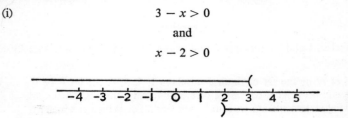

and the intersection of these solution sets is $2 < x < 3$ ... (a).

(ii)
$$3 - x < 0$$
$$\text{and}$$
$$x - 2 < 0$$

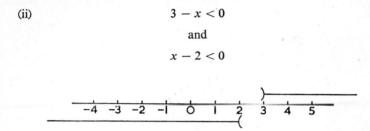

and the intersection of these solution sets is $\emptyset$ ... (b).

The complete solution is the union of sets (a) and (b), in this case $2 < x < 3$. (Note: strictly, the phrase '$x < 3$' does not indicate a set: it indicates a restriction. Properly we should write 'the set of all x such that $x < 3$': the notation favoured for this is $(x; x < 3)$. In this notation the solution to this exercise is $(x; 2 < x < 3)$.)

5. An inequality is a relation in the set of real numbers. Is $a < b$ symmetric, reflexive or transitive? What about $a \leqslant b$?

6. The solution set of a linear inequality in two variables may be represented by the set of points of a half-plane: for example the set for which $x + y \leqslant 9$ is represented by the unshaded area in the diagram below. (The line $x + y = 9$ is included in the unshaded area.)

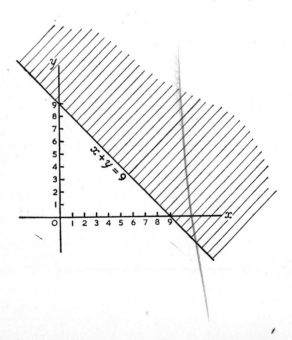

Similarly, the solution set of $2x + 5y \leqslant 35$ is represented by the unshaded area below.

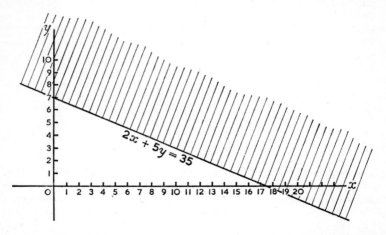

The set which satisfies $x + y \leqslant 9$ and $2x + 5y \leqslant 35$ simultaneously is the intersection of these two unshaded sets. If also $x > 2$ and $y > 3$, the solution set of all four inequalities is the intersection of four sets. This solution set is represented by the unshaded area below together with its boundaries.

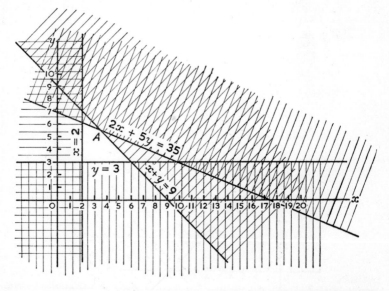

The process by which solution sets of simultaneous linear inequalities involving two variables are obtained by the intersection of half-planes (in general, for n variables, half-spaces) is the basis of the process sometimes called *linear*

programming. For example, the set just obtained corresponds to the following simple situation.

'A firm makes two products, denoted by X and Y, say. The total production capacity is, at most, 9 tons altogether per day. The firm has a permanent contract to supply at least 2 tons of X every day to another firm and another permanent contract to supply at least 3 tons of Y every day to yet another firm. Each ton of X requires 20 machine hours in production, each ton of Y requires 50 machine hours in production, and the number of men and machines available is such that not more than 350 machine hours can be worked per day.'

Let x be the number of tons of X produced, and y the number of tons of Y. Then with this interpretation, any point in the unshaded region corresponds to an output which meets all requirements. This is often called the permissible set. One can proceed to maximize or minimize any appropriate function of the quantities of products. For example, if the profit is £8 on each ton of X and £12 on each ton of Y, then the total profit would be $8x + 12y$ pounds. For any arbitrary value of the profit, say $p = p_1$, the line $p_1 = 8x + 12y$ represents the set of quantities for which the profit is p_1, called the profit set p_1. If the intersection of this profit set p_1 with the permissible set is not empty, then a profit of p_1 may be made and all the requirements are fulfilled. To maximize the profit, one observes that as p increases the line $p = 8x + 12y$ moves parallel to the y-axis, remaining parallel with $p_1 = 8x + 12y$. Hence p is a maximum, and all requirements are fulfilled, at a particular vertex (or along a particular boundary) of the permissible set (assuming that the permissible set is closed in the direction of increasing p, which is the case in our example). In the example the most profitable point is that shown as A in the last diagram, and the values of x and y are obtained as the intersection of the solution sets of $x + y = 9$ and $2x + 5y = 35$.

In practice the number of variables is rarely as small as two and computers are required to evaluate the coordinates of all the vertices of the n-dimensional permissible set. Alternatively a technique called the simplex method may be used.

Note that the equals sign used in this exercise (like the inequality sign used in exercise four) is a linguistic abbreviation in the definition of a set. Thus $x + y = 9$ is the set of all pairs x and y of real numbers which are such that their sum is the real number 9. It would be very forced to explain this use of the equals sign as similar to the use we made of it earlier in the sense 'is the same set as'. When we for instance 'subtract 9 from both sides of this equation' we are saying that the set defined by $x + y = 9$ is the same as the set defined by $x + y - 9 = 0$. In the notation of the note to Exercise 4 we could write this latter statement as

$$(x, y; x + y = 9) = (x, y; x + y - 9 = 0)$$

where the equals sign between the brackets is used in our previous sense.

7. Let A be the set of prime factors of 70, i.e. $A = (2, 5, 7)$. Let B be the set of prime factors of 154, i.e. $B = (2, 7, 11)$. Then if $C = A \cap B$, $C = (2, 7)$ and the set C comprises the prime factors of 14, the 'highest common factor' of 70 and 154. Similarly, if $D = A \cup B$, $D = (2, 5, 7, 11)$ and the set D comprises the prime factors of 770, the 'lowest common multiple' of 70 and 154.

It should be noticed that the above procedure fails to give the H.C.F. or

L.C.M. in the case of such a pair as 24 and 60, and it is of some interest to modify the procedure in such a way that it does not break down. The reason for the failure is that, in general, we do not list the 'same' element of a set twice; but here, the fact that 2 is a three-fold prime factor of 24 and a two-fold prime factor of 60 is essential to our purpose. This means that the three twos in 24 are not the 'same', i.e. the set A of prime factors of 24 is $A = (2, 2, 2, 3)$. To make this distinction the more obvious a possible method is to attach a different suffix to each appearance of the same prime in the factorization of a number, i.e. $A = (2_1, 2_2, 2_3, 3)$.

It might also be observed that such numbers as 6 and 35 apparently have a common factor, 1, but that the intersection of the sets of their prime factors is $\emptyset$. If, therefore, we wish to define common factors in terms of subsets of the intersection of the sets of prime factors (and this seems a very natural definition) we must either say that

    (a) numbers such as 6 and 35 have no common factor,

or (b) accept a convention that the empty set comprises the prime factors of 1,

or (c) admit 1 as a prime number.

Alternative (c) would destroy the so-called 'fundamental theorem of arithmetic', which states that a natural number can be expressed as a product of primes in one and only one way, irrespective of order. (For, if 1 were accepted as a prime, then, for example, $6 = 2 \times 3$ and $6 = 1 \times 1 \times 1 \times 2 \times 3$, which would disprove the theorem.) So we reject (c). A further implication of our rejection of (c) and retention of the fundamental theorem is that 1 is neither prime nor composite. This means that the convention of (b) is unnecessary because the set of prime factors of 1 is the empty set, and (a) is implied by our definition of common factors.

8. Consider the set of all possible displacements of a point in a plane (a displacement being specified by a distance and a direction). Combine any two displacements by merely performing first the one upon some point and then the other upon the resulting point. We denote the result of a displacement d on a point O by $d(O)$. For example, in the diagram, if d_1 and d_2 are two displacements represented by the arrows AB and MN, then the combination of d_1 with d_2 gives the figure OPQ, where P is $d_1(O)$ and Q is $d_2(P)$.

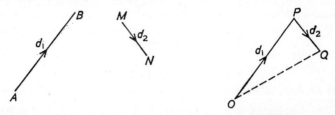

We observe that the combination of d_1 with d_2 is a displacement d_3, where $d_3(O)$ is Q. Further, we observe that combination of displacements is commutative: the order in which we combine them is immaterial to the total distance along the two displacements and to the equivalent single displacement. The combination of displacements is also associative. In the following example we use the associativity and commutativity to prove a simple and elegant result.

Consider the following problem: A and B are two points on either side of a canal. It is required to construct the shortest possible pipe-line from A to B with the condition that that part of the pipe-line which crosses the canal shall be perpendicular to its banks. (The banks are straight and parallel.)

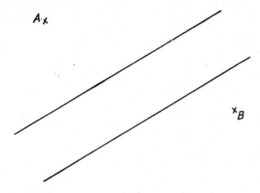

Now this is a problem involving three displacements: from A to the nearest bank: across the canal: from the arrival point on the bank to B. Since only the second of these displacements is known completely (in magnitude and direction) and since the combination of displacements is commutative, perform this displacement first: that is from A lay off AC equal to the width of the canal and in a direction perpendicular to the banks. Call this displacement d_2. Join C to B, letting CB cut the further bank at D. Call CD displacement d_1 and DB displacement d_3. Then the path $AC \cdot CD \cdot DB$ is plainly the shortest path. (Note that we use associativity.) It remains to alter the order of combination so that d_1 is performed first and d_2 second, with d_3 last. This gives a path $AEDB$ of equal (minimum) length with displacement d_2 across the canal, as required.

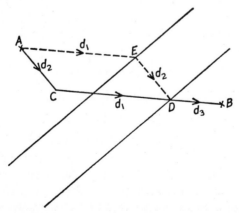

Similar reasoning solves the corresponding problem involving the crossing of two non-parallel canals of unequal width between the two end-points.

The examples we have given here are, on the whole, elementary. They show how one can use the terminology and simple concepts which we have so far introduced in a variety of ways. The number of possible examples is very large, as any teacher who gives a little thought to his today's lessons will readily discover. It is not our purpose, however, to be encyclopaedic, and we shall now continue with a few general remarks before closing the chapter with a much more sophisticated and important example.

One often finds in books that a new combination of elements of a set is introduced using a notation with which the reader is already familiar from other contexts. The effect of this is very often to obscure the necessity for investigating the elementary properties of these concepts, or even in some cases to lead the student into error. (For instance, the ludicrous notation of $\sin^{-1} x$, for what is otherwise often called arc $\sin x$, leads from time to time to $[\sin^{-1} x]^2 = \sin^{-2} x$.) Therefore, we shall use a neutral notation for each new combination we introduce; we shall usually stick to the same symbol, namely a small circle thus o, and indicate in a note the notations commonly used in other texts. Subsequent to its introduction and initial investigation, we may use a more individual symbolism for any particular combination if we have cause to use it often.

An *ordered pair* of two objects a and b is written (a, b) and we shall say that (a, b) is the same as (c, d) if and only if $a = c$ and $b = d$, where '$=$' denotes 'is the same as'. We use the expression 'ordered' because (a, b) is not the same as (b, a) except when $a = b$. Given two sets A and B we can form a new set $A \circ B$ which consists of all ordered pairs of the form (a, b), where a is an element of A and b is an element of B. It follows from our definition of the equality of two ordered pairs that

$$A \circ B \neq B \circ A,$$

i.e. this combination is not commutative: nor is it associative, i.e.

$$[A \circ B] \circ C \neq A \circ [B \circ C],$$

since $((a, b), c) \neq (a, (b, c))$; the first element in the ordered pair on the left-hand side is (a, b), which is not the same as a, the first element in the ordered pair on the right-hand side.

We shall often use the idea of an ordered pair. Many modern authors consider it basic and express the concepts of function, relation, etc., in terms of it. We shall indicate how some of this is done by notes in the appropriate places.

Example O. Let I be the set of natural numbers then $I \circ I$ can be considered as the set of all positive fractions (not in their lowest terms), see Chapter 7.

Example P. Let R be the set of real numbers then $R \circ R$ is the set of all pairs of real numbers (x, y), i.e. a Cartesian coordinate system for the plane. Also if A is the set of real numbers y such that $0 \leqslant y < 2\pi$, $R \circ A$ is a polar coordinate system for the plane. If B is the set of real numbers x such that $0 \leqslant x \leqslant \pi$ then $B \circ A$ is a coordinate system for the surface of a sphere. There is an endless number of examples.

NOTE: The operation 'o' is usually called the *Cartesian product* or *direct product* of two sets and denoted by $A \times B$; we shall denote it by $A \triangledown B$ from now on.

All the operations we have so far mentioned are so-called *binary operations*, that is an operation 'o' on a set of elements such that, given any pair of elements a and b, $a \circ b$ is a uniquely defined element c, not necessarily belonging to the same set. Most of the operations which we shall have cause to consider in this book will be binary operations. We do find it necessary, however, occasionally to introduce other operations: for instance, given three sets A, B and C we can form the new set D of all ordered triples (a, b, c) where a, b and c are members of A, B and C respectively; (a, b, c) is the same as (a', b', c') if and only if $a = a'$, $b = b'$, $c = c'$.

It is clear that we can generalize this latter sort of combination to any number of sets, i.e. n sets can be combined to form a new set of ordered n-tuples. Note that this sort of combination is not the repeated combination obtained by forming successive direct products. For instance D is not the same as either $A \triangledown [B \triangledown C]$ or $[A \triangledown B] \triangledown C$. Since there is some similarity with the direct product (and, in fact, most authors call it the direct product of three sets) we shall denote D by $\triangledown ABC$.

Example Q. Give examples of sets $D = \triangledown ABC$ which are commonly used in mathematics. For instance, the various three-dimensional coordinate-systems.

* * * * *

We shall consider a final example of considerable importance in modern mathematics, which we shall discuss and apply in later chapters. The reason for introducing it here is because the initial unmotivated concept needs only the simple terminology of set theory with which we are familiar.

Let A be any set of elements (often called points, in a geometrical or topological context), and suppose that we have a system of subsets of A which satisfies the following conditions:

(i)   Ø and A are members of the system;

(ii) the intersection of any two subsets of the system is a subset of the system;

(iii) the union of any number of subsets of the system is a subset of the system.

For any set A we denote a system of subsets satisfying conditions (i) to (iii) by $T:A$. The subsets of such a system are called the *open sets* of $T:A$. The subset system is said to form a *topology* for A, and A together with $T:A$ is said to be a *topological space* and written $(A, T:A)$. Clearly the power set of A (i.e. the set of all subsets of A) is a topology for A, and at the other extreme A and Ø also form a topology for A.

Example R. Let A be the set R^+ of positive real numbers (note that zero is excluded), and consider the system of subsets $A_0, A_1, A_2, \ldots, A_m, \ldots$, where A_m is the subset of all positive real numbers less than or equal to the non-negative integer m. Then Ø belongs to the system since $A_0 = $ Ø, but A is not a member of the system; we can rectify matters by specifically including A. $A_{m_1} \cap A_{m_2} = A_{m_1}$ if $m_1 \leqslant m_2$ and so (ii) is satisfied. Finally, the union of any number of subsets is either A or A_m if m is the largest subscript in the union.

Example S. Let A be the set (a, b, c, d). Are the following systems of subsets topologies for A?

(i) A, Ø, (a, b, c), (a, c), (d).

(ii) A, Ø, (a, b, c), (a, b, d), (a, b).

(iii) A, Ø, (a, c), (b, c), (a, d), (c, d), (b, d), (a, b).

Construct two further topologies for A.

Example T. In Exercise 3 on page 30, let A be the set of all line-segments in the figure, i.e. $A = (AF, AC, AE, AB, BC, BD, BE, CG, CF, DE, DF, DG, EF, EG, FG)$. Define some topologies for this set of elements.

Example U. Let S be any set with a topology $T:S$ and let X be a fixed subset of S. Consider subsets of X which can be expressed in the form $A \cap X$ where the A are open sets in $T:S$. Show that the system of all such subsets of X is a topology for X (this is discussed in detail at the end of Chapter 5).

Let S be the set R^+ in Example R and let X be the subset of all real numbers x such that $1\frac{1}{2} \leqslant x \leqslant 3$. Then if the topology for R^+ is the one in Example R, the open sets which form the *induced* topology for X are

$$\varnothing, \ X \text{ and } 1\frac{1}{2} \leqslant x \leqslant 2.$$

What are the open sets for the induced topology for X if X is the subset

$$(\tfrac{1}{2} \leqslant x \leqslant 3) \cup (4 \leqslant x \leqslant 6)?$$

References

A very useful book for teachers is *Sets, Relations, Functions* by Selby and Sweet, (McGraw-Hill) 1963. It contains numerous examples.

For the sophisticated, who would like to go further into set theory in an abstract way, there is *Sets, Logic and Axiomatic Theories* by R. R. Stoll, (Freeman) 1961.

There are, of course, very many other texts on sets at all levels.

CHAPTER 3

EQUIVALENCE RELATIONS

EARLIER we mentioned the concept of an equivalence relation and we now return to this topic. It is an idea which arises naturally whenever we wish to classify and compare objects. It also arises, as we shall see in a number of places throughout this book, when we wish to extend our subject in terms of objects already defined.

We shall denote a general relationship between objects of a set by R, and the objects themselves by a, b, c, . . . Then R is an equivalence relation if it satisfies the three properties,

(i) $a R b$ implies $b R a$ (symmetric)
(ii) $a R a$ (reflexive)
(iii) $a R b$ and $b R c$ imply $a R c$ (transitive).

All objects which are equivalent (i.e. stand in the relation R) to a given object a form a subset called the equivalence class of a. We denote the equivalence class of a by $\{a\}$. Note that in view of the importance of equivalence we reserve braces, $\{\}$, to indicate equivalence classes throughout the book. The significance of the reflexive condition is that it ensures that a always belongs to at least one equivalence class, namely $\{a\}$, even if there exists no other element b to which a is equivalent.

The first relationship we discussed was the equality of two sets. (Here the objects themselves are sets regarded as subsets of what is sometimes called a *universal set*. This should not cause any confusion; whether we call an object a set or a set an object depends on our purpose. At most this is a linguistic difficulty. After all, if you are selling them, boxes of chocolates are the *objects* of your interest; on the other hand, if you are buying them, then the objects of interest are the *set* of chocolates in a box.) The investigation of equality of sets is a classification problem. The equivalence classes of equal sets are made up of sets which have the same elements; in other words, if we take two sets from the same equivalence class then their elements are the same, and if we take them from different equivalence classes, there must be at least one element which they do not have in common. In particular, it would follow

40

here that one set cannot occur in two equivalence classes. If we regard classification as the process of sorting objects into boxes then we would intuitively require that:

(i) every object is put into some box, since otherwise an object would remain unclassified,

(ii) any object taken from a box is just as good as any other from the same box for the purpose for which they were classified, and

(iii) two objects which are the same for the purpose of the classification should not appear in different boxes.

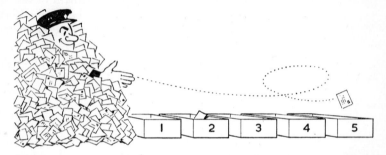

Example A. The local bookshop has shelves of second-hand books: all books on one shelf are 6*d*, all on another 1*s*, and on a third 2*s*. The first property listed above is automatically satisfied, since books not on a shelf are not considered. Our only interest at present is the price of the books and we would expect to pay only 1*s* for any book taken from the second shelf. On the other hand, we might well be annoyed if we were charged 2*s* for a book from the 6*d* shelf.

We shall now show what becomes of this intuitive discussion in terms of a general equivalence relation. We have already remarked, and we may well do so again, that the reflexive law ensures that every object is classified, and is put into some equivalence class. If $b \, R \, a$, then b belongs to $\{a\}$, so we may ask can we equally denote the equivalence class $\{a\}$ by $\{b\}$, i.e. are the elements equivalent to a the same as those equivalent to b? (As remarked earlier, it is sometimes necessary to introduce some space-saving symbols, although we like to keep this down to a minimum. In this case we wish to introduce the symbol $\in$ which means 'is a member of' or 'belongs to'.) To answer the question, suppose $c \in \{a\}$, then by definition $c \, R \, a$, and since $b \, R \, a$ implies $a \, R \, b$, we have by the transitive law $c \, R \, b$, i.e. $c \in \{b\}$. Thus $\{a\} \subseteq \{b\}$. Similarly, we can show that if $c \in \{b\}$ then $c \in \{a\}$, i.e. $\{b\} \subseteq \{a\}$. Hence $\{a\} = \{b\}$, i.e. an equivalence class can be represented by any one of its constituent elements.

Next suppose that $\{a\}$ and $\{b\}$ have an element c in common. Then by the above argument, $\{a\} = \{c\}$ and $\{b\} = \{c\}$, whence it follows that $\{a\} = \{c\}$. Thus two equivalence classes are either disjoint (no elements in common) or identical. In terms of our established notation for sets we can write this

$$\{a\} \cap \{b\} = \emptyset \qquad \text{or} \qquad \{a\} = \{b\},$$

for any two equivalence classes. Since, repeating ourselves for the second time, the reflexive law ensures that every element of the set lies in some equivalence class, we may regard the equivalence classes as a *partition* of a set into non-overlapping classes.

Example B. Rewrite the above arguments showing explicitly where we use each of the three properties of an equivalence relation.

Example C. Consider the map of Europe shown. Give some definitions of equivalence relations which would arise from this sort of map. For instance, the set of all people living in Europe and $a\,R\,b$ if a and b live in the same country. Are there any special cases which must be assumed not to exist?

Conversely, every partition of a set into non-overlapping subsets gives a natural equivalence relation which is defined by saying that two objects are equivalent if they belong to the same subset. The reader should quickly check that this definition of equivalence possesses the three properties.

Example D. A partition of the real numbers is $m \leqslant x < m + 1$, where m takes all integral values (including zero).

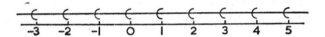

Alternatively, we could have defined two real numbers x and y as equivalent by,

$$x\,R\,y \text{ if } m \leqslant x < m + 1 \text{ and } m \leqslant y < m + 1 \text{ for the same } m.$$

Example E. The three properties of an equivalence relation can, in fact, be replaced by two:

(a) $a\,R\,a$,   (b) $a\,R\,b$ and $b\,R\,c$ imply $c\,R\,a$.

We prove here that (a) and (b) imply the reflexive, transitive and symmetric properties and leave the converse, which is not difficult, to the reader. The reflexive property is contained in both sets of conditions, so this needs no proof. From (b)

$$a\,R\,b \text{ and } b\,R\,b \text{ imply } b\,R\,a$$

but from (a) $b\,R\,b$ is true, therefore, $a\,R\,b$ implies $b\,R\,a$ and the symmetric property is proved. Finally, to prove the transitive property, we use (b) and the symmetric law:

$$a\,R\,b \text{ and } b\,R\,c \text{ imply } c\,R\,a \text{ and } c\,R\,a \text{ implies } a\,R\,c.$$

Example F. The following is suggested as a 'proof' that the symmetric and transitive properties imply the reflexive property. From the symmetric property $a\,R\,b$ implies $b\,R\,a$, which, using the transitive property, implies $a\,R\,a$. Therefore, there is no necessity for the reflexive property at all. What is wrong?

In this connection, consider the set of all males in this country and the relationship of being a brother. What about an only son?

Example G. There are numerous examples of real-life classifications which are equivalence relations. For example, the set of all people who are in the

London postal area, with the equivalence relation $a R b$ if a and b are in the same postal district. Or the set of all people who pay tax under the P.A.Y.E. system who have the same code number, etc. Make up some of your own examples, if you feel like it, but check carefully that they are proper equivalence relations.

'**Example H.** (i) The set of all real numbers and $a R b$ if a is less than b is not a proper equivalence relation. In fact, only the transitive property holds. This is, of course, analogous to the relation of inclusion which we came across in sets.

(ii) The set of all people in the London postal area and $a R b$ if a and b have brown eyes. The reflexive property is the only one which does not hold here, but the effect is clearly serious, because this is hardly a classification at all. In which class shall we put my little blue-eyed niece who lives in the London postal area?

(iii) The set of all real numbers and $a R b$ if

$$m \leqslant a \leqslant m + 1 \text{ and } m \leqslant b \leqslant m + 1, \text{ for the same } m,$$

where m is an integer or zero. Here $\frac{1}{2} R 1$ (with $m = 0$) and $1 R 1\frac{1}{2}$ (with $m = 1$) but $\frac{1}{2}$ and $1\frac{1}{2}$ are not equivalent, so that the transitive requirement is broken. Notice that this relation does not give a partition: it can be converted into a proper equivalence relation by replacing $\leqslant$ by $<$ at the second and fourth occurrence. (See the Example D on page 43.)

(iv) Finally, consider the set of all people in the London area again. We shall say that $a R b$ if a is not taller than b. In this example the only property which does not hold is the symmetric property.

It is suggested that the reader make up a number of his own examples of relations which do not satisfy one or other of the three properties. It is instructive to look for examples, having decided in advance which properties are not to hold.

Although we only consider equivalence relations, we do not wish to suggest that relations which do not satisfy the symmetric property, for instance, are of no interest. After all, very many of our binary operations are not commutative or not associative and we still consider them. The properties which we have listed for both operations and relations, and which we investigate for each new operation and relation, should rather be regarded as the basic properties, the knowledge of which helps us to use the new 'symbol' safely and effectively. Thus, relations which do not possess all our three properties are investigated and classified in various books in connection with the subject of *ordering*. In general, an ordering relation must at least be transitive. The reader who is interested in this complex topic should consult the two references at the end of the previous chapter, inter alia. We have no particular use for ordering within our self-imposed context and so we shall not discuss it all—it is the wood that matters.

Example I. An equivalence relation in a set A can be regarded as defining a subset E of $A \bigtriangledown A$, where (a, b) belongs to the subset if a is related to b. This subset is such that:

   (i)   if $(a, b) \in E$ then $(b, a) \in E$,
   (ii) $(a, a) \in E$ for all $a \in A$,
   (iii) if (a, b) and $(b, c) \in E$ then $(a, c) \in E$.

Conversely, any subset E of $A \bigtriangledown A$ which satisfies (i), (ii) and (iii) defines an equivalence relation in A in an obvious way.

  (a) If A is the set (1, 2, 3, 4) and the relation is '$=$' what is the set E?

  (b) With the same set A, does the set (1, 1), (2, 2), (3, 3), (4, 4), (1, 2), (2, 1) define an equivalence relation? What are the equivalence classes?

  (c) For any set A, does $A \bigtriangledown A$ define an equivalence relation in A? What are the equivalence classes?

  (d) Let A be the set of all integers (with zero). Consider the subset E of $A \bigtriangledown A$ which is made up of all the ordered pairs of the form (a, b), where $a - b$ is divisible by 2. (Note that the form (a, a) is in R for all a since $a - a$ is divisible by 2.) Does this define an equivalence relation? What are the equivalence classes?

Exercises

1. The usual example given to introduce this particular topic is that of a clock-face on which we can count up to twelve and then have to begin again; similarly the milometer in a car usually shows a mileage up to 99,999 miles and then begins all over again.

These examples are typical of what we term *congruence relations* modulo some real number n. We say that two real numbers a and b are congruent modulo n if a and b differ by some integral multiple of n,

i.e. $$a - b = kn,$$

where k is an integer and we write $a \equiv b \pmod{n}$. Thus

$13 \equiv 25 \pmod{12}$, $263 \equiv 95 \pmod{12}$, $3,653,271 \equiv 53,271 \pmod{100,000}$.

This definition of congruence when restricted to integral a, b and n is the same as saying that a and b leave the same remainder when divided by n. We leave the reader to prove this.

We now prove that $a\,R\,b$ if $a \equiv b \pmod{n}$ is an equivalence relation for fixed n.

  (i) if $a \equiv b \pmod{n}$ then $a - b = kn$, for some integer k.

      Therefore, $b - a = [-k]n$, and $b \equiv a \pmod{n}$.

  (ii) $a \equiv a \pmod{n}$ since $a - a = 0.n$.

  (iii) if $a \equiv b \pmod{n}$ and $b \equiv c \pmod{n}$

then $a - b = kn$ and $b - c = ln$,

for some integers k and l.

Therefore

$$a - c = [a - b] + [b - c] = [k + l]n \text{ and } a \equiv c \pmod{n}.$$

There are many examples of such congruence relations: we give a few.

(a) The clock-face example. Two non-negative integers a, b are congruent modulo 12 if $a - b = k.12$. The equivalence (or *residue*) *classes* are the sets

$$(0, 12, 24, \ldots),$$
$$(1, 13, 25, \ldots),$$
$$(2, 14, 26, \ldots),$$
$$\ldots\ldots\ldots\ldots\ldots$$
$$(11, 11 + 12, 11 + 24, \ldots).$$

(b) The integers modulo 2 yield two classes, the odd and even integers.

(c) The real numbers modulo 2π correspond to the rotations in a plane about a point: i.e. a rotation through $\dfrac{\pi}{2}$ is in some sense the same as a rotation through $\dfrac{5\pi}{2}$ and $\dfrac{\pi}{2} \equiv \dfrac{5\pi}{2} \pmod{2\pi}$.

2. Consider the set ∇RRR of ordered triples (x, y, z) where R is the set of real numbers. We say that (a, b, c) is related to (a', b', c') if

$$a = \rho a', \quad b = \rho b', \quad c = \rho c',$$

for some real number $\rho \neq 0$. We write $(a, b, c) = \rho(a', b', c')$. This is an equivalence relation in ∇RRR. We do not include $(0, 0, 0)$. The set of equivalence classes is a set of homogeneous coordinates in the projective plane. We shall investigate the significance of homogeneous coordinates in Chapter 12.

3. In many normal teaching situations we use representatives of equivalence classes suitable to our purpose. We again give a few of the many possible examples.

(a) Evaluate using tables $0 \cdot 036^{\frac{1}{3}}$

No.	Log
$0 \cdot 036$	$\bar{2} \cdot 5563 = \bar{3} + 1 \cdot 5563$
$0 \cdot 3302 = 0 \cdot 036^{\frac{1}{3}}$	$\bar{1} \cdot 5188$

In fact, the logarithm to base 10 of $0 \cdot 036$ is any of $\ldots$ $-1 \cdot 4437$, $\bar{2} \cdot 5563$, $\bar{3} + 1 \cdot 5563$, $\bar{4} + 2 \cdot 5563$, $\ldots\ldots$ and we have a natural equivalence class. It is usually found that $\bar{2} \cdot 5563$ is the most convenient representative of the equivalence class with which to work, but, in particular, when we want to find a cube root we choose a different representative $\bar{3} + 1 \cdot 5563$, for convenience only: $\bar{6} + 4 \cdot 5563$ would have done almost as well and $\bar{4} + 2 \cdot 5563$ would also do but is not so convenient.

(b) Some 'conventions' are examples of the use of equivalence classes. For example, it is conventional when representing a complex number in $r\angle\theta$ form to give the angle such that $-\pi < \theta \leqslant \pi$. Thus $1 + i$ is written $\sqrt{2}\angle\pi/4$ by convention. Here $\pi/4$ is the chosen representative of the equivalence class of all real numbers of the form $\pi/4 + 2k\pi$ where k is any integer. When finding the cube roots of $1 + i$, say, using de Moivre's theorem, we choose three suitable representatives, e.g. $\pi/4$, $\pi/4 + 2\pi$, $\pi/4 + 4\pi$.

(c) The polar coordinates of a point (r, θ) in the plane are usually chosen so that $0 \leqslant \theta < 2\pi$. Again this value is a representative of the equivalence class $(\theta, \theta + 2\pi, \theta - 2\pi, \ldots)$, i.e. all real numbers of the form $\theta + 2k\pi$, where k is any integer. These equivalence classes are the same as those in (b), but conventionally, we choose a different representative. (Also cf. exercise 1 (c), page 46.)

(d) Let F be the set of all real valued differentiable functions of one variable. If f and g belong to F then we shall say that $f R g$ if the derived functions f' and g' are the same, i.e. f and g differ by a real number. This is an equivalence relation in F. The indefinite integral of f' is an equivalence class. For example

$$\int \cos x \, \mathrm{d}x = \{\sin x\}$$
$$= (\sin x, \sin x + 1, \sin x - \pi, \ldots).$$

(e) arc sin $\dfrac{1}{\sqrt{2}} = \dfrac{\pi}{4}$ or $\dfrac{3\pi}{4}$ or $-\dfrac{5\pi}{4}$ or $\ldots$ This again leads to a natural equivalence relation in the set of real numbers, $a R b$ if $\sin a = \sin b$. The 'principal value' of arc sin a is that representative θ of the equivalence class which is such that $-\dfrac{\pi}{2} \leqslant \theta \leqslant \dfrac{\pi}{2}$.

In fact, every 'many-valued' function leads to a natural equivalence relation which will be described in the next chapter.

(f) Consider the set F of all rational numbers. We say that two fractions $\dfrac{a}{b}$ and $\dfrac{c}{d}$ are equivalent if $ad = bc$. This is a proper equivalence relation. The equivalence classes are usually represented by the unique rational number $\dfrac{a}{b}$ where a and b are mutually prime. But this is not always convenient: for instance

$$\frac{2}{7} + \frac{1}{6} = \frac{12}{42} + \frac{7}{42} = \frac{19}{42}.$$

Because $\frac{2}{7}$ was not convenient we chose a different representative of its equivalence class. We shall return to a more detailed consideration of the whole subject of the teaching of rational numbers in a later chapter.

(g) Let V' be the set of all directed straight line-segments in three-dimensional space. We shall say that two line-segments are related if

(i) they have the same length,

(ii) they have the same direction, i.e. they are parallel and have the same sense.

This is an equivalence relation in V'. The equivalence classes are known as *free vectors* (or just vectors) and are the objects investigated in vector analysis as applied to mechanics, hydro- and aerodynamics, electrical and magnetic theory, etc. If P is any point of space then there is one line-segment in each equivalence class which has its starting point at P. Such a representative of a free vector is called a *localized vector*. In particular, if we have chosen a coordinate system in space, then there is a localized vector starting at 0, the origin of the system, representing each free vector. This localized vector is called the *position vector* of its terminal point Q.

These seven examples are only some of the possible uses of the idea of equivalence classes and their convenient or conventional representatives. We think that they are sufficient to make the point that the concept of an equivalence relation can be used in many ways to give the student another initial unifying theme. Mathematics is not a collection of isolated tricks, there are always common ideas which can facilitate learning and understanding. (See also the next exercise.)

4. Geometry abounds in relations between objects some of which are equivalence relations. Which of the following relations are equivalence relations in the sets specified?

(a) The set of all triangles with the relations,

    (i)   congruence,

    (ii) similarity,

    (iii) equality of area.

(b) The set of all lines in space with the relations,

    (i)   parallelism,

    (ii) perpendicularity,

    (iii) skewness, i.e. line 1 is related to line 2 if they are skew,

    (iv) intersection.

(c) The set of all circles in the plane with the relations,

    (i) orthogonal intersection,

    (ii) concentricity.

Let S be a set in which we have a binary operation o and an equivalence relation R. (We shall restrict our present discussion to a binary operation for which if a, $b \in S$, a o b also belongs to S.) Denote the set of equivalence classes by S'. Can we *induce* a binary operation from S to S'? The natural procedure might be as follows.

Let a, b, c, d, ... be elements of S and suppose $a R b$ and $c R d$, i.e. $(a, b, \ldots)$ and $(c, d, \ldots)$ are two elements of S'. Then we define

$$(a, b, \ldots) \text{ o } (c, d, \ldots) = (a \text{ o } c, a \text{ o } d, \ldots, b \text{ o } c, b \text{ o } d, \ldots).$$

But clearly, for this to be a proper definition ($a \circ c$, $a \circ d$, ..., $b \circ c$, $b \circ d$, ...) must be an element of S'. This means that, for instance, $[a \circ c] \, R \, [b \circ d]$, i.e. that any

$$a \, R \, b \text{ and } c \, R \, d \text{ imply } [a \circ c] \, R \, [b \circ d].$$

If this is the case then we obtain a properly defined binary operation in S' and we say that the equivalence relation is *compatible* with the binary operation; we can perform the combination of two elements of S' by combining any representative of the one with any representative of the other, and the result is a representative of the new element of S'. Since the operation in S' is defined in terms of the operation in S we shall use the same symbol and the same name in S'.

Example J. Consider a set S of sets with the equivalence relation of equality.
Then $A = B$ and $C = D$ imply $A \cup C = B \cup D$,
$$A \cap C = B \cap D,$$
$$A \bigtriangleup B = C \bigtriangleup D,$$
where A, B, C, $D \in S$.

Example K. Consider the partition of the real numbers given in Example D on page 43, i.e. that given by

$$x \, R \, y, \text{ where } m \leqslant x < m + 1, \; m \leqslant y < m + 1.$$

Then neither addition nor multiplication give an *induced operation* in the set of equivalence classes. It is left to the reader to show this by specific examples.

Example L. Show that if a binary operation is commutative and associative in S, then the induced binary operation (if it exists) is commutative and associative in S'.

Exercises

We leave the reader to discover which of the many examples of sets S (with the usual operations appropriate to each) given in the previous set of exercises (on pages 45–48) have an induced operation in the corresponding set S'. We shall take the results of such an investigation for granted and give a few interpretations and applications.

1. In Exercise 1(b) S is the set of all integers and both addition and multiplication can be induced into the set of residue classes modulo 2. This can be interpreted as follows:

even + even = even, even + odd = odd, odd + odd = even;
even × even = even, even × odd = even, odd × odd = odd.

2. In Exercise 1(c) the addition of residue classes modulo 2π can be interpreted as the combination of rotations. Is there an interpretation of the multiplication of residue classes?

3. In Exercise 3(e) addition and multiplication in the set of real numbers are not compatible with the equivalence relation, i.e. we do not get induced operations in S'. That addition is not compatible is a result of the fact that if $\sin a = \sin b$ and $\sin c = \sin d$, it does not follow that

$$\sin [a + c] = \sin [b + d].$$

4. In Exercise 3(f) the operations of addition and multiplication are compatible with the equivalence relation, a fact which we constantly use. See also Chapter 7, page 110, where we introduce rational numbers.

5. Occasionally we come across binary operations in a set S with values in another set T. There are two common binary operations of this sort in the set V' of Exercise 3(g). Given two line segments at a point P in space, the product of the length of one with the length of the projection of the other upon it, is a real number: i.e. suppose the two line-segments are PQ and PR as shown in the figure, then

$$PR \circ PQ = (\text{length } PR) \times (\text{length } PM) = (\text{length } PR) \times (\text{length } PQ) \times \cos \theta.$$

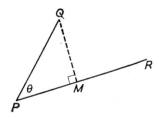

Thus we have a binary operation in V' with values in the set of real numbers. It is commutative; associativity has no meaning.

We shall say that such a binary operation in a set S with values in a set T is compatible with an equivalence relation R in S, if

$$a \, R \, b \text{ and } c \, R \, d \text{ imply } a \circ c = b \circ d;$$

i.e. the result of combining two equivalence classes does not depend on the choice of representatives. It follows that

$$(a, b, \ldots) \circ (c, d, \ldots) = a \circ c$$

is a proper definition.

The binary operation which we introduced in V' is called the *inner product* (or *scalar product*) of two localized vectors and it is compatible with the equivalence relation. Hence we have a scalar product in the set V of free vectors which occurs frequently in all the various applications of vector analysis. For instance, two vectors are perpendicular if the inner product is zero; the inner product of a vector with itself is the square of the length of the vector. In mechanics, if one vector represents the force being exerted on a body which is pulled by this force along a path represented by the other vector, then the inner product represents the work done, etc.

The second binary operation in V', defined in terms of the figure, is

$$PR \circ PQ = (\text{length } PR) \times (\text{length } PQ) \times \sin \theta.$$

It also has values in the set of real numbers and is commutative. Associativity has no meaning. It is compatible with the equivalence relation and can, therefore, be used in V. For instance, two vectors are parallel if the result of this binary operation is zero. In general, it represents the area of the parallelogram defined by any appropriate pair of representatives of the two vectors. However, this binary operation is somewhat modified in vector analysis, so we shall not pursue it further here.

*   *   *   *   *

We conclude with an example from topology.

Let S be a set with a topology $T : S$ and an equivalence relation R. Let S' be the set of equivalence classes and consider each of the subsets U of S' for which all the individual elements in all the equivalence classes in U together form an open subset of $T : S$. For instance, in Example R of Chapter 2, page 38, suppose that the set of positive reals has the equivalence relation

$$x \, R \, y \text{ if } m < x \leqslant m + 1 \text{ and } m < y \leqslant m + 1,$$

where m takes all positive integral values (including zero). Denote each of the equivalence classes by $[m]$ for the appropriate m. Then the single element $[0]$, i.e. all x such that $0 < x \leqslant 1$, is such a set U since this corresponds to the open set A_1 in A. But $[m]$, $m \neq 0$, is not such a set U, whereas any subset of the form $([0] \cup [1] \cup [2] \cup \ldots)$ is.

In general, the set of all such subsets U in S' forms a topology for S' (denote this subset system by X). To prove this we shall use the following notation: if A' is a subset of S' then we shall denote by A the subset of S which consists of all the individual elements in the classes of A'; similarly B and B', etc.

(i) $S' \in X$ because S is open in $T : S$. Also $\emptyset \in X$ because it corresponds to $\emptyset$ in S.

(ii) Any element in $A \cap B$ will appear in some equivalence class in $A' \cap B'$. Further, if $a \in A$ but does not belong to B, then since equivalence classes are made up of disjoint subsets of S, the equivalence class corresponding to a belongs to A' and not B'. It follows that $A \cap B$ in S corresponds to $A' \cap B'$ in S'. Hence if A' and B' belong to X (i.e. A and B are open in $T : S$ and so is $A \cap B$) $A' \cap B'$ also belongs to X.

(iii) A union of subsets $A' \cup B' \cup \ldots$ in S' corresponds to $A \cup B \cup \ldots$ in S. Therefore, if A', B', C', $\ldots$ all belong to X then their union also belongs to X. Hence we have shown that X is a topology for S'.

Example M. Consider the same set (positive reals) and the same topology as in the text above but with the equivalence relation

$$x \, R \, y \text{ if } m \leqslant x < m + 1 \text{ and } m \leqslant y < m + 1, \, m \neq 0$$
and
$$x \, R \, y \text{ if } 0 < x < 1 \text{ and } 0 < y < 1.$$

Show that the only open sets in the induced* topology for S' are S' and $\emptyset$.

Example N. Let S be the positive integers with zero. Consider the system of sets of the form $(3r, 3r + 1, 3r + 2)$, where r is any positive integer or zero, together with all unions of such sets. If we include S and $\emptyset$ this is a topology for S.

If the equivalence relation is the clock-face one given in Exercise 1(a) on page 46, show that the individual elements of S', regarded as sets, are open.

* Where a topology arises from some existing relation we shall usually say that it has been 'induced' by it. The usual procedure is to reserve 'induced' for subset topologies (see Chapter 2, Example U, page 38) while that above, arising from an equivalence relation, is called the 'identification' topology.

CHAPTER 4

MAPPINGS

ONE of the simplest and most important, and yet most neglected, of basic mathematical concepts is that of a mapping. Let A and A' be any two sets, then any rule which assigns to any given element $a \in A$ a subset of elements of A' is said to be a *mapping* of A to A'. We say that a is mapped onto the subset; the latter is called the *image* of a under the mapping. In general, we shall denote the image by $(a', \ldots)$, where a' is an element in the image set of a. When the image is one element a' only, then we shall omit the brackets.

Example A. Consider the set of natural numbers and the rule which assigns each natural number to its prime factors, then 12 is mapped onto 2 and 3, 70 is mapped onto 7 and 2 and 5, and 4 is mapped onto 2. The set of images or image set is, of course, the set of prime numbers.

It is convenient to give a mapping a label, i.e. to denote the mapping by a letter such as f, say: then we write symbolically

$$f: a \rightarrow (a', \ldots) \text{ or* } f(a) = (a', \ldots).$$

When we wish to consider the image of more than one element of A this notation is naturally extended to subsets of A. Thus

$$f: S \rightarrow S' \text{ or } f(S) = S',$$

where S is a subset of A and S' is a subset of A'. In particular $f(A)$ would mean the image of the complete set A. Note that it is not to be assumed that $f(A) = A'$. In fact, if every element of A' *is* the image of some element of A (i.e. $f(A) = A'$) then the mapping is said to be *onto* A', otherwise (i.e. $f(A) \subset A'$) it is said to be *into* A'. When we do not wish to specify whether a mapping is onto or into A' we just say that it is to A'.

* The second of these forms seems to tend to focus attention on the image under the mapping, while the first gives more weight to the mapping itself. In the past much trouble has been caused by the careless identification of the mapping with the image: in an attempt to rectify this we shall often prefer the first form. This is not to claim any particular merit for the first form: it is merely that its less traditional nature may cause more careful reading.

To invert a mapping, we must find the subset of A which maps onto any element a' of A' under f; we say that this subset is the *inverse image* of a' under f.

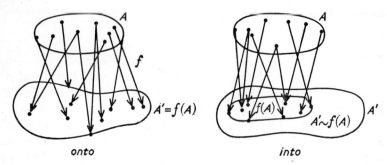

onto   *into*

Example B. If the sets and the mapping are those in the example above, then the inverse image of the prime number 2 is

$$(2, 4, 6, \ldots),$$

i.e. the set of all even numbers. The inverse image of any prime number is the set of all multiples of that prime.

If f is an into mapping then any element $a' \in A'$ may be the image of no element of A. This would be the case if a' is not in $f(A)$, i.e. using the notation introduced in Chapter 2, page 28, we could say that $a' \in [A' \sim f(A)]$.

We shall denote the *inverse mapping* of f by an inverted f, thus $\mathcal{f}$, and we write

$$\mathcal{f}: a' \rightarrow (a, \ldots) \quad \text{or} \quad \mathcal{f}(a') = (a, \ldots),$$

and in particular, $\mathcal{f}: f(A) = A$. We shall say that $\mathcal{f}$ is undefined on $A' \sim f(A)$.

A is usually called the *domain* of the mapping f and A' the *range** of the mapping. We distinguish three main classes of mapping:

(i) if to each element a of A there corresponds only one element a' of A', then the mapping f is said to be *many-one*;

(ii) if f maps $a' \in f(A)$ onto just the one element $a \in A$, then f is said to be *one-many*;

(iii) if (i) and (ii) hold simultaneously, that is, if f maps each element a of A onto just one element a' of A' and conversely, if f

---

* Strictly, the term 'range' should be reserved for $f(A)$. We prefer to use the word loosely and achieve precision, where required, by the use of 'onto'. (See example L, page 57.)

maps each element a' of $f(A) \subseteq A'$ onto just one a, then the mapping f is said to be *one-one*.

The last case is very important. If f is a one-one onto mapping then A and A' are said to be in *one-one correspondence*, meaning that to every element of A there corresponds just one element of A' and to every element of A' there corresponds just one element of A.

We have introduced a considerable number of terms in the last few paragraphs and we shall now attempt to clarify the concepts in the notes and examples which follow.

NOTE: There are many synonyms for some of the terms we have used. On the other hand, different authors adopt different usages, so that it is not easy to give a list of synonyms and usages. It is always advisable to find out exactly how an author defines his terms. There is one word which we should like to mention expressly, and that is the word '*function*' which is often taken to be synonymous with our word mapping. Yet it is used in a slightly different form in many cases, a form which is also different from the classical use of the word function. It is restricted, by many authors, to apply only to what we have called a many-one mapping (including, of course, a one-one mapping). In classical terminology this would be a single-valued function. This use of function has the following typical consequences.

(a) The mapping of the real numbers R onto the positive reals R^+ defined by $f: x \longrightarrow x^2$ or $f(x) = x^2$, where x is a real number, is a many-one mapping and, therefore, also a function in the new sense. The inverse mapping $f: R^+ \longrightarrow R$ is, however, not a function since, for example, $f: 4 \longrightarrow (2, -2)$. The approach must be changed a little if we want our function to have an inverse which is also a function. We would have to consider two functions, $f: R^+ \longrightarrow R^+$ and $f: R^- \longrightarrow R^+$, where R^- has the obvious meaning. Thus although the mapping looks the same in both cases, its domain differs, and both mappings are now one-one. We leave the reader to make these functions explicit.

In the theory of complex numbers many-one mappings of the complex plane onto (or into) itself are made one-one by the construction of appropriate Riemann surfaces.

(b) Sine: $x \longrightarrow \sin x$ is a many-one mapping of R into R and hence also a function. It maps R into R, or R onto the subset $-1 \leqslant x \leqslant 1$ of R. The inverse mapping arc sine: $x \longrightarrow \arcsin x$ is not a function. Arc sine is a function, however, if its range is restricted to $-\frac{\pi}{2} \leqslant x \leqslant \frac{\pi}{2}$, say. (Classical terminology achieves the same end by the use of some such phrase as 'principal values only'.) Alternatively, sine may be regarded as the mapping of a set of equivalence classes, i.e.

$$\text{sine}: \{x\} \longrightarrow \sin x$$

where $x R y$ if $\sin x = \sin y$. This is a particular example of a general concept given in one of the following examples.

It is clear that only a one-one function can have an inverse function in this sense of the word.

In consequence of the above note, and also because many-one mappings are of considerable importance, we shall call a many-one mapping a *function*, and retain the word mapping to be used in the general sense of many-many mappings of which many-one, one-many and one-one mappings are special cases.

Example C. Consider a mapping f of the set A of all different words in this sentence to the alphabet A', defined by taking as the image of each word the last letter in the word. (We do not count f, A or A' as words.) Thus

$$f(\text{the}) = e, \quad f(\text{mapping}) = g$$

and $f(e) = (\text{sentence, the, image})$, $f(d) = (\text{word, defined})$. Is this mapping a function? Is it into or onto? What is the set $f(A)$ on which f is defined, and is f a function?

If a and b are words of the sentence, define $a R b$ if both words have the same last letter. Then the sentence is partitioned into equivalence classes and the mapping of the equivalence classes into the alphabet has an inverse which is a function.

Example D. Consider the set A of natural numbers less than nine and the set A' which is the same as the set A in the previous example. A mapping f is defined so that to each natural number in A corresponds the words with that number of letters. Investigate this mapping as indicated in the previous example.

Example E. The mapping f which maps each person onto his navel is a one-one mapping of the set of all people onto the set of all navels. The mapping which assigns to the 'centre' of each town in England its latitude and longitude (to the nearest second) is also a one-one mapping (we hope). It maps the set of all towns in England into the set of pairs (a, b) where a is a latitude value and b is a longitude value. If, however, the latitude and longitude values were assigned to the nearest degree the mapping would be many-one.

ROD

Example F. The reader is advised to make up many examples of his own and investigate them. In particular find examples of,

(i) a many-one mapping onto,

(ii) a one-one mapping into,

(iii) a one-many mapping into.

Example G. If a mapping f of a set A to a set A' is one-many we can define an equivalence relation on $f(A)$ in a similar fashion to the two examples considered above. Let a' and $b' \in f(A)$, then we shall say that

$$a' \, R \, b' \text{ if } f(a') = f(b') = a, \text{ say.}$$

Verify that this is a proper equivalence relation. Denote the set of equivalence classes by A_1. The mapping f_1 which maps a to $\{f(a)\} \in A_1$ is one-one. Construct an example.

Example H. Let A to be a set on which an equivalence relation R has been imposed. Let A_1 be the set of equivalence classes. Then there is a natural many-one map of A onto A_1 defined by $f(a) = \{a\}$.

Example I. A mapping may also be regarded as defining a set of ordered pairs (a, a'), where the first element in each pair is an element belonging to the domain of the mapping and the second element is an image of this element in the range. Conversely, a set of ordered pairs defines a mapping by taking all first elements as the domain and all second elements as the range. The correspondence is then the natural one: a first element a corresponds to all second elements of ordered pairs in which a has appeared as first element. Thus in Example C on page 56 typical ordered pairs would be

(the, e), (sentence, e), (mapping, g), etc.

Notice, that as we have explained, (Jim, Mary) is not the same as (Mary, Jim).

Example J. In Example I on page 45 in the last chapter we showed that an equivalence relation defines a set of ordered pairs of a particular type. This set of ordered pairs, in turn, may be regarded as defining a mapping of A onto itself or the equivalence relation. So we see that by an 'abuse of language' we may say that an equivalence relation is a special type of mapping.

Example K. Under what conditions is a set of ordered pairs a function? Is the following set of ordered pairs a function?

(Lolita, Nabokov), (St. Joan, Shaw), (Agnes Grey, Brontë), (Phoebe Thirsk, Meyerstein), (Emma, Brontë), (Salomé, Wilde). Is the inverse a function? Can you suggest a simple literary improvement to make it a function?

Example L. It may be asked why we bother with into mappings at all. Why not always restrict A' to the image set of A? The answer to this is that we can very often determine a set outside of which the image cannot lie without being able to determine very easily the exact set of all images. Thus the mapping of a name in the current London telephone directory onto the telephone number (excluding the letters) is a mapping into the set of all four digit numbers. It would be difficult to define the set for which this map would be onto (except, of course, as the set of all four digit numbers in the telephone directory), although the Post Office might know. Alternatively, one could go through the four volumes and make a list if one really wanted. The point is that the essential information is described by the mapping into. Is this mapping a function? Make up your own examples of mappings for which the into concept is useful.

A rather sophisticated example arises from the fallacy which asserts that every angle is an integral multiple of π. Consider the mapping of the complex numbers to the complex numbers defined by

$$\text{tangent}: z \longrightarrow \tan z.$$

(For the reader unfamiliar with the definition of tan in this context, we mention that all the 'usual' formulae of 'real' trigonometry still apply.) One does not often hear a teacher remark that tangent is a many-one mapping of some of the real numbers onto the real numbers (ignoring $\dfrac{\pi}{2}$ and such-like), so let us suppose that tangent, as a mapping of the complex numbers to the complex numbers, had also been introduced without comment. Let z_1 be a complex number which maps onto i ($i^2 = -1$)* under tangent, i.e.

$$\tan z_1 = i.$$

Let a be any number, then

$$\tan [z_1 + a] = \frac{\tan z_1 + \tan a}{1 - \tan a \tan z_1}$$

$$= \frac{i + \tan a}{1 - i \tan a}$$

$$= \frac{i[1 - i \tan a]}{1 - i \tan a}$$

$$= i$$

$$= \tan z_1$$

$$\therefore z_1 + a = z_1 + k\pi, \text{ for any integer } k,$$

whence $a = k\pi$, as previously asserted.

The fallacy lies not in the individual steps in the 'proof' but in the very first assumption, i.e. 'let $\tan z_1 = i$'. In fact, tangent is a mapping of the complex plane (possibly excluding points of the form $[2k + 1]\dfrac{\pi}{2}$, k any integer) onto the complex plane except for the two points $\pm i$, i.e. there is no number z_1 whose image is i.

Exercises

The general concept of a mapping (like many other general ideas) is much easier to grasp than the particular concept of a real-valued function. Moreover, one does not need to revise or enlarge one's ideas when faced with slight

---

* There is no good reason why one should always use the label i as here, and we do not do so. The i–j confusion in the minds of some students is a typical consequence of misplaced 'consistency'. For an introduction to complex numbers see the article by M. Bruckheimer and N. Gowar in *Mathematics Teaching*, May, 1965.

variants; the same terminology will get one through all mathematics. Another point is that one can give what one might call 'non-numerical' examples of the terms introduced, which usually tends to add to the interest.

Having introduced the general ideas one can then use the terminology whenever convenient and useful. We give a few examples.

1. The range and domain of a mapping are useful things to know; for instance, in the following cases, suggest a domain and determine the corresponding (onto) range.

$$x \longrightarrow \text{(i)} \ \sqrt{1 - x^2}, \quad \text{(ii)} \ \frac{1}{1 - x}, \quad \text{(iii)} \tan x, \quad \text{(iv)} \log x.$$

What are the inverse mappings? Are they functions? Into or onto?

In this way we gain a knowledge of the mappings and add to the precision and accuracy of our statements.

2. A particular class of mappings of special interest are the constant mappings, i.e. f is a constant mapping if it maps all elements in its domain A onto a single element b, say. An example of such a mapping is

$$x \longrightarrow \sin^2 x + \cos^2 x = [\sin x]^2 + [\cos x]^2$$

which maps the real numbers onto the single element 1.

3. The idea of the composition of independent mappings allows us to analyse our particular examples further.

If f maps A to A' and g maps A' to A'' then we can combine f and g to form a map h of A to A''. h is defined by saying that

$$h(a) = g(f(a))$$

and we write $h = g \circ f$. This combination of two mappings is clearly in general not commutative (e.g. $x \longrightarrow \sin [2x] \neq x \longrightarrow 2 [\sin x]$), but it is associative. Analyse the following mappings (using a suitable domain) by decomposing them into simpler mappings. State the intermediary ranges and domains.

$$x \longrightarrow \text{(i)} \sin [x^2], \quad \text{(ii)} [\sin x]^2, \quad \text{(iii)} \sin [\sin x], \quad \text{(iv)} \sqrt{1 - x^2}.$$

4. One should be careful to distinguish between a mapping and an image in the range. It is a general and confusing abuse of language to refer to a function $f(x)$. $f(x)$ is very rarely a function, it is very often a real number: f is a function. This confusion can easily be avoided by a little more precision in statement and, in some cases, a better notation. Incidentally, if the derivative of a real-valued function f (where f is a many-one mapping of the reals into the reals) is denoted by f' then $f'(0)$ means the value of the function f' at zero; but if the function is said to be $f(x)$ and its derivative $f'(x)$, then $f'(0)$ is a notation which confuses many students.

5. Consider the set of all differentiable real-valued functions. Then the mapping D defined by

$$D:f \longrightarrow f'$$

is a many-one mapping of the set into the set of all real-valued functions, and D is, therefore, a function. The inverse $\int$ of D is not a function, since the inverse image of f' is the set of all functions of the form

$$f + c$$

where c is any real number. But if we introduce the natural equivalence relation mentioned in Exercise 3(d) on page 47 in the previous chapter, then the inverse mapping is a function.

6. The *graph* of a mapping is the set of ordered pairs defined by the mapping. Thus the graph of the function square:$x \longrightarrow x^2$, mapping the real numbers onto the positive reals, is the set of ordered pairs of the form (x, x^2) where x is any real number. In general, if f maps A into A' then the graph of f is the set of ordered pairs $(a, f(a))$.

Sometimes we can draw pictures to represent the graph of a mapping. For instance, if f maps the reals into the reals we can use the conventional Cartesian coordinate system and represent the element $(a, f(a))$ of the graph by the point with coordinates $(a, f(a))$.

When one has developed the idea of a continuous function one can use it to define a curve in any space A as the image under a continuous many-one mapping of the interval $0 \leqslant x \leqslant 1$ of the set of real numbers into A. (See Chapter 8, page 135, and Mansfield & Bruckheimer, *Mathematics: A New Approach*, Book 5.) This definition is then seen to tie up with the intuitive concept of a curve.

7. A binary operation in a set S with values in a set T can be represented as a mapping of $S \triangledown S$ to T. Thus if $a \circ b = c$, we write

$$0:(a, b) \longrightarrow c.$$

The binary operation is commutative if $0((a, b)) = 0((b, a))$. We leave the reader to express the associative property in these terms: notice that our definition of associativity is meaningful only if $T \subseteq S$.

Are the following binary operations commutative and/or associative?

(i) $(a, b) \longrightarrow a^b$, (ii) $(a, b) \longrightarrow |a-b|$, where $|a-b|$ denotes the absolute value of $a-b$.

Suppose that we have a set S with a binary operation $\circ$ with values in S and a set T with a binary operation $\square$, and a many-one mapping f of S onto T. f is said to be a *homomorphic mapping* (or a *homomorphism*) if it preserves the structure of S in T, i.e. if

$$f(a \circ b) = f(a) \square f(b).$$

The structure of T is said to be a *homomorphic image* of the structure of S. When the mapping f is one-one then f is called an *isomorphic mapping* (or an *isomorphism*); the structures are said to be *isomorphic*.

These concepts are of the utmost importance and we shall study them in more detail, for the particular case when the binary operation gives group structure, in subsequent chapters. Here we shall give a few general examples.

Example M. Suppose that we have a set S with a binary operation o and an equivalence relation R which is compatible with o. Then the *natural mapping* f of an element $a \in S$ to the equivalence class $\{a\} \in S_1$ is a homorphism. For, by definition of the compatibility of R and o we have

$$f(a \circ b) = \{a \circ b\} = \{a\} \circ \{b\}$$
$$= f(a) \circ f(b).$$

(Note that this becomes clearer if we use different symbols for the operations, for instance, if we use $\square$ for the combination of equivalence classes, the above reads

$$f(a \circ b) = \{a \circ b\} = \{a\} \square \{b\}$$
$$= f(a) \square f(b).$$

We do not, in general, use different symbols because the operations are closely linked and a mass of unusual symbolism makes a book unreadable.)

An example of such a situation is given by Exercise 1 in Chapter 3, page 49, where we took the set of natural numbers N with the operation of multiplication and the equivalence relation $a \, R \, b$ if $a \equiv b \pmod 2$. We stated there that multiplication is compatible with the equivalence relation and, therefore, we get the induced multiplication in the set of equivalence classes. This latter set P consists of the two elements $E = (2, 4, \ldots)$ and $0 = (1, 3, 5, \ldots)$ and the induced multiplication (which is commutative) is

$$E \times E = E, \quad E \times 0 = E, \quad 0 \times 0 = 0.$$

The natural many-one correspondence f illustrated below is a homomorphism. It maps the odd numbers onto 0 and the even numbers onto E.

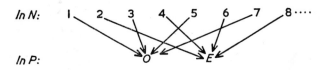

Taking a particular example we have

$$f(2 \times 3) = \{2 \times 3\} = E$$
$$= \{2\} \times \{3\} = E \times 0 = E.$$

CHAPTER 4

62

Example N. The above case is very simple; but suppose we have two sets each with its operation and we are required to decide whether they are isomorphic or homomorphic or neither. For instance, consider the set of all real numbers with addition and with multiplication. We shall denote the two structures by $(R, +)$ and $(R, \times)$. Since we have the same fundamental set we clearly have a one-one mapping (in fact, many such) between $(R, +)$ and $(R, \times)$; is there an isomorphic mapping? Let us suppose that f is an isomorphic mapping, then

$$f(a + 0) = f(a) \times f(0), \qquad \text{because } f \text{ is an isomorphism,}$$
but $\quad f(a + 0) = f(a),$

where a is any real number. It follows that $f(0) = 1$. Also

$$f(a + - a) = f(a) \times f(-a), \qquad \text{because } f \text{ is an isomorphism,}$$
but $\quad f(a + - a) = f(0) = 1.$

Therefore, $f(a) \times f(- a) = 1$ so that $f(a) = \dfrac{1}{f(- a)}$.

Now f is a one-one mapping, therefore (since $f(0) = 1$) there is an element $b \neq 0$, $b \in (R, +)$ which maps onto 0 in $(R, \times)$. The last result implies that $- b$ maps onto $1/0$, which is not a real number and hence there is no isomorphism between $(R, +)$ and $(R, \times)$.

Another way of showing that no isomorphism exists is as follows: let $b \in (R, +)$, then there is always an a, such that $a + a = b$. This implies that under an isomorphism f

$$f(a) \times f(a) = f(b) . \qquad . \qquad . \qquad . \qquad . \quad (1)$$

Now if f is one-one, then $f(b)$ is any element of $(R, \times)$, and the equation (1) is certainly not satisfied for all elements of $(R, \times)$.

Exercise

Well-known examples of isomorphisms between $(R^+, \times)$ and $(R, +)$ are

$$\log_a : a^x \rightarrow x,$$

where a is any positive real number $(\neq 1)$ and R^+ is the set of all positive real numbers (without zero). The inverse mapping is $\text{antilog}_a : x \rightarrow a^x$ and is also an isomorphism (see next example). Incidentally, it is because these mappings are isomorphisms that we use 'logs' to solve our problems. The statement

$$\log bc = \log b + \log c$$

tells us that the two structures are homomorphic, and if the mapping were not one-one we might have considerable difficulty in obtaining an answer—consider, for instance, the slide-rule as an example of a homomorphism.

Example O. If f is an isomorphism* of S onto T, then f is an isomorphism of T onto S. For, f is one-one because f is, and if $a, b \in S$, then, because f is

---

* Notice that an isomorphism implies the existence of binary operations in each of the two sets and, to be precise, one ought to specify them. See footnote to Example Q.

an isomorphism,

$$f(f(a) \square f(b)) = f(f(a \circ b)),$$
$$= a \circ b, \qquad \text{(because } f \text{ is one-one)}$$
$$= f(f(a)) \circ f(f(b)), \qquad \text{(again because } f \text{ is one-one).}$$

Example P. If we consider a collection of sets, each with a binary operation, then the relationship $S\,R\,T$ if S is isomorphic to T is an equivalence relation.

(i) We have just shown that $S\,R\,T$ implies $T\,R\,S$.

(ii) The identity mapping which maps each element of S onto itself is an isomorphism of S onto itself, and so $S\,R\,S$.

(iii) $S\,R\,T$ and $T\,R\,U$ imply $S\,R\,U$. For, let the binary operations in S, T and U be $\circ$, $\square$ and $\triangleright$ respectively, and denote an isomorphism of S onto T by f and of T onto U by g. Then if a and b are any elements of S we have

$$f(a \circ b) = f(a) \square f(b)$$
$$g(f(a) \square f(b)) = g(f(a)) \triangleright g(f(b)).$$

Now consider the combination h of f and g as defined in Exercise 3 on page 59. It is a one-one mapping of S onto U and

$$h(a \circ b) = g(f(a \circ b))$$
$$= g(f(a) \square f(b)) = g(f(a)) \triangleright g(f(b))$$
$$= h(a) \triangleright h(b).$$

Is a 'homomorphism' an equivalence relation on sets? If not, why not?

Example Q. If $(S, \circ)$* is mapped homomorphically onto $(T, \square)$, then show that if $\circ$ is commutative and/or associative, $\square$ is commutative and/or associative.

$$* \quad * \quad * \quad * \quad *$$

We finish the chapter in the usual way with an example from topology. Let S_1 be a set with a topology $T: S_1$ and let S_2 be another set with topology $T: S_2$, then a many-one mapping f of S_1 onto S_2 is said to be *continuous* if for every set $U \in T: S_2$, $f(U) \in T: S_1$. In words this can be expressed by saying that the function f is continuous if the inverse image of any set open in the topology of S_2 is open in the topology of S_1. The following example should clarify why we adopt this definition.

Example R. A 'real valued function f of one real variable' (i.e. a many-one mapping of the reals onto a subset of the reals) is defined to be continuous in text-books on analysis in the following way.

'f is continuous at a point $x = a$ if given any real number $\epsilon > 0$, there exists a $\delta > 0$ such that

$$|f(x) - f(a)| < \epsilon,$$

for all $0 < |x - a| < \delta$.' In general, f is continuous over a range if it is

* $(S, \circ)$ indicates 'the set S with binary operation $\circ$'.

continuous at all points a of the range. If we represent the situation pictorially thus

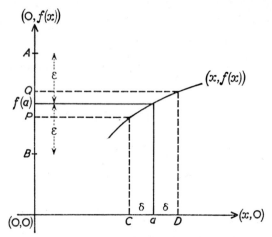

then the definition means that 'f is continuous at the point $x = a$ if given any *interval* AB* about $f(a)$ on the line representing the values of $(0, f(x))$ then there exists an interval CD about a on the line representing the values of $(x, 0)$ such that for all points x in CD, $f(x)$ lies within AB'.† Now f is a one-one mapping (in the case illustrated) of a subset of the line $(x, 0)$ onto a subset of the line $(0, f(x))$, and AB contains the interval PQ which is the image of CD. Thus we can again restate the result as 'f is continuous at a point $x = a$, if for any interval PQ about $f(a)$, $f(PQ) = CD$ is an interval'. Now if we wrote 'open set' for 'interval', we would be back, almost word for word, to our general definition above. Nevertheless, the two terms are *not* synonymous.

In fact the set of all intervals do not form a topology for the real line, since the union of any two intervals is not necessarily an interval. For instance,

$$(\tfrac{1}{2} < x < 1) \cup (2 < x < 85)$$

is not an interval. So we define the *natural topology for the real line* to be the set of all intervals and their unions (including the real line and Ø, of course). (See, however, the next example.)

* By interval we mean an interval like $0 < x < 1$ throughout which is usually called an 'open interval' in analysis, in contrast to a 'closed interval' (like $0 \leqslant x \leqslant 1$) or a 'half-open interval' (like $0 \leqslant x < 1$). We do not use the expression 'open' with this meaning in the text, in order not to create a confusion with the more general topological term.

† We could take this statement as motivation for a topological definition of continuity as follows:

A many-one mapping f from S_1 to S_2 with topologies $T:S_1$ and $T:S_2$ is continuous at the point $x \in S_1$, if for any set V such that $f(x) \in V$ and $V \in T:S_2$ there exists an open set $U \in T:S_1$ such that $x \in U$ and $f(U) \subseteq V$. If f is continuous at every point x of S_1 then f is continuous on S_1.

This definition can be proved equivalent to our previous definition. We do not give the proof since we make no use of it. The proof can be found in, for instance, M. J. Mansfield, *Introduction to Topology* (Van Nostrand).

Example S. A subset of the open sets of a topology $T:S$ is said to form a *base* for the topology if every open set of $T:S$ is a union of sets of this subset. (Thus the natural topology of the real line has a base made up of all intervals.) Conversely, given a system of subsets of a set S such that the intersection of any two subsets also belongs to the system, we can define a topology in S by forming all the unions of these subsets.

We can now prove very easily that, if B is a base for $T:S_2$, then a function f of S_1 onto S_2 is continuous if and only if $f(U_B)$ is open in $T:S_1$ for every set $U_B \in B$. (The U_B are the sets of the base B.)

Let U be an arbitrary open set of $T:S_2$ and $U_B \in B$. Then suppose that $f(U_B)$ is open in $T:S_1$ for all U_B. U is a union of sets U_B and so $f(U)$ is a union of sets of the form $f(U_B)$, all of which are open in $T:S_1$, therefore $f(U)$ is open in $T:S_1$.* Conversely, suppose that f is continuous, then, since U_B is an open set of $T:S_2$, by the definition of continuity, $f(U_B)$ is open in $T:S_1$. This proves the result.

Using this result, we see that we can replace 'interval' by 'open set in the natural topology of the real line' in the above example. For although 'open set' is more general than 'a set of the base', we see that we can generalize.

Example T. The natural mapping f (Example M, page 61) of a set S onto a set of equivalence classes S_1 of S is continuous if the topology in S_1 is defined from the topology of S as at the end of the last chapter.

Example U. Using the topological definition of continuity and the idea of a base, show that the following functions are continuous mappings of the real numbers onto the real numbers with the natural topology in each case.

$$\text{(i) } x \longrightarrow x, \qquad \text{(ii) } x \longrightarrow x^3.$$

Example V. Consider the following function illustrated by its graph in the normal way.

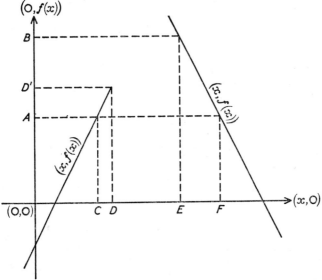

* We should have verified that the inverse image of a union of sets U_B is the union of the inverse images of the U_B. We leave this to the reader.

The inverse image of the interval AB is $CD \cup EF$ and this set contains the inverse image of the point D' which is D itself. Such a set, which contains an end point, is not an open set in the natural topology of the real line since it is not an interval of the form $a < x < b$ nor is it a union of any such intervals. Therefore the function is not a continuous mapping of the real line into itself with the natural topology of the real line. This does not, of course, preclude it from being continuous if different topologies are defined for the real line.

CHAPTER 5

CARDINALS

In the last three chapters we defined our fundamental concepts. Before discussing the idea of a group and associated topics, we will give an intuitive idea of cardinal numbers defined in terms of set, mapping and equivalence relation. In this section all maps considered will be *onto*.

We take two sets A and A' to be equivalent if there exists a one-one map $f: A \to A'$. We verify that this is a proper equivalence relation. By definition f is one-one and so $A \, R \, A'$ implies $A' \, R \, A$. Also $A \, R \, A$ since the map $f: a \to a$, the identity map, is a one-one mapping of A onto A. Further, if

$$f: A \to A' \quad \text{and} \quad g: A' \to A''$$

are one-one onto, then we can define a mapping $h: A \to A''$ by

$$h(a) = g(f(a)) = g(a') = a''.$$

This mapping is one-one and onto because f and g are one-one and onto, which completes the verification.

So we can form the equivalence classes of all sets which are in one-one correspondence with each other. We shall as usual denote these equivalence classes by $\{A\}$, and we shall call the equivalence class associated with A the *cardinal number associated with A*. We emphasize that cardinal number is the name of a class of elements, the elements being sets. Thus all sets which belong to the same equivalence class as A (i.e. are in one-one correspondence with A) will have the same associated cardinal number.

We hope that the reader will excuse the repetition in the previous paragraph, but we wished to make what seemed to us an important point, which is often found difficult.

NOTE: In spite of what we have written above, what we have done is not really unusual at all. We have re-worded in our terms the common enough statement that 3 is an abstraction (in the sense of Chapter 2, page 18) from 3 men, three oranges, a set containing a boy, a dog and a football, a piano trio, a trilogy, etc. The idea that three is what all these sets have in common is an intuitive idea, since any number of triples may have some property in common other than their three-fold quality, whereas our present approach can be used as a beginning for the precise grounding of much mathematics. (See also later!)

We define the cardinal number associated with the null set to be 0. The set whose only member I am will have an associated cardinal denoted by 1. The reader may go on to assign labels, of his own choosing, to various other sets which cannot be put into one-one correspondence with each other. He is warned, however, that nothing is to be gained by being unconventional in this respect. Just because he changes his spectacles there is no need to change the car number-plates. Labels have no intrinsic value; it is the properties of the labelled objects which are of interest and these remain to be discovered.

It is of interest to note that the equivalence classes here defined are quite different from those we could have obtained using the idea of equality of sets, which was our first equivalence relation. In the present case the sets are not necessarily equal by any means; we have just selected one property that they have in common, i.e. they can all be put into one-one correspondence with each other. Equal sets are equivalent in this sense also, but equivalent sets are not necessarily equal.

NOTE: We should add one further word of warning before continuing. We are not trying to establish a logically complete system, even if this were possible. One man's logic is another man's fallacy. (See, for example, Nidditch, *Introductory Formal Logic of Mathematics* (University Tutorial Press), who writes, 'In its whole literature, from Euclid to Bourbaki inclusive, there are scarcely any proofs in the logical sense.') Our aim is rather to develop some of the ideas of mathematics and to show some of their applications, as we have tried to explain in Chapter 1. Therefore, there are large gaps in our present development as there will be gaps in many other places. We rely very much on intuition rather than on axioms, and the reader who is interested in the logical foundations must consult more sophisticated works. We do not wish to obscure entirely one of our main purposes which was to write a book which would give the teacher some background to 'modern mathematics' as well as indicate some elementary applications.

Since we have gone to great lengths to establish the idea of equivalence classes, and especially in the last case to make the concept as clear as words will allow, we propose to use our definition of a cardinal number to develop the properties of cardinals as equivalence classes.

Let A and A' be any two sets such that $A \cap A' = \emptyset$. We shall show that union for two such sets is compatible (in the sense of Chapter 3, page 49) with the equivalence relation of one-one correspondence. That is, we show that

$$A \; R \; B \text{ and } A' \; R \; B' \text{ imply*} \; [A \cup A'] \; R \; [B \cup B']$$

where $A \cap A' = \emptyset = B \cap B'$. (Once we have proved this we are entitled to extend union to equivalence classes, as we shall explain.) By definition of the equivalence classes, there exist one-one maps f and g such that

$$f: B \rightarrow A \quad \text{and} \quad g: B' \rightarrow A'.$$

Define the map $h: B \cup B' \rightarrow A \cup A'$ by

$$h(b) = \begin{cases} f(b) \text{ if } b \in B \\ g(b) \text{ if } b \in B'. \end{cases}$$

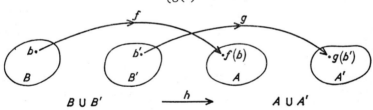

We wish to show that h is one-one onto. Certainly since $B \cap B' = \emptyset$ and f and g are one-one, corresponding to an element $b \in B \cup B'$ there is just one element $h(b)$ of $A \cup A'$. Also h is onto, because any element $a \in A \cup A'$ which is in A is the image of some element b of $B \subseteq B \cup B'$, and similarly for any $a' \in A \cup A'$ which is in A'. Thus h is at worst many-one onto, and we shall finally show that it is one-one. Let b_1 be any element, other than b, $b_1 \in B \cup B'$. Then if b

---

* There is a symbol in common use for 'implies', viz. $\Rightarrow$. For example, 'A implies B' is written 'A $\Rightarrow$ B'. If, also, B implies A one writes 'A $\Longleftrightarrow$ B'.

and $b_1 \in B$, $f(b) \neq f(b_1)$ since f is one-one and so $h(b) \neq h(b_1)$. Similarly if b and $b_1 \in B'$, $g(b) \neq g(b_1)$ so $h(b) \neq h(b_1)$. On the other hand if $b \in B$ and $b_1 \in B'$ then $h(b) = f(b) \in A$ and $h(b_1) = g(b_1) \in A'$; thus, once again, since $A \cap A' = \emptyset$, $h(b) \neq h(b_1)$. This completes the proof that h is a one-one map of $B \cup B'$ onto $A \cup A'$, i.e. $[A \cup A']\ R\ [B \cup B']$.

We have rather laboured this proof, but it is very important to make sure that our statements are meaningful. Subsequent proofs of this kind will usually be left explicitly to the reader. Eventually one achieves a sort of intuitive feeling for a result of this kind and this makes the proof little more than a formality.

If we now define

$$\{A\} \cup \{A'\} = \{A \cup A'\}$$

then this is a proper definition if $A \cap A' = \emptyset$, i.e. if the chosen representatives of the equivalence classes are disjoint: we may not choose our representatives arbitrarily.

Example A. $\{(\text{Mary}, \text{Jim})\} \cup \{(1, 2, 3)\} = \{(\text{Mary}, \text{Jim}, 1, 2, 3)\}$, which in terms of the usual labels for cardinal numbers reads

$$2 \cup 3 = 5.$$

But $\{(\text{Mary}, \text{Jim})\} \cup \{(\text{Jim})\}$ is undefined as it stands: we could, however, take a different representative for the second class.

The binary operation here defined for cardinal numbers is usually called *summation* of the two cardinal numbers; we also speak of *adding* two cardinal numbers and *addition*. The usual symbol for this binary operation is $+$, but it is perhaps not a good idea to introduce this symbol with all its implications yet.

Example B. Show that the summation of cardinals is a commutative and associative operation (where all the sets used are disjoint in the sense that their intersections are empty). This is a special case of Example L, Chapter 3, page 49.

Example C. $\{A\} \cup \{\emptyset\} = \{A\}$. (Note that although $\emptyset \subseteq A$, $\emptyset \cap A = \emptyset$.)

Example D. If B is a subset of A, verify that

$$\{A \sim B\} \cup \{B\} = \{A\}.$$

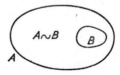

Example E. Let A and A' be any two sets, such that $A \cap A' = \emptyset$, and let B and B' be two further sets in one-one correspondence with A and A' respectively. Show that $A \cup A'$ is in one-one correspondence with $B \cup B' \cup C$ where C is in one-one correspondence with $B \cap B'$, but such that

$$B \cap C = B' \cap C = \emptyset.$$

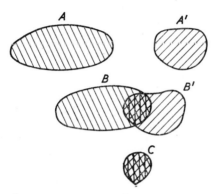

$\left(\text{Sets in one-one correspondence are represented}\right.$
$\left.\text{by similar shading}\right)$

Using this we can obtain a result for the sum of two cardinal numbers in the case where the representative sets intersect, as follows:

$$\{B\} \cup \{B'\} = \{A\} \cup \{A'\} = \{A \cup A'\} = \{B \cup B' \cup C\}$$
$$= \{B \cup B'\} \cup \{C\} = \{B \cup B'\} \cup \{B \cap B'\}.$$

Hence $\{B\} \cup \{B'\} = \{B \cup B'\} \cup \{B \cap B'\}$ is consistent with the definition for the sum of two cardinal numbers when the representatives chosen are not disjoint.

Clearly, what we have so painstakingly defined above are the *natural numbers* with zero and the addition of these numbers . . . or have we? Before we investigate this any further we shall discuss a few exercises, and adopt the more usual notation for the cardinal number associated with A, and that is $n(A)$. We shall also now use $+$. When, however, we wish to emphasize the fact that the cardinal numbers are names of equivalence classes, we shall return to the original notation. The addition formula for cardinal numbers is now

$$n(A) + n(A') = n(A \cup A') + n(A \cap A').$$

Exercises

1. The relation $n(A) + n(B) = n(A \cup B) + n(A \cap B)$ can be demonstrated by means of Venn diagrams. In the diagram below the crosses represent the elements of the sets.

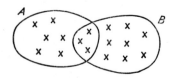

It is evident that if we count the crosses in A, to obtain $n(A)$, and count the crosses in B, to obtain $n(B)$, then, in the sum $n(A) + n(B)$ the crosses in $A \cap B$ have been counted twice. Hence $n(A) + n(B)$ exceeds $n(A \cup B)$ by $n(A \cap B)$ and this is the required result,

$$n(A) + n(B) = n(A \cup B) + n(A \cap B) . \qquad . \qquad . \quad (1)$$

Pupils of above average ability will be able to discover for themselves, by similar means, the corresponding result for three sets.

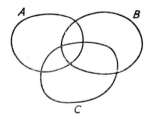

It may, however, be thought advisable to deduce this result from the previous one, using the known properties of union and intersection, as follows. First demonstrate, using the diagram, that

$$[A \cap C] \cap [B \cap C] = A \cap B \cap C . \qquad . \qquad . \quad (2)$$

Then expressing $A \cup B \cup C$ as $[A \cup B] \cup C$ according to the associative property of $\cup$, we have

$$n(A \cup B \cup C) = n([A \cup B] \cup C) = n(A \cup B) + n(C) - n([A \cup B] \cap C),$$
$$\text{from equation (1)*}$$

$$= n(A) + n(B) + n(C) - [n(A \cap B) + n([A \cup B] \cap C)],$$
$$\text{using equation (1) again,}$$

$$= n(A) + n(B) + n(C) - [n(A \cap B) + n([A \cap C] \cup [B \cap C])],$$

* We have not introduced '$-$' in our main text, but, as we have explained more than once, the examples and exercises are not in logical or teaching sequence. In Chapter 7 (page 113) we shall extend our number system and introduce subtraction; for the purpose of these exercises we assume that this has been done. One could, of course, avoid the use of $-$, but the proof would be stilted.

using the fact that $\cap$ is distributive over $\cup$,

$$= n(A) + n(B) + n(C) - [n(A \cap B) + n(A \cap C)$$
$$+ n(B \cap C)] + n([A \cap C] \cap [B \cap C]),$$

using equation (1) again.

Finally, using equation (2) to reduce $n([A \cap C] \cap [B \cap C])$ to $n(A \cap B \cap C)$, we have the result

$$n(A \cup B \cup C) = n(A) + n(B) + n(C) - [n(A \cap B) + n(A \cap C)$$
$$+ n(B \cap C)] + n(A \cap B \cap C) \quad . \quad . \quad (3)$$

2. It is of interest to find, in some numerical cases, the number of elements in each of the sections of a Venn diagram of three sets. If the numbers are small the results can be obtained by trial and error, working 'from inside outwards'. For example if, of 8 boys all of whom are wearing at least one article of school uniform, it is known that

5 wear school blazers,	2 wear blazers and ties,
4 wear school ties,	3 wear ties and caps,
5 wear school caps,	3 wear caps and blazers,

then one does not need result (3) above to discover that the only possible arrangement is as shown below.

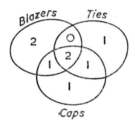

From this diagram questions like 'How many of these boys are wearing all three articles of school uniform?', 'How many of these boys are each wearing just one article of school uniform?' can be answered.

If the numbers are large trial and error becomes impracticable and pupils see that result (3) is useful. Let us imagine that every house in a village of 426 houses has one or more of the gas, electricity or telephone services connected, and 250 have gas, 200 have electricity, 150 have a telephone, while 78 have gas and electricity, 76 have electricity and telephone, and 56 have telephone and gas. Then the question 'How many of these houses have all three services?' is not readily answered by trial and error.

Result (3), however, gives

$$426 = 250 + 200 + 150 - [78 + 76 + 56] + n(A \cap B \cap C)$$

so that the number required is 36.

Other questions from the same problem, such as 'How many houses have gas only?' can then be answered by inserting the numbers in the Venn diagram, with 36 in the triple intersection and proceeding outwards.

3. An agency is asked to make a survey on the viewing and listening habits of people in this country. It employs women to make door-to-door calls. They fill in on a prepared sheet the answers to the questions. From the returns of one of these women, the following information is taken.

She visited 475 homes and found that 433 watched B.B.C. television, 362 commercial television, and 231 listened to the radio. Also 312 watched both commercial television and B.B.C., 130 received commercial television and radio, 196 received B.B.C. television and radio, and 98 received all three.

Do you think that the agency should make use of this woman in any further surveys they conduct?

We proceed somewhat intuitively to investigate our definition of cardinal number. We shall say that two labels are different if they have different markings on them. Thus the label with a 0 on it, which was attached to the class with representative the empty set, and the label with a 1 on it, which was attached to the class with representative myself, are different. But either of these labels could be hung round my neck—i.e. each single label (whatever its marking) can be put in one-one correspondence with myself— i.e. label 0 and label 1 are both representatives of the cardinal number 1.

Thus

$$n(\text{label } 0) + n(\text{label } 1) = 1 + 1$$

(sometimes denoted by the shape 2). So we can have a new label with the device $1 + 1$ on it, and

$$1 + 1 = n(\text{label } 0) + n(\text{label } 1)$$
$$= n(\text{label } 1) + n(\text{label } 1 + 1)$$
$$= n(\text{label } 1, \text{label } 1 + 1)$$
$$= n(\text{myself, you}).$$

We can go on in this way. For instance, next time

$$n(\text{label } 0, \text{label } 1) + n(\text{label } 1 + 1) = (1 + 1) + 1$$
$$= n(\text{label } 0, \text{label } 1, \text{label } 1 + 1)$$
$$= n(\text{myself, you, Khrushchev}),$$

assuming that you, myself and Khrushchev are all distinct.

Suppose now that a label r has been assigned to the set of all labels previously allocated. Call this set L_r, then

$$n(L_r) = r,$$

and $\qquad n(L_r) + n(\text{label } r) = r + 1,$

since label r does not occur in L_r, and we have another label with which to continue the process. It would seem, therefore, that the process is unending. The problem is how to express this within our defined terms, and of what significance is it?

The fact that the process is unending is easily dealt with. Consider the set of such labels L and define a mapping of L to L by mapping any label r onto label $r + 1$. Then 0 is mapped onto 1 and 1 onto $1 + 1$, etc., but nothing is mapped onto 0, that is with the exception of 0 every label is of the form $r + 1$ (where we use the identity

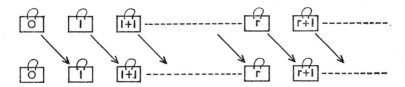

$0 + 1 = 1$) and is the image of the label r. Thus we have established a one-one correspondence of L *into* L; precisely L onto (L less the label 0). Any set in one-one correspondence with L can also be mapped one-one into itself. Hence this is a property of the equivalence class.

A study of what we have done will show that such a mapping is only possible because given any label r we can invent a new one $r + 1$, or at least we feel we can.

Example F. Consider all the words as listed in any dictionary and map each word into the one succeeding it. This is a map of the set into itself. In the dictionary I have before me this mapping looks like this

... abate, abatis, abattoir, abature, ...

... abate, abatis, abattoir, abature. ...

Of course, the first entry in the second row, which is usually 'a', has no arrow leading to it, i.e. it is the image of no element in the row above. But if I now turn my attention to the other end of the dictionary, the last entries are

. . . zyme, zymome, zymurgy, zythum,

. . . zyme, zymome, zymurgy, zythum,

and zythum in the first row has no image in the second row, unless I map it onto 'a' back at the beginning. This set thus does not have the character of our labels above. In fact, no set which is completely within our experience has this property, however large the set may be.

We shall say that a set which can be put into one-one correspondence with a *proper subset of itself* has an associated *infinite* cardinal number. Remember that all we are saying is that the equivalence class, of which the set of all labels described above is a representative, shall have the name 'infinite'. Sets which do not have the above property of being in one-one correspondence with a subset of themselves will be said to have an associated *finite* cardinal number.

From now on we shall say briefly that a set has a cardinal number, where we mean the associated equivalence class of the set. Thus the cardinal number of a set A is $\{A\}$ or $n(A)$.

Example G. The cardinal number 1 is finite.

Any number as the word is commonly understood is a finite cardinal number. We have so far introduced one infinite cardinal number $n(L)$. The symbol very often used for this number is the first letter of the Hebrew alphabet with a suffix 0, viz. $\aleph_0$ (aleph 0). The set of finite cardinal numbers or natural numbers with zero we shall denote by N. These finite cardinal numbers are, of course, the symbols on our labels, thus L and N are in one-one correspondence. Any set which belongs to the same equivalence class as N (i.e. is in one-one correspondence with N) is said to be *countably infinite*. All countably infinite sets have the cardinal number $\aleph_0$. We shall from now on use 0, 1, 2, . . . for the elements of N.

Example H. Show that if a finite number of objects is removed from a countably infinite set then it is still countably infinite. This means that it does not make sense to say that all the natural numbers are more or less than all the natural numbers greater than ten. (See also the exercises which follow.)

Example I. $\aleph_0 + \aleph_0 = \aleph_0$, i.e.

$$n(L \cup N) = n(L) = n(N),$$

whereas if A and B are sets each with finite cardinal number m, it is never true that

$$n(A) + n(B) = m,$$

unless $m = 0$.

Notice here that we are running into no real trouble when dealing with the addition of infinite cardinal numbers. But notice, also and again, that although $L \subset L \cup N$, $n(L) = n(L \cup N)$.

Exercises

1. The obvious fact that in any finite set of consecutive natural numbers there are more natural numbers than even numbers leads pupils to a false generalization when talking about 'all' natural numbers. To correct this, a one-one correspondence may be displayed as follows

$$
\begin{array}{cccccccc}
N & 1 & 2 & 3 & 4 & 5 & 6 & 7 \ldots \\
 & \updownarrow & \updownarrow & \updownarrow & \updownarrow & \updownarrow & \updownarrow & \updownarrow \\
E & 2 & 4 & 6 & 8 & 10 & 12 & 14 \ldots
\end{array}
$$

and emphasis laid on the statement that both sequences are to be imagined as continuing indefinitely. Then, to each and every member of N there corresponds just one member of E and to each and every member of E there corresponds just one member of N. Hence it cannot be true that one set has more numbers than the other, although one is a subset of the other.

Pupils may be asked to set up a one-one correspondence between the set of natural numbers and the set of multiples of three, between the set of natural numbers and the set of multiples of four, between the set of multiples of three and the set of multiples of four, and so on. In all these cases the mappings and their inverses are one-one and onto and can be represented as algebraic functions: for instance, in the correspondence set out above, if n_i is the ith member of N and e_i is the ith member of E, then $e_i = 2n_i$ and $n_i = \frac{1}{2}e_i$.

Consider also the set of primes, P. Then there is a one-one correspondence between the members of N and P, viz.

$$
\begin{array}{cccccccc}
N & 1 & 2 & 3 & 4 & 5 & 6 & 7 \ldots \\
 & \updownarrow & \updownarrow & \updownarrow & \updownarrow & \updownarrow & \updownarrow & \updownarrow \\
P & 2 & 3 & 5 & 7 & 11 & 13 & 17 \ldots
\end{array}
$$

where again, both sequences continue indefinitely. Again, this mapping and its inverse are both one-one and onto, but it can be proved that there is no exact algebraic relation between p_i and n_i. Nevertheless, both mappings are functions and p is a subset of N.

2. It follows from Exercise 1 that the even numbers are countably infinite, the multiples of three are countably infinite, the primes are countably infinite

and so on. The statement that the set of positive rationals F is countably infinite requires a little more work. Let us, for the moment, define the set of positive rationals as the set of all pairs $\frac{a}{b}$ where a and b are natural numbers.

Then there is a one-one correspondence between these pairs and the set of crosses below (continued indefinitely).

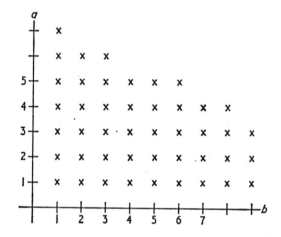

Now, by describing a path from cross to cross, the crosses are passed in order, and hence a one-one correspondence is established between the crosses (and, hence, the positive rationals) and the natural numbers. There are many possible paths; a specimen path is shown below. The first few terms of the resulting correspondence between N and F are shown on page 79.

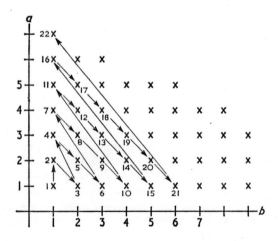

N	1	2	3	4	5	6	7	8	9	10	11 ...
	↕	↕	↕	↕	↕	↕	↕	↕	↕	↕	↕
F	$\dfrac{1}{1}$	$\dfrac{2}{1}$	$\dfrac{1}{2}$	$\dfrac{3}{1}$	$\dfrac{2}{2}$	$\dfrac{1}{3}$	$\dfrac{4}{1}$	$\dfrac{3}{2}$	$\dfrac{2}{3}$	$\dfrac{1}{4}$	$\dfrac{5}{1}$ ...

If we wish to count only those fractions which are in their lowest terms, then we merely omit appropriate members as we come to them: having counted $\dfrac{1}{1}$ we do not wish to count $\dfrac{2}{2}$ so we omit it, the 5 in N then corresponds to $\dfrac{1}{3}$ in F and so on. Other modifications may be made as desired.

3. As in Exercise 1, pupils feel that there must be 'more' points on a line segment 2 inches long than on a coplanar line segment 1 inch long. Again, a correspondence can be displayed between the two sets of points but, it should be stated clearly, this time neither set is countably infinite (see below).

Let AB and CD be the line segments. Let AC intersect BD in O. Then if P is any point on AB and OP intersects CD in P', we may put P and P' in correspondence.

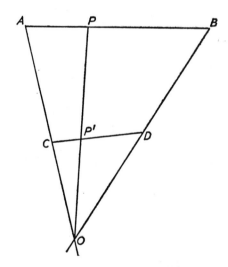

Similarly each point on AB has just one corresponding point on CD and vice-versa.

To demonstrate that the set of all points on a finite line segment is not countably infinite, proceed as follows. Let the segment be AB: with A associate the number ·00000 . . .; with B associate the number ·9999 . . .; with every other point associate the non-terminating decimal corresponding to the distance of the point from A in terms of the appropriate unit. (A rational whose decimal representation terminates may be regarded as non-terminating by the addition of zeros: e.g. $\frac{1}{2} = \cdot 500000 \ldots$). Then, if possible, let a correspondence between the natural numbers and these decimals be

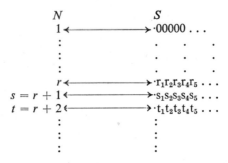

where the r_i, s_i, t_i, etc., are the digits 0, 1, 2, 3, 4, ..., 9 in some order. ($\frac{1}{2} = \cdot 50000 \ldots = \cdot 49999 \ldots$, and if we admit the second decimal representation of $\frac{1}{2}$ we shall get into difficulties. Therefore we exclude all decimal representations ending in an infinite succession of 9's except $\cdot 999 \ldots$ itself.) Now form a decimal whose first digit is 1, whose second digit is a 1 if the second digit in the second decimal is 0 and otherwise is one less than that second digit, and in general, whose nth digit is

or

    (a) a 1 if the nth digit in the nth decimal is 0,
    (b) is one less than the nth digit in the nth decimal,

if that digit is not zero. Plainly, this decimal differs in at least one place from every decimal in the list, and does not end in an infinite succession of 9's: hence the point corresponding to this decimal is not associated with any number of N: hence the correspondence is not one-one, and the set of all points is not countably infinite. We denote the cardinal number of this set by $\aleph$. It is an example of an infinite cardinal number different from $\aleph_0$.

So far we have introduced the idea of cardinal numbers (finite and infinite) and their addition. Clearly, even as far as the basic concepts are concerned, we have only scratched the surface. However, the immediate subsequent development is relatively straightforward, and so we shall indicate it with comments in the following examples. The reader who wishes to skip them is welcome to do so; it should not prejudice his understanding of subsequent chapters. On the other hand, for the reader who is interested in this topic, more information can be found in *A Survey of Modern Algebra* by Birkoff and Mac Lane (Macmillan). An interesting book of rather a different type is *Number, The Language of Science*, by T. Dantzig (Allen and Unwin).

Example J. In Chapter 2 we introduced the binary operation ▽. This binary operation is compatible with our equivalence relation of one-one correspondence, i.e.

$$A \ R \ B \text{ and } A' \ R \ B' \text{ imply } [A \ ▽ \ A'] \ R \ [B \ ▽ \ B'].$$

The details are left to the reader, we merely remark that if f is a one-one map of A onto B and g a one-one map of A' onto B' then h is a one-one map of $A \ ▽ \ A'$ into $B \ ▽ \ B'$, where

$$h(a, a') = (f(a), g(a')).$$

We can, therefore, induce the binary operation ▽ onto the set of equivalence classes, and we get

$$\{A\} \ ▽ \ \{B\} = \{A \ ▽ \ B\},$$

or in more usual notation

$$n(A) \times n(B) = n(A \ ▽ \ B).$$

We call this new binary operation for cardinal numbers *multiplication*.

Example K. ▽ as applied to sets (rather than the equivalence classes) is neither commutative nor associative; as applied to equivalence classes, however, it is both. For, although $A \ ▽ \ B \neq B \ ▽ \ A$, there is a one-one correspondence between $A \ ▽ \ B$ and $B \ ▽ \ A$. Similarly, there is a one-one correspondence between $A \ ▽ \ [B \ ▽ \ C]$ and $[A \ ▽ \ B] \ ▽ \ C$.

Example L. In Example I, page 77, we mentioned that $\aleph_0 + \aleph_0 = \aleph_0$. This means that the equation $a + x = a$, where a is a cardinal, does not necessarily have the solution $x = 0$. This is only true if a is a finite cardinal.

One can further show that multiplication of cardinal numbers is distributive over addition, i.e. that

$$\{A\} \ ▽ \ [\{B\} \cup \{C\}] = [\{A\} \ ▽ \ \{B\}] \cup [\{A\} \ ▽ \ \{C\}],$$

or in more usual notation that

$$n(A) \times [n(B) + n(C)] = [n(A) \times n(B)] + [n(A) \times n(C)].$$

This proof can be supplied by the reader by exhibiting a one-one correspondence between

$$A \ ▽ \ [B \cup C] \text{ and } [A \ ▽ \ B] \cup [A \ ▽ \ C].$$

(They are, in fact, equal.)

It follows that $\aleph_0 + \aleph_0 = [1 + 1] \times \aleph_0 = 2 \times \aleph_0 = \aleph_0$, but $2 \neq 1$. Thus we cannot 'cancel' in either addition or multiplication, unless we know that our cardinals are finite. We have not, of course, proved the latter half of the last sentence; the reader might like to put forward some reasoning of his own.

Example M. Can any of the other binary operations on sets be induced onto the cardinal numbers (with suitable provisos, if necessary)?

*   *   *   *   *

We conclude this chapter with another short topological note. Let S be a topological space with topology $T : S$, and let V be any subset of S. We gave V an induced topology (cf. Example U at the end of Chapter 2) known as the subset topology. A topology for V was there suggested as the system of all sets of the form $V \cap U$ where $U \in T : S$. We shall now prove that this system is a topology for V.

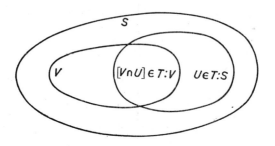

(i) $V \cap \emptyset = \emptyset$ and $V \cap S = V$, therefore V and $\emptyset$ belong to the system.

(ii) Let U_1 and U_2 be any two open sets of $T : S$. Then $V \cap U_1$ and $V \cap U_2$ belong to the system and their intersection is $(V \cap U_1) \cap (V \cap U_2) = V \cap (U_1 \cap U_2)$. But $U_1 \cap U_2$ is open in $T : S$, therefore $V \cap (U_1 \cap U_2)$ belongs to the system.

(iii) Finally, consider any system of sets of the form $V \cap U$ where the U are open in $T : S$. Intersection is distributive over union, therefore the union of all sets of the system is of the form $V \cap W$, where W is the union of all the U. But the sets $U \in T : S$, therefore W is open in $T : S$, and hence $V \cap W$ belongs to the system.

Example N. Consider the subset $0 \leqslant x \leqslant 1$ of the real line. (We discussed the natural topology of the real line at the end of the last chapter.) The base for its *subset topology* is the sets of the forms

$$0 \leqslant x < k, \quad l < x \leqslant 1, \quad l < x < k$$

where $l \geqslant 0$, $k \leqslant 1$, $l < k$. These sets together with all unions of them and the sets $\emptyset$ and $0 \leqslant x \leqslant 1$, are the open sets of the subset topology.

$x \longrightarrow |\sin x|$ is a many-one mapping of the real line onto this subset. Is it a continuous mapping of the real line with the natural topology? (Remember that to show this we need only show that the inverse images of the sets of the base for the subset topology are open sets in the natural topology for the real line.)

Example O. Consider N (the subset of natural numbers with zero) of the real numbers with the natural topology. Every element of N is open in the subset topology; for if $n \in N$, $N \cap (n - \frac{1}{2} < x < n + \frac{1}{2}) = n$. Any topology in which every element is itself an open set is said to be the *discrete topology*. Thus the subset topology for N is the discrete topology.

Consider the function f which maps any real number onto its integral part (ignoring the sign). For instance

$$f(- 2 \cdot 3) = 2, \quad f(7 \cdot 005) = 7, \quad f(\tfrac{1}{2}) = 0.$$

This function is not a continuous mapping of the reals onto N with the above topologies: the inverse image of the open set 2, for instance, is the set

$$(- 3 < x \leqslant - 2) \cup (2 \leqslant x < 3)$$

and this is not an open set in the topology for the reals. Note the exception: the inverse image of the open set 0 in $T: N$ is the set

$$- 1 < x < 1$$

which is open in the topology for the reals.

Example P. In the text the subset V was not itself specified as being open in $T: S$ and, therefore, the open sets in the subset topology for V were not necessarily open in $T: S$. If, however, V is open in $T: S$, then any open set of the subset topology is open in $T: S$.

CHAPTER 6

GROUPS

GIVEN any two sets A and B their union $A \cup B = C$, say, is uniquely defined. On the other hand, given any two sets A and B, a set X such that $A \cup X = B$ is not necessarily uniquely defined and, indeed, may not exist. In fact, the set X is uniquely defined if and only if $A = \emptyset$, in which case $X = B$. The set X is defined, but not uniquely, if $A \subseteq B$ and $A \neq \emptyset$; X is then given by an expression of the form $[B \sim A] \cup C$ where $C \subseteq A$. Since A is not empty, at least two solutions exist, corresponding to $C = \emptyset$ and $C = A$. If A is a finite set with cardinal number n, then there are 2^n solutions, corresponding to all possible subsets of A. If A is an infinite set there is an infinity of solutions. If $A \neq \emptyset$ and $A \nsubseteq B$ then the set X does not exist.

Example A. The reader should draw Venn diagrams illustrating some special cases, e.g.

(a) $A \cap B = \emptyset, A \neq \emptyset, B \neq \emptyset$

(b) $B \subset A, B \neq \emptyset$

and verify that no set X can be found to satisfy $A \cup X = B$. He should also illustrate

(c) $A \subset B, A \neq \emptyset$

and verify the existence of several solutions of $A \cup X = B$.

A somewhat similar situation obtains for the intersection operation. Given two sets A and B, their intersection $A \cap B = C$, say, is uniquely defined, but, given two sets A and B a set X is not necessarily uniquely defined to satisfy $A \cap X = B$.

Example B. The reader should illustrate each of the possible cases and put them in three categories according to whether $A \cap X = B$ gives

(a) X uniquely defined,

(b) X defined, but not uniquely,

(c) X non-existent.

The situation is quite different with the operation called 'symmetric difference'. We shall, as before, in Chapter 2, write the symmetric difference of two sets A and B as $A \triangle B$. It is the set whose members are those members of A which are not members of B together with those members of B which are not members of A.

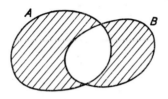

A △ B is shaded

Example C. We mentioned symmetric difference in the second chapter and asked the reader to discover some of its properties. Since we are going to investigate one property in detail it might be as well if the reader were to revise his knowledge and reconsider this binary operation. For instance, is it associative? Commutative? Distributive with respect to union and/or intersection? Can it be expressed in terms of union and intersection only? Can it be expressed in terms of union, intersection and $\sim$?

Given any two sets A and B, their symmetric difference $A \triangle B = C$, say, is uniquely defined. Given two sets A and B, a set X such that $A \triangle X = B$ is also uniquely defined as $X = A \triangle B$, as we shall show in general later.

Example D. Verify that no matter what case of two gives sets A and B is chosen, the set $X = A \triangle B$ is uniquely defined and satisfies $A \triangle X = B$.

The question now arises, why this fundamental distinction between the one operation and the others? We shall answer this question by deriving $A \triangle X = B$ from $X = A \triangle B$ and considering the properties required to perform the derivation. If the union and intersection operations do not possess these properties then the reason for the distinction will be clear.

(1) We know that given any two sets A and B, $A \triangle B$ defines a unique set. Call this set X. Then

$$X = A \triangle B.$$

(2) We wish to find the set $A \triangle X$. Now, since X and $A \triangle B$ are equal sets, that is, they have the same members, $A \triangle X$ and

$A \triangle [A \triangle B]$ will be equal. Also since $\triangle$ is associative, $A \triangle [A \triangle B]$ may be written as $[A \triangle A] \triangle B$. Hence

$$A \triangle X = [A \triangle A] \triangle B.$$

(3) Consider $[A \triangle A] \triangle B$. Now $A \triangle A$ is the set consisting of those members of A which are not members of A, that is $A \triangle A = \emptyset$. Hence

$$A \triangle X = \emptyset \triangle B.$$

(4) $\emptyset \triangle B$ is the set consisting of those members of $\emptyset$ which are not members of B (and there are no such members) together with those members of B which are not members of $\emptyset$ (and none of the members of B are members of $\emptyset$). Hence

$$\emptyset \triangle B = B.$$

Thus $A \triangle X = B$ and the solution is valid.

Now let us list the properties which have been used.

(1) states that the symmetric difference of any two sets A and B exists and is a uniquely defined set.

(2) states that $\triangle$ is associative.

(4) and (3) together state that

(a) for any set B a particular set exists (in fact, $\emptyset$) such that its symmetric difference with B is B itself,

and (b) that this particular set can be obtained as the result of combining any set A with some set (in fact, A itself) by the operation of symmetric difference.

Example E. Union and intersection possess the properties stated under (1) and (2). (a) is also satisfied for union since $B \cup \emptyset = B$ for all B. Property (a) is also satisfied for intersection if we regard all our sets B as subsets of some 'universal set' U, for then $B \cap U = B$. But consider (b). For union and any set A we must have a set A' such that

$$A \cup A' = \emptyset$$

and this is clearly impossible if $A \neq \emptyset$.

For intersection and any set A we must have a set A' such that

$$A \cap A' = U, \text{ the universal set}$$

and this is again impossible if $A \neq U$.

So it would seem that the essential difference (in the context of our present argument) between union and intersection on the one hand, and symmetric difference on the other, is that for the latter for any set A we have a set $A'(A' = A)$ such that $A \triangle A' = \emptyset$, where $\emptyset \triangle B = B$ for all B. We shall now show that this difference is, in fact, essential in that it guarantees a solution to the problem $A \triangle X = B$, and a unique one at that.

Let us generalize the properties above. Consider a set S with elements $a, b, \ldots$ (the elements may, of course, themselves be sets) and an operation o which is such that

(i) $a \circ b$ is a uniquely defined member of S for all $a, b \in S$;

(ii) o is associative;

(iii) there is a member of S, called a *neutral element* or *identity*, and written e, such that
$$e \circ a = a$$
for all $a \in S$;

(iv) corresponding to every $a \in S$ there is an element in S, say c, called an *inverse* of a, such that
$$c \circ a = e.$$

We shall now show that, under these conditions, the equation $a \circ x = b$ has a unique and specific solution in S for all $a, b \in S$. (Note that we do not wish to imply that there is a unique identity element, or a unique inverse element corresponding to any element a. For the time being we only assume that an identity element exists and an inverse for each element a. We shall prove later that it is a necessary consequence of properties (i) to (iv) that the identity is unique in S and that each element has a unique inverse.)

Consider the equation $a \circ x = b$.

By (iv) there exists an element c which is such that $c \circ a = e$, and we can write
$$c \circ [a \circ x] = c \circ b.$$

This gives $\qquad [c \circ a] \circ x = c \circ b \qquad$ (from (ii))

i.e. $\qquad\qquad\qquad e \circ x = c \circ b \qquad$ (from (iv))

whence $\qquad\qquad\qquad\quad x = c \circ b \qquad$ (from (iii))

and this is defined and belongs to S (from (i)).

So we see that the equation has at least one solution in the set S; we still need to show that it has only one. To prove this, suppose that it has two solutions, x_1 and x_2 say, i.e.
$$a \circ x_1 = b \quad \text{and} \quad a \circ x_2 = b.$$

Then $\qquad\qquad\qquad a \circ x_1 = a \circ x_2$

and $\qquad\qquad c \circ [a \circ x_1] = c \circ [a \circ x_2]$

where c is an inverse of a (from (iv)). Whence, by (ii) and (iii) we have

$$[c \text{ o } a] \text{ o } x_1 = [c \text{ o } a] \text{ o } x_2$$

i.e. $\qquad\qquad\qquad e \text{ o } x_1 = e \text{ o } x_2$

and hence $\qquad\qquad\qquad x_1 = x_2.$

Hence the solution $x = c \text{ o } b$ is unique.

A set S, with an operation o, which possesses the properties (i), (ii), (iii) and (iv) is called a *group*. If the number of elements of S is infinite, S is called an infinite group, otherwise it is called a finite group.

Example F. The set S of all subsets of some set, with the operation of symmetric difference, forms a group. $A \triangle B$ is a uniquely defined subset for all subsets A and B, $\triangle$ is associative, $\varnothing$ is the neutral element since $\varnothing \triangle A = A$ for all $A \in S$, and, lastly $A \triangle A = \varnothing$ for all $A \in S$.

It is precisely the last property, the existence of an inverse for any set A, which neither union nor intersection possess.

We have shown that the defining properties of a group are sufficient to guarantee a solution of the equation

$$a \text{ o } x = b.$$

But what about the equation $x \text{ o } a = b$, when the binary operation o is not commutative? We shall show that this also has a solution by showing that for the same e and c as in the defining properties above

$$a \text{ o } e = a \quad \text{and} \quad a \text{ o } c = e.$$

It is then clear that an analysis similar to the one given for the solution of $a \text{ o } x = b$ will provide the solution, x, of $x \text{ o } a = b$, and show that it is unique.

(a) To prove $a \text{ o } e = a$. Consider

$$
\begin{aligned}
c \text{ o } [a \text{ o } e] &= [c \text{ o } a] \text{ o } e \quad \text{(by (ii))} \\
&= e \text{ o } e \qquad\;\; \text{(by (iv))} \\
&= e \qquad\qquad \text{(by (iii))} \\
&= c \text{ o } a
\end{aligned}
$$

Now c is an element of S and, therefore, by (iv) must itself have a 'left' inverse, d say, whence

$$d \text{ o } [c \text{ o } [a \text{ o } e]] = d \text{ o } [c \text{ o } a]$$

i.e. $\qquad [d \text{ o } c] \text{ o } [a \text{ o } e] = [d \text{ o } c] \text{ o } a \quad \text{(by (ii))},$

i.e. $\qquad\qquad e \text{ o } [a \text{ o } e] = e \text{ o } a,$

whence $\qquad\qquad\quad a \text{ o } e = a \qquad\qquad \text{(by (iii))}.$

(b) To prove $a \circ c = e$. Consider

$$c \circ [a \circ c] = [c \circ a] \circ c \quad \text{(by (ii))}$$
$$= (e \circ c) \quad \text{(by (iv))}$$
$$= c \quad \text{(by (iii))}.$$

Whence using the d mentioned above, we have

$$[d \circ c] \circ [a \circ c] = d \circ c,$$
i.e.
$$e \circ [a \circ c] = e$$
$$a \circ c = e \quad \text{(by (iii))}.$$

So we see that in any group a 'left' identity is also a 'right' identity: also, for any element a 'left' inverse is a 'right' inverse.

It follows that if a and b are members of a group S, then there exists in S a member x such that $a \circ x = b$, and there exists in S a member y such that $y \circ a = b$. If, in accordance with property (iv) $c \circ a = e$ (and hence $a \circ c = e$), then $x = c \circ b$ and $y = b \circ c$.

We proved earlier that the solution, x, of $a \circ x = b$ is unique. Consider the two special cases

$$\text{(i)} \quad a \circ x = a, \qquad \text{(ii)} \quad a \circ x = e.$$

They will have unique solutions. But we know one solution of (i), i.e. e, hence this is the only one; the identity element in a group is unique. We also know a solution of (ii), i.e. the inverse of a which we denoted by c. Again this is the only solution; the inverse of any element a in a group is unique.*

Example G. The reader should verify that the set of all positive rational numbers forms a group under multiplication, that 1 is the neutral element and that the inverse of a is a^{-1}. Hence, if a and b are positive rationals, it is always possible to find a positive rational x such that $ax = b$ (see Chapter 7, Exercise 7, page 110 et seq.). He should also verify that the same set does not form a group for addition, and that if a and b are positive rationals it is not always possible to find a positive rational x such that $a + x = b$.

It is perhaps unfortunate that the example above has had a powerful influence on notation. The effect has been (i) that the neutral element in any group is often denoted by the symbol I, (ii) that the inverse of an element a is usually denoted by a^{-1} and, (iii) that the symbol for the operation is often omitted altogether, the result of combining two elements a and b by the defined operation being written ab, the operation being understood from the

* Notice that this implies that the d mentioned above is a.

context. We shall not adopt this notation and the reader is warned that its attractive suggestiveness is not without disadvantages. (The reader who wishes to discover these disadvantages should rework some of the examples and exercises in the later part of this book, using the I, a^{-1} notation.) We prefer, when we are talking about an abstract group or groups in general, to retain the notation already introduced, that is, to represent the operation by 'o' and the neutral element by 'e'. We shall, from now on, represent the inverse of a by '$\tilde{a}$'.

In this notation we can define a group as follows.

If G is a set of elements for which an operation o is defined, then G is a group if and only if

(a) the operation o, applied to any pair of elements a, $b \in G$, gives a unique element $c \in G$, and we write $a \circ b = c$; (This is called the requirement of *closure*.)

(b) for all a, b, $c \in G$

$$a \circ [b \circ c] = [a \circ b] \circ c = a \circ b \circ c;$$

(This is called the requirement of *associativity*.)

(c) there is an element $e \in G$ (called the neutral element) such that for each and every $a \in G$,

$$e \circ a = a \circ e = a;$$

(This is the requirement of a *neutral element*.)

(d) to each $a \in G$ there corresponds an element $\tilde{a} \in G$ (called the inverse of a) such that

$$a \circ \tilde{a} = \tilde{a} \circ a = e.$$

(This is the requirement of *inverses*.)

It should be noted that (as proved above) the neutral element e is a single, specific, unique element, which is the neutral element for *every* member of G, but that each element a possesses its *own* unique inverse $\tilde{a}$. Thus if a and b are distinct members of G

$$a \circ e = e \circ a = a$$
and
$$b \circ e = e \circ b = b,$$
but although
$$a \circ \tilde{a} = \tilde{a} \circ a = e,$$
it is not true that $b \circ \tilde{a} = e$, or that $a \circ \check{b} = e$.

We would also point out that (c) and (d) differ slightly from the properties (iii) and (iv) we gave earlier. We proved that $e \circ a = a$ and $\tilde{a} \circ a = e$ imply $a \circ e = a$ and $a \circ \tilde{a} = e$. Therefore, although we have no need to include the latter two properties in our definition, it seems advisable to do so in order to emphasize that, even though the group may not be commutative, the left inverse of any element is also its right inverse, and that there is only one neutral element, whether from the left or the right.

If a group G possesses the additional property that, for every $a, b \in G$,

$$a \circ b = b \circ a$$

then G is said to be a *commutative* (or *Abelian*) *group*.

Example H. The reader may verify that the set of all integers (i.e. directed numbers) forms a group for addition (see Chapter 7, Exercise 8, page 112 et seq.), that 0 is the neutral element and that the inverse of a is $-a$. Hence if a and b are integers it is always possible to find an integer x such that $a + x = b$. He may also verify that the same set does not form a group for multiplication, and that, if a and b are integers, it is not always possible to find an integer x such that $a \times x = b$.

The group of integers under addition compares with the group of positive rationals under multiplication in that it also has led to some authors adopting '+' as the symbol for any group operation, with 0 as the neutral element and $-a$ as the inverse of a. (We shall not adopt this notation either.)

Example I. (a) Is the set of all integers a group for subtraction?

(b) Is the set of negative rationals a group for multiplication?

(c) Is the set of all integers, including zero, together with all positive and negative rationals, a group for addition?

(d) Is the set of all integers, including zero, together with all positive and negative rationals, a group for multiplication?

To these four questions, three of the answers are 'No': the reader is strongly urged to check carefully all the defining properties in each case.

Example J. Is the set of all subsets of a set a group for the operation $\sim$?

If G is a group* and $a, b \in G$, then $a \circ x = b$ and $y \circ a = b$ are always rigorously, explicitly and uniquely solvable, using the operation 'o' only, by the process of operating on both sides with $\tilde{a}$, from the left and right respectively, and using the properties of associativity and the neutral element. If a set S is not a group under operation o it does not necessarily follow that $a \circ x = b$ and $y \circ a = b$ are not solvable. For example, an explicit solution can be obtained in any set S closed under o for which a mapping f exists

---

* Strictly we should say 'If (G, o) is a group'.

of S into itself so that $f(a) \circ (a \circ b) = b$ for all a and b in S. Also, of course, other methods such as trial and error may be successful.

Example K. The set of all integers does not form a group for subtraction but if a and b are integers it is always possible to find an integer x such that $a - x = b$. The reader may solve this equation rigorously using the subtraction operation only.

Example L. The set of natural numbers does not form a group under multiplication, but if a and b are natural numbers it is sometimes possible to find a natural number x such that $a \times x = b$. The reader should attempt to solve this equation rigorously, using the multiplication operation only. (It must not be assumed that the inverse of a exists.)

It may be noted that the usual process, that is, to divide both sides by a and then to decide whether $b \div a$ is a natural number, is equivalent to recognizing that the set of natural numbers is a subset of the *group* of positive rationals under multiplication. In this group $\frac{1}{a} \times b$ always exists and it merely remains to decide whether or not $\frac{1}{a} \times b$ is a member of the equivalence class identified with some natural number (see Chapter 3, Exercise 3(f), page 47 and Chapter 7, Exercise 7, page 110).

In Chapter 2, page 29, we asked the reader to verify that if A, B and C are sets and $\triangle$ represents the operation of symmetric difference, then

$$A \triangle B = A \triangle C$$

implies $\qquad B = C,$

that is, 'left-cancellation' is possible. The analogous result holds for any group, for, if a, b and c are members of a group $(G, \circ)$, then both sides of

$$a \circ b = a \circ c$$

may be operated on, from the left, by $\tilde{a}$, giving, by the associative property

$$e \circ b = e \circ c$$

that is, $\qquad b = c.$

Similarly, in a group, 'right-cancellation' is always valid.

If group structure is not present as, for example, with the subsets of some set as elements and union (or intersection) as the operation, then 'cancelling' is not necessarily valid. (Examples were given in Chapter 2, Example N, page 28.)

Because group structure guarantees

(i) the explicit solution of $a \circ x = b$ (i.e. $x = \tilde{a} \circ b$) and $x \circ a = b$ (i.e. $x = b \circ \tilde{a}$), and

(ii) the validity of left and right cancellation (i.e. $a \circ b = a \circ c$ or $b \circ a = c \circ a$ imply $b = c$),

it naturally follows that sets and operations with group structure occupy a privileged position.* It would be possible to argue that among the important tasks of mathematics is that of investigating existing sets and operations to discover which of them form groups: at the same time, where possible, by extensions of sets or modifications of operations, to introduce group structure where it did not previously exist.

The ideas implicit in the last paragraph underlie the whole structural approach to mathematics; groups and higher structures (which possess the group properties together with others) are singled out and defined because of the facilities they guarantee or the frequency of their occurrence. They are then studied in their abstract form, and existing concepts are categorized according to the structures they exhibit. Thus the solution of a problem or the establishment of a property in the abstract structure automatically solves the analogous problem, or establishes the analogous property, in a multitude of existing algebraic systems all of which possess the same structure. Where a problem arises in an algebraic system which does not already possess the structure necessary to provide its solution then modifications are attempted in order to achieve that degree of structure.

In respect of groups, we shall postpone further investigation of the abstract structure until a few examples have been given

(a) of further existing sets possessing group structure,

(b) of the modifications directed to producing group structure where it did not previously exist.

This we shall do in the next chapter. We shall finish this chapter with one further example and our usual section on topology.

---

* A group may be defined directly in terms of (i) as a non empty set closed under an associative operation o so that for all a and b in the set there exists an x and y in the set such that

$$a \circ x = b = y \circ a.$$

Such a definition is not very satisfactory in the teaching situation since its conciseness and completeness make the motivation of further discussion difficult and the crucial ideas of neutral and inverse elements have to be artificially extracted by formal analysis.

Example M. The well-known 'method of dimensions' in school physics states that to every physical quantity (or class of equivalent quantities) there corresponds a dimensional expression of the form $M^\alpha L^\beta T^\gamma$ where α, β and γ are real: the values of α, β and γ are obtained by expressing the particular quantity in terms of a set of 'fundamental' physical quantities, say mass (M), length (L) and time (T). For example, the quantity 'acceleration' has the corresponding expression $M^0 L^1 T^{-2}$, since acceleration is change of distance (i.e. a length) per unit time per unit time. The set of all such dimensional expressions forms a group under the operation of multiplication according to the usual process of addition of indices, so that, typically,

$$M^{\alpha_1} L^{\beta_1} T^{\gamma_1} \times M^{\alpha_2} L^{\beta_2} T^{\gamma_2} = M^{\alpha_1 + \alpha_2} L^{\beta_1 + \beta_2} T^{\gamma_1 + \gamma_2}.$$

The group property is an immediate consequence of the fact that the set of reals forms a group for addition.

In the traditional introductory example it is assumed that the time (t) of swing of a simple pendulum in vacuo depends, at most, upon the mass (m) of the bob, the length (l) of the pendulum and the acceleration (g) due to gravity, and it is required to find the precise form of the dependence. For our purposes we take the assumption to imply

$$t = m^x l^y g^z, \qquad \text{where } x, y \text{ and } z \text{ are to be determined.}$$

Each quantity is now replaced by the corresponding element from the group, giving

$$M^0 L^0 T^1 = [M^1 L^0 T^0]^x [M^0 L^1 T^0]^y [M^0 L^1 T^{-2}]^z,$$

that is $\qquad M^0 L^0 T^1 = M^x L^{y+z} T^{-2z},$

whence $x = 0$, $y = \frac{1}{2}$, $z = -\frac{1}{2}$, giving, apparently, $t = \sqrt{\dfrac{l}{g}}$. Now this expression is incorrect: the correct result is $t = 2\pi \sqrt{\dfrac{l}{g}}$. After answering the following questions the reader should be able to explain the discrepancy.

(a) What is the result of combining the neutral element of any group with any other element of that group?

(b) What is the neutral element of the particular group under discussion, the group of dimensions?

(c) To what class of entities does this neutral element correspond?

(d) Can the method of dimensions (in the above elementary form) predict the presence or absence of one of these entities?

Any reader unfamiliar with the above technique might also solve the following example. Newton's law of gravitation states that the force (F) between two particles of masses m_1 and m_2 at a distance r apart is given by

$$F = \frac{Gm_1m_2}{r^2},$$

where G is sometimes called the 'gravitational constant'. Find the dimensional expression for G. (Force, being defined as mass $\times$ acceleration, has the dimensional expression $M^1 L^1 T^{-2}$.)

$$* \quad * \quad * \quad * \quad *$$

Now to our concluding topological section. The concept of continuity is at the heart of topology. For instance, two geometrical figures in three-dimensional space which can be continuously deformed into each other are topologically equivalent. Note that this is only an example, not a definition. A rectangle can be continuously deformed into a circle, and vice versa, therefore we would say that a rectangle is topologically equivalent to a circle. But a cube within a cube cannot be deformed physically and continuously into two cubes next to each other, but, nevertheless, the two configurations are topologically equivalent because we can map them mathematically and continuously into each other. (See Chapter 8, Example I, page 134.) It may make the situation clearer if we point out that our intuition tends to accept continuity only if it can provide us with a set of pictures showing the stages through which one object passes in its deformation into the other; on the other hand, topological equivalence is not concerned with the intermediate stages at all. We use the intuitive idea of continuous deformation at the end of Chapter 7 to discuss the theory of braids and at the ends of Chapters 9, 10 and 11 to construct the group associated with the continuous deformation of curves.

The above may or may not be helpful; however, the discussion has no real meaning since the continuity of a mapping depends upon the topologies chosen in the domain and the range. For instance, *any* two sets A and B in one-one correspondence may be continuously mapped into one another if we take the open sets for A to be A and $\emptyset$ and the open sets for B to be B and $\emptyset$. (These are proper topologies.) Then the one-one correspondence is a continuous mapping.

However, such a truism as the above is not useful: if topological equivalence is to be a useful idea we must restrict the choice of topologies. For example, the previous discussion could be made meaningful by allocating to three dimensional space and the mentioned subspaces that topology which is implicit in real analysis, in the same way as our previously defined natural topology for the real line coincides both with our intuition and the ideas used in analysis. In this and subsequent topological notes we shall assume, unless otherwise stated, that three dimensional space has been given this topology, and that any surfaces in this space have been given the corresponding subset topology. This is an important point, for changing the topology may alter the results.

So clearly our imagination is not sufficient to provide us with a definition of topological equivalence. Real and complex classical analysis do, of course, deal with the idea of continuity, but this is far too special and ill founded for our purpose. After all, continuity in analysis is defined in terms of distance, and distance is certainly not necessarily unaltered under a continuous mapping. If we were to use this definition, then not only would we restrict ourselves to spaces in which distance (or a quantity, known as a metric, which has the same essential property as distance) could be defined, but all our definitions and results, although themselves unaltered by a continuous mapping, would be given in terms of a quantity (distance) which is not.

But analysis does provide us with the clue. We must just rework our ideas until distance is eliminated and a more general concept is found instead. At the end of the last chapter we did this in reverse. We showed that the topological definition of continuity, in the special case of a real-valued function of one real variable, was the same as the definition in terms of distance. Further, we see that in analysis we use the idea of distance to define an interval $0 < |x - a| < \delta$, say, where the important point is that the interval does not include the end-points. Now this property of an interval is preserved under the continuous mappings of analysis; deform the interval continuously by any one of these mappings and an interval of the real line without its end-points will become the arc of some curve, but still without its end points. So the 'open set' which replaced 'interval' as at the end of Chapter 4 has become the fundamental concept in topology. In terms of open sets we define the topology of a set (as at the end of Chapter 2) and the idea of a continuous function (as at the end of Chapter 4).

This then justifies the use of open set as a basic element in our definition of continuity, but not the actual definition of a topological space (a set with its topology is called a topological space) as given by us at the end of Chapter 2. Now although this can again be explained as a generalization of the interval in analysis, the process is a little more sophisticated and yet common enough in mathematics. It is precisely the same process as could have led us from, say, the positive rational numbers with multiplication to the concept of a group. We abstract those defining properties which, while common to a large number of particular examples, are convenient to develop a general theory. Now only experience*

---

* In fact the definition given is a synthesis of the various definitions which have arisen in the historical development of the subject.

can teach us what is convenient, and although, in teaching, one naturally tries to motivate the choice of defining properties, we demand so little of a topological space that we could well accept the definition and go on to see what we can get out of such a structure. We propose to do this.

Example N. We have already given one topology for the real numbers R, i.e. that topology whose base is the set of all (open) intervals. Another topology is given by taking the open sets to be

(i) R and $\emptyset$, and

(ii) all the sets of the form $x < a$ for $a \in R$.

The reader might like to invent some of his own topologies for R: in particular there is, of course, the discrete topology (see Chapter 5, page 83) and the *indiscrete topology* whose open sets are just R and $\emptyset$.

We stated above that a rectangle and a square are topologically equivalent, because each can be continuously deformed into the other. Now this intuitive idea can easily be made precise. We require some definition of topological equivalence for abstract topological spaces, and we would like such a definition to provide us with an equivalence relation for spaces. In the first place we shall require the points of the two topological spaces $(A, T : A)$ and $(B, T : B)$ to be in one-one correspondence. (A many-one mapping of a set A onto a set B will not give us an equivalence relation, since there is not necessarily a many-one mapping of B onto A.) Then from our discussion above, we shall clearly require the existence of a one-one mapping of $(A, T : A)$ onto $(B, T : B)$ which is continuous. But this again is not sufficient; perhaps there is no continuous mapping of $(B, T : B)$ onto $(A, T : A)$: examples of such a situation are known to exist (see Example Q, page 101). Therefore, we go one step further, and require the existence of a bi-continuous mapping, i.e. it and its inverse must be continuous. To summarize then; we shall say that a topological space $(A, T : A)$ is topologically equivalent to a topological space $(B, T : B)$ if there is a one-one bi-continuous mapping of $(A, T : A)$ onto $(B, T : B)$. Such a mapping is called a *homeomorphism* (note the '*e*') and the spaces are said to be *homeomorphic*.

We have not quite proved that 'homeomorphism' is an equivalence relation on spaces. In obtaining our definition we made sure that the relation was symmetric, but paid no attention to the other two required properties of an equivalence relation. The reflexive property is self-evident; the identity mapping of $(A, T:A)$ onto $(A, T:A)$ which maps every point onto itself, is a homeomorphism. The transitive property is, however, far from evident. If f is a homeomorphism of $(A, T:A)$ onto $(B, T:B)$ and g is a homeomorphism of $(B, T:B)$ onto $(C, T:C)$ then we have a mapping $h = g \circ f$ of $(A, T:A)$ onto $(C, T:C)$ which is one-one (see Chapter 5, page 67). It remains to prove that h is bi-continuous. We shall prove, in a little while, the stronger result that if f and g are continuous many-one mappings then their combination h is also continuous. It will follow that if f and g are homeomorphisms that $h = g \circ f$ is a homeomorphism; for the inverse of h is the combination $f \circ \mathcal{S}$ and f and $\mathcal{S}$ are, of course, continuous by definition.

Before we prove the outstanding result, let us consider a different approach which is not only relevant to this chapter, but also of great importance in mathematics, as we intend to show in subsequent chapters. Distance we said is not a useful topological concept. Now what exactly does this mean? Suppose that we are given a topological space $(A, T:A)$ in which distance is defined and that the images of two elements P, Q of A under a continuous mapping f of A onto itself are $f(P)$ and $f(Q)$, then the distance between P and Q is not necessarily the same as the distance between $f(P)$ and $f(Q)$.

Example O. Suppose that the real line and its subsets have the natural topology and the usual distance. Then $x \rightarrow + \sqrt{x}$ is a homeomorphism of, say, $0 \leqslant x \leqslant 1$ onto itself. The points $\frac{1}{4}$ and 1 map onto the points $\frac{1}{2}$ and 1.

We shall say that distance is not a *topological invariant*, i.e. it is not necessarily preserved under a homeomorphic mapping. Topology concerns itself with those things which are invariant under homeomorphic mappings, for homeomorphisms give rise to group structure (see page 99).

Example P. A common elementary example of a topological invariant is that usually illustrated by a torus and a sphere. It is intuitively evident that we cannot remove the hole in the torus without regarding different points as identical and thus breaking the one-one requirement, so we cannot deform the surface of the torus into the surface of the sphere. (Try it with a ring and ball.) We can express a difference between the two in very loose topological terms as follows. We can imagine any closed curve drawn on the surface of a sphere being deformed continuously into any other closed curve on the sphere, and a closed curve is intuitively a topological invariant. But we can find two closed curves on a torus which cannot be continuously deformed into each other; for instance the two shown in the diagram. Therefore, it would seem that the sphere and torus cannot be topologically equivalent (see also the topological notes to Chapter 9 and Chapter 11).

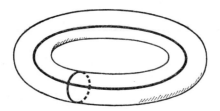

Now consider a topological space $(A, T: A)$ (remember that a topological space is a set with a definite topology) and the set of all mappings which are homeomorphisms of the topological space onto itself. This set of homeomorphisms H, under the usual binary operation for the combination of two mappings, forms a group. What is more, the mappings which we rejected earlier (e.g. many-one, continuous one-one but not bi-continuous) in our attempt to find a proper equivalence relation, do not form groups, and for the same reasons. We shall illustrate this point while showing that H does form a group.

(a) The combination of any two elements f, $g \in H$, i.e.

$$h = g \circ f,$$

is uniquely defined, and will be a member of H when we prove the result which is already outstanding from our previous considerations.

(b) Let h, g, f be members of H and let a be any point of A, such that

$$f(a) = b, \ g(b) = c \text{ and } h(c) = d,$$

then $[[h \circ g] \circ f](a) = [h \circ g](b) = h(g(b)) = h(c) = d$

and $[h \circ [g \circ f]](a) = h(g(f(a))) = h(g(b)) = h(c) = d.$

Hence the combination is associative.

(c) The identity mapping e of A onto itself is a homeomorphism and

$$[e \circ f](a) = e(f(a)) = e(b) = b = f(a)$$

and $[f \circ e](a) = f(e(a)) = f(a).$

(d) Since f is a homeomorphism so is $\bar{f}$, and $\bar{f} \circ f$ (and $f \circ \bar{f}$) maps any element of A onto itself, i.e. $\bar{f} \circ f = f \circ \bar{f} = e$.

It is in this last point that we need our mapping to be bi-continuous (and not merely continuous) in order that the inverse $\bar{f}$ is guaranteed continuous. Similarly f must be one-one, in order that $\bar{f}$ should be one-one; if f were many-one, then $\bar{f}$ would be one-many.

Let us summarize the two aspects of topology which we have described.

(i) Two topological spaces are equivalent if there is a one-one bi-continuous mapping of one space onto another.

(ii) A topological invariant in a space is an object, or quantity determined by an object, which is invariant under the group of homeomorphisms of the space onto itself.

We now propose to prove the outstanding result. Suppose that f is a continuous many-one mapping of a topological space $(A, T: A)$ onto a topological space $(B, T: B)$ and that g is a continuous many-one mapping of $(B, T: B)$ onto a topological space $(C, T: C)$ and consider the mapping $h = g \circ f$ of A onto C. We shall show that h is continuous. Let U be any set open in $T: C$, then $\bar{h}(U) = Y$, say, is the set of all those elements of A which are mapped onto U by $h = g \circ f$; i.e., by definition, $\bar{f}(Y) = Z$, say, is the set of all those elements of B which are mapped onto U by g; in other words $Z = \bar{g}(U)$ and

$$Y = \bar{f}(\bar{g}(U)).$$

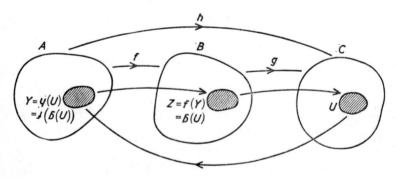

But g is continuous, therefore $\bar{g}(U)$ is open in $T: B$; similarly $\bar{f}(\bar{g}(U))$ is open in $T: A$, i.e. Y is open in $T: A$, whence h is continuous. This completes the proof.

NOTE: As we said above, the set of all homeomorphisms of a space onto itself form a group. Therefore, we shall now adopt the group notation for mappings and denote the inverse of f by $\tilde{f}$ (and we shall henceforth use this notation for *any* mappings even when the structure is not a group).

Example Q. In Example N on page 97 we gave various topologies for the set of real numbers R. Consider the mapping f, defined by

$$f(x) = x.$$

Is it a continuous mapping of R (with one topology) onto R (with another topology)? Is it a homeomorphism?

For example, consider

$(f: R_i$ (R with the 'natural topology') $\longrightarrow R_d$ (R with the discrete topology).

(i) f is not continuous, for any $x \in R$ is open in R_d, but its inverse image x is not open in R_i.

(ii) $\tilde{f}$ is continuous, for the image of any (open) interval in R_i is open in R_d because this image is the union of its discrete elements, each of which is open in R_d.

References

For more information on the topological note in this chapter see, for example,

Arnold: *Intuitive Concepts in Elementary Topology* (Prentice-Hall), 1963, Chapter 8.

Mansfield : *Introduction to Topology* (Van Nostrand), 1963, Chapters 2 and 3.

Patterson: *Topology* (Oliver and Boyd), 2nd edition, Chapter 2.

CHAPTER 7

EXERCISES

IN this chapter we shall give examples of groups and modifications of existing sets to obtain groups.

1. Certain objects have the property of *symmetry*: that is, there is more than one way in which they can be fitted into a close-fitting fixed framework. For example, a cube can be fitted into a close-fitting cubical box in many different ways. (How many?)

Imagine an equilateral triangle cut out of some transparent material with the vertices lettered *A*, *B* and *C*. This triangle can be fitted into a close-fitting fixed frame in precisely six ways, as shown in the diagram below. (In the diagrams the letters are shown the right way up in spite of the fact that they would really be tilted or seen in reverse. The fixed frame is shown in dotted lines.)

Now imagine the frame to have axes *dd'*, *ee'* and *ff'* as shown together with

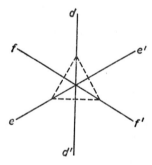

an axis *OO'* through the centre of the frame and perpendicular to its plane. Then if we start, in each case, with position (*a*), the other five positions may be obtained by performing the following rotations:

Rotation *b*: 120° anticlockwise about *OO'*
,,   *c*: 240°   ,,   ,,   *OO'*
,,   *d*: 180° about *dd'*
,,   *e*: 180° about *ee'*
,,   *f*: 180° about *ff'*.

To this list we add a sixth, a rotation of 0° called rotation *a*.

These six rotations are the elements of a group. The elements are combined by starting with position (*a*) and performing first one rotation and then performing the other upon the result of the first. (We call this the operation of 'subsequent performance' and indicate it by the symbol o, as usual.) Thus *b* o *e* means (starting from position (*a*)) 'rotate 180° about *ee'*, then rotate through 120° anticlockwise about *OO''*. (Note that the *e* rotation is performed first.) The position arrived at is

which is the same as that produced by the single rotation *d*. Hence we write

$$b \text{ o } e = d.$$

Notice that we do *not* imply by the equals sign that rotating 180° about *ee'* followed by rotating through 120° about *OO'* *is the same as* rotating 180° about *dd'*. The equals sign here implies, merely, that the final position is the same.

In a similar way, $\qquad e \text{ o } b = f.$

(i) Copy and complete the following table, noticing that the two results *b* o *e* = *d* and *e* o *b* = *f* have been inserted in the appropriate places. (By convention the result *b* o *e* is placed in row *b*, column *e*, while the result *e* o *b* is in row *e*, column *b*.)

o	a	b	c	d	e	f
a						
b					d	
c						
d						
e		f				
f						

(ii) The statement that the system forms a group implies that the operation is known to be associative. How do we know this?

(iii) What is the neutral element of the group?

(iv) List the inverses of the six elements.

(v) Is the group commutative?

(vi) Solve the equations *c* o *x* = *d* and *x* o *c* = *d*.

(vii) The two elements a and f form a group by themselves, with the same operation. The group table is:

o	a	f
a	a	f
f	f	a

Such a group, using the same operation as the original group, but using only some of its elements, is called a *subgroup* of the original group. Find two other subgroups with two elements and find also a subgroup with three elements.

The interested reader will find Herman Weyl's beautiful book *Symmetry*. (Princeton University Press) well worth reading.

2. In Chapter 3, Exercise 1, page 45, we discussed residue classes and mentioned subsequently that congruence to a modulus is an equivalence relation compatible with the operations of multiplication and addition. Consider, in particular, the set of all integers and the residue classes modulo 7, i.e. the classes

$$(\ldots -21, -14, -7, 0, \quad 7, 14, 21, \ldots) \text{ class O}$$
$$(\ldots -20, -13, -6, 1, \quad 8, 15, 22, \ldots) \text{ class } A$$
$$(\ldots -19, -12, -5, 2, \quad 9, 16, 23, \ldots) \text{ class } B$$
$$(\ldots -18, -11, -4, 3, \quad 10, 17, 24, \ldots) \text{ class } C$$
$$(\ldots -17, -10, -3, 4, \quad 11, 18, 25, \ldots) \text{ class } D$$
$$(\ldots -16, -\ 9, -2, 5, \quad 12, 19, 26, \ldots) \text{ class } E$$
$$(\ldots -15, -\ 8, -1, 6, \quad 13, 20, 27, \ldots) \text{ class } F$$

Since multiplication is compatible with the equivalence relation we can multiply two residue classes using any representatives from each class, and the class to which the result belongs is independent of the choice of representatives.

Thus, for example, we can calculate $E \times B$ by taking, say, 9 from class B and -2, say, from E, then

$$E \times B = \text{the residue class containing } (-2 \times 9 = -18),$$
i.e. $E \times B = C$.

(i) It would certainly be instructive (if the reader has the patience) to verify again that multiplication is compatible with the equivalence relation. In general, for an equivalence relation R and an operation o, we defined this to mean

$$a \, R \, b \text{ and } c \, R \, d \text{ imply } [a \text{ o } c] \, R \, [b \text{ o } d].$$

In particular, we want to show

$$a \equiv b \pmod 7 \text{ and } c \equiv d \pmod 7 \text{ imply } [a \times c] \equiv [b \times d] \pmod 7.$$

(ii) Taking the six classes A, B, C, D, E, F as elements, and using the operation of multiplication, verify that the structure is a group and copy and complete the following table. Is the group commutative (cf. Example L, Chapter 3, page 49)?

×	A	B	C	D	E	F
A						
B						
C						
D						
E	C					
F						

(iii) Verify that the structure obtained by using the same operation on all seven classes O, A, B, C, D, E, F is not a group. Is it a group under addition?

The structures obtained in Exercises 1(i) and 2(ii) are two different groups each having six elements. (Finite groups are said to be different if one table cannot be obtained from the other by renaming elements or altering the order of rows and columns, i.e. the groups are not isomorphic.) It can be shown that, in this sense, no other groups of six elements exist, that is, that every other group table of six elements can be transformed into one of the above two by renaming or re-ordering (see Chapter 11).

3. Consider the set whose elements are the six mappings of the reals into the reals

$$f_1 : x \longrightarrow x, \quad f_2 : x \longrightarrow \frac{1}{1-x}, \quad f_3 : x \longrightarrow \frac{x-1}{x}$$

$$f_4 : x \longrightarrow \frac{1}{x}, \quad f_5 : x \longrightarrow \frac{x}{x-1}, \quad f_6 : x \longrightarrow 1-x,$$

and take as operation o the combination of two mappings, so that, for example

$$f_4 \circ f_2 = \left[x \longrightarrow \frac{1}{x} \right] \circ \left[x \longrightarrow \frac{1}{1-x} \right] = x \longrightarrow \frac{1}{\frac{1}{1-x}}$$

$$= x \longrightarrow 1-x$$

$$= f_6.$$

(i)   Verify that this system is a group.

(ii) Relabel the elements with the letters a, b, c, d, e, f in such a way that the group table becomes identical with that of Exercise 1(i).

(iii) Verify that it is impossible to relabel with the letters A, B, C, D, E, F so that the table becomes identical with that of Exercise 2(ii).

4. Consider the set of all symmetries of a regular hexagon with centre O.

(i) Show that the subset of all symmetries, obtainable by rotating the hexagon about an axis through O and perpendicular to the plane of the hexagon, form a group with the operation described in Exercise 1. Construct the group table.

(ii) Relabelling the rotations (or re-ordering the columns or rows of the group table) if necessary, show that the group table is identical with one of Exercise 1(i) or Exercise 2(ii).

(iii) Construct the group table for the set of *all* symmetries of the hexagon and find as many subgroups as you can. (The group has twelve elements.)

5. For those familiar with vector analysis we remark that the set of all vectors with the vector product as operation does not form a group. The operation is not associative and there is no neutral element (and, *ipso facto*, inverses are not defined). The inherent difficulty in manipulating equations involving the vector product certainly stems from this fact. (The generalization of vectors as quaternions removes this difficulty but has the disadvantage that the physical interpretation of quaternions is not so obvious.)

6. The group in this exercise is usually associated with more advanced mathematics. Consider the set of all complex functions, i.e. the set of all many-one mappings of the complex numbers (or some subset) into the complex numbers. A complex function f is usually represented as a correspondence between two complex planes; if $z = x + iy$ is any complex number in the domain of f and if w is the image of z under f,

and $$w = u + iv = f(z),$$

then we would represent z in one complex plane and w in another.

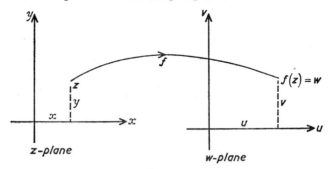

In particular the mapping $f : z \longrightarrow \dfrac{1}{z}$ is a one-one mapping of the z-plane onto the w-plane except that the origin, $z = 0$, has no image point. Rather than make a special statement it is usual to adjoin a special point, the *point at infinity*,* to the complex plane; in other words we adjoin a point which is

---

* This is an unfortunate name since it implies that we have a point in the plane at an infinite distance from the origin and this is pure nonsense. The point at infinity is extra to all the points of a complex plane: it can be represented by any point *not* in the plane (e.g. by a point one inch above the origin).

defined to be the image of $z = 0$ under the mapping $f: z \longrightarrow \frac{1}{z}$. The point is usually denoted by ∞. (There are, incidentally, other good reasons for introducing the point at infinity, but these do not concern us.)

Now the set of all many-one mappings of the complex plane onto the complex plane is far too general a class of functions to be of any special mathematical interest (see for example Titchmarsh, *The Theory of Functions*, (Oxford) pages 64 et seq.). So we consider a subset of all those functions which are differentiable in some domain. Such functions are called *analytic* (in the domain). The theory of analytic functions is probably one of the most beautiful in mathematics. In particular we note that an analytic function of an analytic function is analytic. In our terminology this means that if we combine two analytic functions we get another member of the set.* The identity mapping, $e: z \longrightarrow z$, is also analytic, so, following the train of thought in this chapter, it remains to investigate the existence of the inverse of any function f.

It is clear that a general function f has no inverse, because if f is many-one then the inverse mapping is not a function; and, generally, in the theory of analytic functions this is of no consequence. Only in particular branches do we require inverse functions; for instance, in the applications of the theory of mappings to hydrodynamics, electrical theory, etc. Here we are interested only in the existence of group structure, so we shall restrict our analytic functions to be one-one mappings (often called bi-uniform). This is still not sufficient restriction, for if f is any one-one analytic function there is no guarantee that $\tilde{f}$ is analytic.

Suppose that f and $\tilde{f}$ are analytic and write

$$w = f(z),$$

and so
$$z = \tilde{f}(w) = \tilde{f}(f(z)).$$

Differentiating with respect to z, we have

$$1 = \frac{d\tilde{f}(w)}{dz} = \frac{d\tilde{f}}{dw} \cdot \frac{dw}{dz} = \frac{d\tilde{f}}{dw} \cdot \frac{df}{dz}.$$

It follows that
$$\frac{d\tilde{f}}{dw} = \frac{1}{\dfrac{df}{dz}}, \text{ if } \frac{df}{dz} \neq 0.$$

Thus, a necessary condition that $\tilde{f}$ should be analytic is that $\frac{df}{dz}(z) \neq 0$. This condition is also sufficient.

In general, as we saw earlier, the combination of functions is associative, and so we now have a group structure for this restricted set of analytic functions (see the footnote). There is a result which states that the most general

---

* If f is analytic in a domain D and g is analytic in a domain D', then we can say very little about the domain in which $f \circ g$ is analytic. So the statement in the text is not true without some limitation. We run into the same difficulties when dealing with associativity. We have, however, glossed over these difficulties, because, in the end, we shall give an example of a set of functions which forms a group and in which the domain of each function is the whole complex plane.

one-one analytic mapping of the whole complex plane onto the complex plane is

$$z \longrightarrow \frac{az+b}{cz+d}, \qquad ad - bc \neq 0.$$

where a, b, c, d are (complex) constants. Such a mapping is variously called a *linear*, *bilinear* or *Möbius transformation*.

(i) Find the inverse of the mapping.

(ii) Show that the derivative of this mapping is non-zero if $ad - bc \neq 0$.

(iii) Show, by direct substitution, that the combination of two such mappings is again such a mapping.

(iv) $c = b = 0$, $d = a = 1$ gives the identity mapping $e : z \longrightarrow z$.

(v) Any bilinear mapping can be composed of four basic mappings.

   (a) $z \longrightarrow z + \alpha$, α any complex number. This represents a translation in the plane.

   (b) $z \longrightarrow ze^{i\theta}$, θ any real number. This represents a rotation in the plane, about the origin.

   (c) $z \longrightarrow az$, a any real number. This represents a dilation ($a > 1$), or a contraction ($a < 1$), i.e. a figure is mapped onto a similar figure with a scale of $1 : a$.

   (d) $z \longrightarrow \dfrac{1}{z}$. This represents an inversion in the unit circle, centre the origin.

Now consider the mapping $z \longrightarrow \dfrac{az+b}{cz+d}$.

(A) If $c = 0$, then this can be written $z \longrightarrow a'z + b'$, where $a' = \dfrac{a}{d}$ and $b' = \dfrac{b}{d}$. Then if $a' = \rho e^{i\phi}$, ρ and ϕ real, we can decompose this mapping into

$$z \xrightarrow{\text{(c)}} \rho z \xrightarrow{\text{(b)}} \rho e^{i\phi} z = a'z \xrightarrow{\text{(a)}} a'z + b'.$$

(B) If $c \neq 0$, then write

$$\frac{az+b}{cz+d} = - \frac{[ad-bc]}{c} \cdot \frac{1}{cz+d} + \frac{a}{c}$$

and suppose $c = \rho e^{i\phi}$ and $\dfrac{bc-ad}{c} = K = re^{i\theta}$, where ρ, ϕ, r and θ are real. Then the decomposition is

$$z \xrightarrow{\text{(c)}} \rho z \xrightarrow{\text{(b)}} \rho e^{i\phi} z$$

$$= cz \xrightarrow{\text{(a)}} cz + d \xrightarrow{\text{(d)}} \frac{1}{cz+d} \xrightarrow{\text{(c)}} \frac{r}{cz+d} \xrightarrow{\text{(b)}} \frac{r}{cz+d} e^{i\theta}$$

$$= \frac{K}{cz+d} \xrightarrow{\text{(a)}} \frac{K}{cz+d} + \frac{a}{c} = \frac{az+b}{cz+d}.$$

The only one of the mappings (a), (b), (c) or (d) which changes the shape of figures in the complex plane is the inversion (d). Since the inversion of a circle or a straight line is a circle or a straight line, it follows that circles and straight lines are transformed into circles and straight lines by a bilinear mapping.

(vi) Show that each of the sets of mappings (a), (b) and (c) forms a subgroup of the group of all bilinear mappings. What about (d)?

(vii) Under the mapping $z \longrightarrow \dfrac{az + b}{cz + d}$, which point z maps onto the point at infinity? What is the image of the point at infinity? Answer the same questions for the mappings (a) to (d).

We shall now leave the straightforward examples of groups and turn to another aspect of the use of group ideas. There will, of course, be many more examples of groups in subsequent chapters.

The following two examples of extensions of sets to form groups may, with suitable pupils, be made the basis for the teaching of much elementary arithmetic. Suitable pupils are those who are

(a) familiar with the properties of natural numbers under addition and multiplication,

(b) familiar with simple group structures and the fact that simple problems of the type $a \circ x = b$ are solvable in a group,

(c) either completely unacquainted with the properties of fractions and directed numbers or, although acquainted with them, sufficiently academically inclined to be prepared to reconsider these properties in a more unified way.

(For a discussion of this topic within the general teaching scheme see Mansfield and Thompson, *Mathematics: A New Approach*, Teachers' and Pupils' Books 3, Chapters 1 and 9 (Chatto and Windus).)

The work may well be introduced once some simple examples of groups have been considered, and the specific advantages of the structure realized, by constructing the following table, which is intended to show whether or not the set of natural numbers, 1, 2, 3, 4, . . . possesses the four group properties under the operations of addition, subtraction, multiplication and division.

Natural numbers	+	−	×	÷
Closure	√	×	√	×
Associativity	√	×	√	×
Neutral element	×	×	√ (1)	×
Inverses	×	×	×	×

Evidently the set does not form a group under any of these operations and hence the situation is unsatisfactory in that if a and b are natural numbers there may not always be an x in the set such that $a \circ x = b$ where $\circ$ stands for any of the four operations. Our purpose is to extend the set so that groups are formed where possible, and we shall use the properties of the natural numbers only. The extended system will include a subset which can be identified (under an isomorphism, see Chapter 4, page 61) with the natural numbers. Plainly the operations of subtraction and division may be discarded since they fulfil none of the four conditions. Of the remaining two operations we consider multiplication first since it fails in respect of one property only.

7. We wish to invent a new set, using natural numbers only, so that it 'contains' the natural numbers, but so that the equation

$$ax = b$$

always has a solution in the set, when a and b are members of the set. Now in the cases where a natural number x does exist to satisfy $ax = b$ (where a and b are natural numbers) the value of x is completely specified by the values of a and b and we want to preserve this property*. (The asterisk, here and subsequently, is inserted for future reference.) Hence we may define x by the pair of natural numbers (a, b):

if x_1 satisfies $a_1 x_1 = b_1$ we define x_1 by (a_1, b_1),
and   if x_2 satisfies $a_2 x_2 = b_2$ we define x_2 by (a_2, b_2).

But if x_1 and x_2 are as defined, and they are natural numbers, we have, necessarily,

$$a_1 a_2 \, x_1 x_2 = b_1 b_2$$

and we also wish to preserve this property*. Hence

$$x_1 x_2 \text{ is defined by } (a_1 a_2, b_1 b_2)$$

which implies that our combination operation (which we shall denote by a simple dot, because we are extending multiplication of natural numbers) for these pairs of natural numbers is

$$(a_1, b_1) . (a_2, b_2) = (a_1 a_2, b_1 b_2) \ . \qquad . \qquad . \qquad . \quad (1)$$

If we now take all pairs of natural numbers (a, b) (and not only those which correspond to a natural number x) as the members of a set, then equation (1) defines an operation by which any two pairs of natural numbers may be combined to produce another pair of natural numbers. (Note that since a_1, a_2, b_1 and b_2 are natural numbers so also are $a_1 a_2$ and $b_1 b_2$.)

Plainly $(1, 1)$ is an identity element, since

$$(a, b) . (1, 1) = (1, 1) . (a, b) = (a, b),$$

but so far, the system does not possess inverses: there is, for example, no pair (a, b) such that

$$(2, 3) . (a, b) = (1, 1).$$

However, we observe that if x is a natural number satisfying $ax = b$ (so that x is defined by (a, b)), we have, necessarily, for any natural number k,

$$kax = kb$$

so that the same x is defined by (ka, kb) and we also (and finally) wish to retain this property*. Hence

$$(ka, kb) = (a, b),$$

where the equals sign is used in the sense that both pairs define the same x. It is convenient to write this in the equivalent form

$$(a_1, b_1) = (a_2, b_2) \text{ if } a_1 b_2 = a_2 b_1. \qquad . \qquad . \qquad . \quad (2)$$

Now the relation (2) is an equivalence relation for the set of all pairs of natural numbers. It partitions the set into non-overlapping equivalence classes and the combination defined by equation (1) is compatible with the equivalence relation, i.e. if

$$(a_1, b_1) = (a_2, b_2) \text{ and } (c_1, d_1) = (c_2, d_2) \text{ then } (a_1 c_1, b_1 d_1) = (a_2 c_2, b_2 d_2),$$

for $\qquad a_1 c_1 b_2 d_2 = [a_1 b_2][c_1 d_2] = [b_1 a_2][d_1 c_2] = b_1 d_1 a_2 c_2.$

It follows that we can take these equivalence classes as the elements of a set and that classes can be combined by applying the operation given by equation (1) to any two representative members of the two classes, and then identifying the class to which the result belongs. Then, with the equivalence class containing $(1, 1)$ as identity element, the system forms a group. It may be seen that operation defined by equation (1) is necessarily associative, since multiplication of natural numbers is associative. It may also be seen that if $\{(a, b)\}$ is a class, then

$$\{(a, b)\}.\{(b, a)\} = \{(ab, ab)\} \qquad \text{by equation (1)}$$
$$= \{(1, 1)\} \qquad \text{by relation (2)}.$$

Thus the class whose representative is (a, b) has as inverse the class whose representative is (b, a).

Further, as required, there always exists a class $\{(x, y)\}$ such that

$$\{(a, b)\}.\{(x, y)\} = \{(c, d)\},$$

for operating on both sides with $\{(b, a)\}$, the inverse of $\{(a, b)\}$, we have

$$\{(1, 1)\}.\{(x, y)\} = \{(b, a)\}.\{(c, d)\},$$
$$\{(x, y)\} = \{(bc, ad)\}. \qquad . \qquad . \qquad . \quad (3)$$

Since the operation is commutative, $\{(bc, ad)\}$ automatically satisfies

$$\{(x, y)\}.\{(a, b)\} = \{(c, d)\}.$$

Thus our object has been achieved, in that we have defined a group structure purely in terms of natural numbers. It remains to be seen that the systems 'contains' the natural numbers; more precisely that it has a subset which can be identified isomorphically with the natural numbers. It is already obvious that many of the properties of the natural numbers have been deliberately retained (see the three occurrences of an * above).

Some of the equivalence classes have members of the form (m, ma). In each such class there is a member for which the first element of the ordered pair is least, viz. the pair $(1, a)$. The mapping i

$$i : a \rightarrow \{(1, a)\}$$

is clearly one-one. Also

$$i(ab) = \{(1, ab)\} = \{(1, a)\}.\{(1, b)\} = i(a).i(b),$$

and so i is an isomorphism between the natural numbers and the subset of equivalence classes of the form $\{(1, a)\}$.

It is inconvenient to continue repeating 'class whose representative is' or using the multiple brackets $\{(\ )\}$, so we usually denote each whole equivalence class by that one of its members for which the first element of the ordered pair is least: if this member is (a, b) it is usually written as b/a and the whole equivalence class is called the *positive rational b/a*.

It is suggested that pupils in the category 'unacquainted with fractions' should now be introduced to the usual physical interpretations and that some corresponding interpretations of the operation defined by equation (1) above should also be investigated (noticing that multiplication of a fraction by a fraction and of a fraction by a natural number are obtained directly from equation (1), while division of a fraction or a whole number by a whole number or a fraction are obtained from equation (3): 'cancellation' and 'reduction to lowest terms' follow from relation (2)).

8. We now construct a set, using only natural numbers, forming a group for an operation corresponding to addition, so that the system, in the sense explained in the previous exercises, 'contains' the natural numbers, and so that if a and b are members of the set there is always an x such that

$$a + x = b$$

and a y such that

$$y + a = b,$$

where the $+$ denotes the operation of addition extended to the new set.

The construction is analogous to that in the last example and will, in consequence, be abbreviated. In the cases where a natural number x_1 exists to satisfy $a_1 + x_1 = b_1$ (a_1 and b_1 are natural numbers), we define x_1 by (a_1, b_1). If a natural number x_2 satisfies $a_2 + x_2 = b_2$, we define x_2 by (a_2, b_2). Now it follows that

$$[a_1 + a_2] + [x_1 + x_2] = b_1 + b_2,$$

so we define $x_1 + x_2$ by $(a_1 + a_2, b_1 + b_2)$. Hence

$$(a_1, b_1) + (a_2, b_2) = (a_1 + a_2, b_1 + b_2) \quad . \quad . \quad . \quad (1)$$

Again, if x is a natural number and satisfies

$$a + x = b,$$

then for any natural number k,

$$a + k + x = b + k,$$

so that the same x is defined by (a, b) and by $(a + k, b + k)$.

We write $\qquad (a + k, b + k) = (a, b)$

in the more convenient form

$$(a_1, b_1) = (a_2, b_2) \text{ if } a_1 + b_2 = a_2 + b_1. \quad . \quad . \quad (2)$$

Now the set of all pairs of natural numbers is partitioned into equivalence classes by the relation (2). We take the equivalence classes as elements, and as in the previous exercise show that addition is compatible with the equivalence relation. Therefore, we can combine any two equivalence classes by combining two representative members by the operation defined by equation (1) and identifying the equivalence class to which the result belongs.

The set is closed under this operation since $a_1 + a_2$ and $b_1 + b_2$ are natural numbers if a_1, a_2, b_1 and b_2 are natural numbers.

The operation is associative because addition of natural numbers is associative.

The identity element is the class containing $(1, 1)$, for

$$\{(a, b)\} + \{(1, 1)\} = \{(a + 1, b + 1)\} \quad \text{from equation (1)}$$
$$= \{(a, b)\} \quad\quad\quad\quad \text{by relation (2).}$$

The class $\{(a, b)\}$ has as inverse the class $\{(b, a)\}$, for

$$\{(a, b)\} + \{(b, a)\} = \{(a + b, a + b)\} \quad \text{from equation (1)}$$
$$= \{(1, 1)\} \quad\quad\quad\quad \text{by relation (2).}$$

Hence this system of equivalence classes forms a group.

Again, for conciseness, each equivalence class is allotted a name, determined as follows: in any class choose a pair (r, s). Then, if $r > s$, $r - s$ is a natural number, say t. The whole class is given the name the *integer*, or *directed number*, $-t$. If $r < s$, $s - r$ is a natural number, say t. The whole class is given the name the integer, or directed number, $+t$. If, finally, $r = s$, the whole class is given the name the integer 0. (If $r = s$, (r, s) is a member of the class $(1, 1)$; it follows that 0 is the neutral element.)*

The mapping $i: a \longrightarrow \{(1, a + 1)\} = + a$ is clearly a one-one mapping of the natural numbers onto a subset of the integers. The mapping is an isomorphism:

$$i(a + b) = \{(1, a + b + 1)\} = \{(2, a + b + 2\}$$
$$= \{1, a + 1)\} + \{(1, b + 1)\} = i(a) + i(b).$$

Hence the natural numbers may be identified with the classes $+1$, $+2$, $+3$, ... and the system in this sense 'contains' the natural numbers.

Since the system is a group, if

$$\{(a, b)\} + \{(x, y)\} = \{(c, d)\}$$

we may add the inverse of $\{(a, b)\}$, that is $\{(b, a)\}$, to both sides, obtaining

$$\{(1, 1)\} + \{(x, y)\} = \{(b + c, a + d)\},$$
i.e. $\quad\quad\quad \{(x, y)\} = \{(b + c, a + d)\}$. $\quad$. $\quad$. $\quad$. $\quad$. (3)

It is suggested that appropriate pupils perform such calculations as $+3 + +5$, $-3 + +5$, $+3 + -5$ and $-3 + -5$, by choosing particular representatives of the equivalence classes and using equation (1) and relation (2). For example, to calculate $+3 + -5$ they might take $(1, 4)$ as representing $+3$ and $(7, 2)$ as representing -5. Then

$$(1, 4) + (7, 2) = (8, 6) \quad\quad\quad \text{by equation (1)}$$

and the class which $(8, 6)$ represents is named -2. Hence

$$+3 + -5 = -2.$$

Again subtraction may be performed by equation (3). For instance $-3 - -5$ may be calculated by taking $(4, 1)$ as representing -3 and $(8, 3)$ as representing -5. It is required to find (x, y) such that

$$(8, 3) + (x, y) = (4, 1)$$

---

* This, the traditional notation for the integers, is offensive and obscure. In order to distinguish the elements from the operations many teachers now write, for example, $^-1 + {}^+2 = {}^+1$.

and, by equation (3), $(x, y) = (7, 9)$ and $\{(7, 9)\}$ has the name $+2$. Hence

$$-3 - -5 = +2.$$

The usual interpretations in terms of thermometer scales, altitudes and bank balances may follow.

9. The process which we have described in the last two exercises can be continued (with variations) until the whole system of rationals with addition and multiplication has been constructed. But after the last two exercises the process may well become too tedious for both pupil and teacher, and, therefore, for teaching purposes a compromise is suggested as outlined in Mansfield and Thompson, *Mathematics. A New Approach* (Chatto & Windus) (especially, Teachers' Book 3, Chapter 9). Nevertheless, it is advisable that the teacher should be aware of the fact that the structural approach can be continued to develop the whole system of rationals. We do this in Chapter 13, where it is more appropriate.

*   *   *   *   *

Our last example of a group structure in this chapter is a topological one.

10. There are many fascinating topics which belong to the byways of topology. Although they may once have been associated with 'recreational mathematics' their theory has been developed and has engaged the attention of many famous mathematicians. Such topics are the map colouring problem, the theory of knots and braids and many topics now included in the theory of graphs. All these belong properly to the wide field of topology and they have all led to much serious mathematics, and in a number of cases to problems still unsolved.

As an example to end this chapter we shall describe the group associated with the theory of *braids*: for more information the reader is referred to Reidemeister, *Knotentheorie*, (Chelsea), 1948, and the bibliography given by him.

Let l_1 and l_2 be two equal parallel lines and let $A_1, \ldots, A_n$ and $B_1, \ldots, B_n$ be n points equidistantly spaced on each line respectively.* Then a braid of order n is a system of n threads (mathematically represented by non-intersecting space curves) joining the A's to B's: only one thread terminates at any of the points. Also we shall require that the projection of the threads into the plane of l_1 and l_2 is such that any line l parallel to l_1 and l_2 meets each curve once only. Thus a typical projection of a braid would look like the figure on page 115, where over and under crossings of the threads are shown in an obvious way. As we shall see later, it is inconvenient to have exactly the situation depicted where l passes through two double-points, so we deform the pattern slightly so that no two double-points lie on the same parallel l. In fact

---

* Our definition might seem somewhat special, but it is given in this form for subsequent convenience. If the points were not equidistantly spaced we would just allow a further continuous deformation which moved the points into the required positions without reordering, etc.

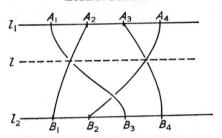

we shall allow any continuous* deformation of the threads, and two braids will be said to be equivalent if they have the same number of threads and if they can be continuously deformed into each other. This is a proper equivalence relation.

We can combine braids of the same order by sticking them end to end. We can formalize this as follows: Let the braids be denoted in an obvious way by $Z_1 = l_1, l_2; A_1, \ldots, A_n; B_1, \ldots, B_n$ and $Z_2 = l_1', l_2'; A_1', \ldots, A_n'; B_1', \ldots, B_n'$, then we define the combination by laying l_2 along l_1' so that the points $B_1, \ldots, B_n$ and $A_1', \ldots, A_n'$ are matched. (If the distances between the A's and B's are not the same then we can always perform an affine transformation (see Chapter 12) to arrange this.) We then suppress l_2 and l_1' and imagine the threads to run uninterruptedly from l_1 to l_2'. The new braid is again of order n and we shall denote it by $Z_1 \circ Z_2$. We give an example.

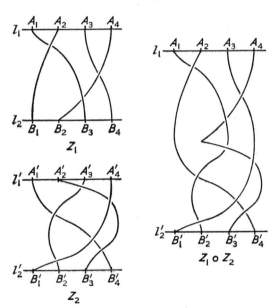

If Z_1 is equivalent to Z_1' and Z_2 to Z_2' then $Z_1 \circ Z_2$ is equivalent to $Z_1' \circ Z_2'$.

* By 'continuous deformation' we mean the physical deformation of a thread in three dimensional space without breaking it or making joins.

This means that we can combine equivalence classes according to the definition

$$\{Z_1\} \circ \{Z_2\} = \{Z_1 \circ Z_2\}.$$

Combination of braids is associative: the braid in which each A_i is joined to B_i without crossings defines a class $\{e\}$ and clearly

$$\{Z_1\} \circ \{e\} = \{e\} \circ \{Z_1\} = \{Z_1\}.$$

Therefore, if we can define the inverse of $\{Z_1\}$, we shall have a group structure for the set of all braids of given order n. In fact $\{\tilde{Z}_1\}$ is the inverse, where $\tilde{Z}_1$ is the mirror image of Z_1 in l_2. We shall, however, develop the inverse otherwise.

Instead of combining braids we can chop them up into elementary sections by lines parallel to the lines l_1 and l_2 so that each section contains one crossing only. Thus Z_2 illustrated above would be divided into six elementary sections as shown below.

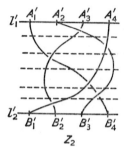

Z_2

If in any elementary section the i-th thread crosses over the $(i + 1)$-th thread, counting from the left along the top line of the section, then we denote that section by S_i: if the i-th thread passes under the $(i + 1)$-th thread we denote it by $\tilde{S}_i$. It is clear that

$$\{S_i\} \circ \{\tilde{S}_i\} = \{\tilde{S}_i\} \circ \{S_i\} = \{e\}.$$

Note that the numbering of the threads will change from section to section and that we work from the top to the bottom of the braid. In the above figure we have

$$Z_2 = S_2 \circ \tilde{S}_3 \circ \tilde{S}_1 \circ \tilde{S}_2 \circ \tilde{S}_3 \circ \tilde{S}_1.$$

Hence $$\{Z_2\} = \{S_2\} \circ \{\tilde{S}_3\} \circ \{\tilde{S}_1\} \circ \{\tilde{S}_2\} \circ \{\tilde{S}_3\} \circ \{\tilde{S}_1\} \qquad . \qquad . \ (1)$$

Since the combination of braids is associative, it follows* that

$$\{\tilde{Z}_2\} = \{S_1\} \circ \{S_3\} \circ \{S_2\} \circ \{S_1\} \circ \{S_3\} \circ \{\tilde{S}_2\},$$

which exhibits the inverse explicitly. The reader might like to draw this braid.

Every equivalence class $\{Z\}$ can be written as a combination of $\{S_i\}$ and $\{\tilde{S}_i\}$, therefore we say that the $\{S_i\}$ are *generating elements* of the group. If the braids are of order n, then there are $n - 1$ generating elements,

$$\{S_1\}, \ldots, \{S_{n-1}\}.$$

Two braids of order n will be equivalent if the corresponding combinations of generating elements define the same group element. For instance in

* Note that the inverse of an expression like $g_1 \circ g_2$ is $\tilde{g}_2 \circ \tilde{g}_1$.

the braid Z_2, the thread $A_4'B_1'$ passes over all the other threads and we can alter its position arbitrarily. Thus an equivalent braid would be Z_2'

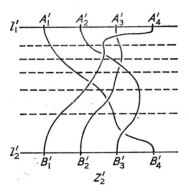

$$Z_2'$$

whence $\qquad \{Z_2'\} = \{Z_2\} = \{\tilde{S}_3\} \circ \{\tilde{S}_2\} \circ \{S_3\} \circ \{\tilde{S}_1\} \circ \{\tilde{S}_2\} \circ \{\tilde{S}_3\} . \qquad . \quad (2)$$

Thus (1) and (2) would define the same group element.

Reidemeister shows that any continuous transformation of braids can be obtained from three elementary transformations. By examining the effect of these elementary transformations on any combination of generating elements one can obtain the following two relations satisfied by the generating elements of a braid group

$$\{S_i\} \circ \{S_j\} = \{S_j\} \circ \{S_i\} \quad j \neq i+1, i-1 \qquad (3)$$

and $\qquad \{S_i\} \circ \{S_{i+1}\} \circ \{S_i\} = \{S_{i+1}\} \circ \{S_i\} \circ \{S_{i+1}\}. \qquad (4)$

These are the defining relations for the group and they are the algebraic expression of the geometrical concept of a continuous transformation: the relations can be verified by drawing the corresponding braids. The reader is recommended to do this in order to appreciate their geometric significance.

Given two braids Z_1 and Z_2 one can form the corresponding expressions in the group. If Z_1 and Z_2 are equivalent then their corresponding expressions can be transformed into each other using the defining relations (3) and (4). Alternatively we can examine the expression corresponding to $\{Z_1\} \circ \{Z_2\}$ using the defining relations. If the braids are equivalent then we must so be able to simplify the expression corresponding to $\{Z_1\} \circ \{\tilde{Z}_2\}$ that we obtain $\{e\}$. For instance, using the example $\{Z_2\}$ above consider

$$\{Z_2'\} \circ \{\tilde{Z}_2\}$$
$$= \{\tilde{S}_3\} \circ \{\tilde{S}_2\} \circ \{S_3\} \circ \{\tilde{S}_1\} \circ \{\tilde{S}_2\} \circ \{\tilde{S}_3\} \circ \{S_1\} \circ \{S_3\} \circ \{S_2\} \circ \{S_1\} \circ \{S_3\} \circ \{\tilde{S}_2\}.$$
$$= \ldots \circ \ldots \ldots \ldots \ldots \circ \{\tilde{S}_3\} \circ \{S_3\} \circ \{S_1\} \circ \ldots \ldots \quad \text{by (3)}$$
$$= \ldots \circ \ldots \ldots \ldots \circ \{\tilde{S}_1\} \circ \{\tilde{S}_2\} \circ \{S_2\} \circ \{S_1\} \circ \{S_2\} \circ \{S_3\} \circ \{\tilde{S}_2\} \text{ etc.} \quad \text{by (4)}$$

The following are elementary exercises on this topic.

(a) Prove that if Z_1 is equivalent to Z_2 then in $Z_1 \circ \tilde{Z}_2$ each A_i must be joined to B_i.

(b) Show that the group of braids of order 2 is an infinite group generated by the element $\{S_1\}$.

(c) Draw the braids of order 3 corresponding to

    (i) $\tilde{S}_2 \circ S_1 \circ \tilde{S}_2 \circ \tilde{S}_1$ (ii) $\tilde{S}_2 \circ \tilde{S}_2 \circ \tilde{S}_1 \circ S_2$

    (iii) $S_1 \circ \tilde{S}_2 \circ \tilde{S}_1 \circ \tilde{S}_2$.

(When drawing braids corresponding to combinations of generating elements it is best to construct them section by section using straight lines, e.g. $S_1 \circ \tilde{S}_3$ in a four braid would be shown as follows.)

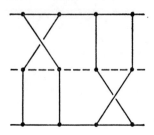

Are any of the three braids equivalent?

(d) Show that the braids of order n in which A_i is joined to B_i for all i, form a subgroup of the general group (see also the end of Chapter 11).

CHAPTER 8

ISOMORPHISMS

IN this chapter we shall return to our investigation of group structure: we shall be concerned with isomorphisms. We defined this term in Chapter 4, which is now a long way off, so we shall repeat ourselves.

Consider the set of natural numbers, $N = (1, 2, 3, 4, \ldots)$, with the operation of addition. Consider also the set of positive integral powers of two, $P = (2, 4, 8, 16, \ldots)$, with the operation of multiplication. It is well known that a one-one correspondence can be set up between the members of these two sets, N and P, so that the result of combining any two elements from one set (by the operation defined for that set) corresponds to the result of combining the corresponding elements from the other set (by the operation defined for that set). The correspondence is shown below:

$$
\begin{array}{ccccccc}
N & 1 & 2 & 3 & 4 & 5 & 6 \ldots \\
  & \updownarrow & \updownarrow & \updownarrow & \updownarrow & \updownarrow & \updownarrow \\
P & 2 & 4 & 8 & 16 & 32 & 64 \ldots
\end{array}
$$

and we have, for example,

$$
\begin{array}{lccc}
\text{in } N & 2 + 4 = & 6 \\
 & \updownarrow & \updownarrow & \updownarrow \\
\text{in } P & 4 \times 16 = & 64.
\end{array}
$$

Any two sets, each with its defined operation, which together exhibit the property described in the last paragraph, are said to be isomorphic to each other (or isomorphic structures). The one-to-one correspondence in such a case is called an isomorphic mapping (or isomorphism): either set may be taken as domain and the other as range, and the image of the combination of two elements in the domain is the combination of the corresponding elements in the range.

In the particular example quoted above the sets do not form groups for the stated operations but, in view of the importance of group structure, we shall be mainly concerned with *isomorphic groups*. Two groups, G and H, with elements $(g_1, g_2, g_3, \ldots)$ and $(h_1, h_2, h_3, \ldots)$ respectively, and operations symbolized by o and □

respectively, are said to be isomorphic if a one-one (onto) mapping can be established between the elements of the two sets so that if any two elements g_i and g_j of G correspond to h_p and h_q of H respectively, and

$$g_i \circ g_j = g_{k'}$$

and
$$h_p \,\square\, h_q = h_{r'}$$

then g_k corresponds to h_r. We can put this in other words. Let i be the one-one mapping of G onto H, then i is an isomorphism if

$$i(g \circ g') = i(g) \,\square\, i(g'),$$

where g and g' are any elements of G.

Example A. Extend the two sets in the example with which this chapter began so that they become isomorphic groups, retaining as subsets the sets N and P and retaining the same operations. Describe the isomorphic mapping precisely (cf. Chapter 4, the exercise on page 62).

Example B. Let G and H be two isomorphic groups as in the text above and let e and e' be their identity elements respectively. Show that

$$i(e) = e',$$

and that if
$$i(g) = h \text{ then } i(\tilde{g}) = \tilde{h}.$$

(Cf. Chapter 4, Example N, page 62.)

Exercises*

1. In the first exercise (Chapter 7, page 103) and the third exercise (Chapter 7, page 105) in the previous chapter the following two group combination tables should have been obtained.

o	a	b	c	d	e	f		o	f_1	f_2	f_3	f_4	f_5	f_6
a	a	b	c	d	e	f		f_1	f_1	f_2	f_3	f_4	f_5	f_6
b	b	c	a	f	d	e		f_2	f_2	f_3	f_1	f_5	f_6	f_4
c	c	a	b	e	f	d		f_3	f_3	f_1	f_2	f_6	f_4	f_5
d	d	e	f	a	b	c		f_4	f_4	f_6	f_5	f_1	f_3	f_2
e	e	f	d	c	a	b		f_5	f_5	f_4	f_6	f_2	f_1	f_3
f	f	d	e	b	c	a		f_6	f_6	f_5	f_4	f_3	f_2	f_1

* Since most of this chapter is concerned with exercises, we have numbered the exercises sequentially for easy reference. There are minor interruptions throughout: these are either general statements which are used subsequently, or examples which have no apparent direct application to the teaching situation.

The one-to-one correspondence set out below

$$\begin{array}{cccccc} a & b & c & d & e & f \\ \updownarrow & \updownarrow & \updownarrow & \updownarrow & \updownarrow & \updownarrow \\ f_1 & f_2 & f_3 & f_4 & f_5 & f_6 \end{array}$$

does NOT establish an isomorphism, for

$$b \circ e = d,$$

and f_2 corresponds to b, f_5 corresponds to e, but

$$f_2 \circ f_5 = f_6$$

and f_6 does *not* correspond to d.

An isomorphism does in fact exist and is established by the isomorphic mapping

$$\begin{array}{cccccc} a & b & c & d & e & f \\ \updownarrow & \updownarrow & \updownarrow & \updownarrow & \updownarrow & \updownarrow \\ f_1 & f_2 & f_3 & f_4 & f_6 & f_5 \end{array}$$

and the correspondence indicates the relabelling required in Exercise 3(ii) on page 105 in the previous chapter.

Two isomorphic groups must necessarily have the same structure (hence the term 'isomorphic'): they are, abstractly, the *same* group, i.e. in the classification of groups they belong to the same equivalence class (cf. Chapter 4, Example O, page 62). It is sometimes evident, from dissimilarities in structure, that two groups are not isomorphic. For example, the group table obtained in Exercise 2(ii) on page 105 in the previous chapter contains six elements like the tables above: however, it is immediately evident that it is not isomorphic to them because it is commutative, while the group we have been discussing is non-commutative (cf. Chapter 4, Example Q, page 63).

2. Pupils may be asked to consider the two groups whose tables are set out below: they can be asked either to establish an isomorphic mapping (i.e. 'relabel') or to give good reasons why no isomorphism exists.

$\circ$	a_1	a_2	a_3	a_4
a_1	a_1	a_2	a_3	a_4
a_2	a_2	a_3	a_4	a_1
a_3	a_3	a_4	a_1	a_2
a_4	a_4	a_1	a_2	a_3

$\square$	b_1	b_2	b_3	b_4
b_1	b_1	b_2	b_3	b_4
b_2	b_2	b_1	b_4	b_3
b_3	b_3	b_4	b_1	b_2
b_4	b_4	b_3	b_2	b_1

(Sufficient reasons are, for example,

  (i) the 'a' group contains only one subgroup with two elements while the 'b' group contains several such subgroups, or

  (ii) in the 'b' group b_1 is the neutral element and the combination of every element with itself is the neutral element: in the 'a' group a_1 is the neutral element but the combination of a_2 with itself, or a_4 with itself, is not a_1.)

Example C. Both the statements made at the end of the above exercise can be proved quite generally. We use the notation of the groups G and H above.

(1) If G_1 is a subgroup of G then $i(G_1) = H_1$, the image of G_1 under the isomorphism i of G onto H, is a subgroup of H.

This can be proved as follows

  (a) H_1, is closed, for let $h_1, h_1' \in H_1$ and let $i(g_1) = h_1$ and $i(g_1') = h_1'$, then

  $$h_1 \square h_1' = i(g_1) \square i(g_1') = i(g_1 \circ g_1'),$$ because i is an isomorphism
  $= i(g_1'')$, where $g_1'' \in G_1$, because G_1 is a group, and hence
  $$i(g_1'') = h_1'' \in H_1.$$

  (b) Combination in H_1 is associative because it is the same as in H.

  (c) The identity element $e \in G$ belongs to G_1 (prove this) and its image $i(e)$ belongs to H_1 and is the identity element (cf. Example B, page 120).

  (d) If $h_1 \in H_1$ then $\tilde{h}_1 \in H_1$. For suppose $i(g_1) = h_1$, then $i(\tilde{g}_1) = \tilde{h}_1$ (cf. Example B, page 120), and $\tilde{g}_1 \in G_1$.

(2) Show that if $g \in G$ and $g \circ g = e$, then $i(g) = h$ also satisfies $h \square h = e'$, where e' is the identity element of H. In general, if $g^n = e$, where n is an integer, then $h^n = e'$. (We here use the index notation to represent repeated combination of the element with itself.)

3. Pupils are usually interested in the statement that the two groups in Exercise 2 represent the only possible groups of four elements, that is, that every other group of four elements is isomorphic to one of these. This (and similar statements) follows from Lagrange's Theorem which we shall prove subsequently.

Teachers, who, knowing that the only two different groups of six elements are those obtained in Chapter 7, Exercise 1(i), page 103, and Exercise 2(ii), page 105, propose to challenge their pupils to produce group tables not isomorphic to either of these should beware of the fact that apparently satisfactory tables can be produced which are certainly not isomorphic to them. Such tables do not, of course, represent groups at all and at least one of the group properties will not hold: unfortunately, if the associative requirement is the only one broken, this has to be demonstrated by the very tedious process of trial with every triple of elements until a case of failure is found.

4. Consider the eight rectangular patterns of four numbers.

$$A = \begin{pmatrix} 0 & 1 \\ 1 & 0 \end{pmatrix}, \ B = \begin{pmatrix} 0 & -1 \\ 1 & 0 \end{pmatrix}, \ C = \begin{pmatrix} 0 & 1 \\ -1 & 0 \end{pmatrix}, \ D = \begin{pmatrix} 0 & -1 \\ -1 & 0 \end{pmatrix},$$

$$E = \begin{pmatrix} 1 & 0 \\ 0 & 1 \end{pmatrix}, \ F = \begin{pmatrix} -1 & 0 \\ 0 & 1 \end{pmatrix}, \ G = \begin{pmatrix} 1 & 0 \\ 0 & -1 \end{pmatrix}, \ H = \begin{pmatrix} -1 & 0 \\ 0 & -1 \end{pmatrix}.$$

The operation by which two patterns may be combined to produce a pattern is symbolized by o, as usual, and is given below. (The double suffix notation by which, for example, a_{21} is the number in the second row and first column, is sometimes convenient but not essential.)

$$\begin{pmatrix} a_{11} & a_{12} \\ a_{21} & a_{22} \end{pmatrix} \circ \begin{pmatrix} b_{11} & b_{12} \\ b_{21} & b_{22} \end{pmatrix} = \begin{pmatrix} a_{11}b_{11} + a_{12}b_{21} & a_{11}b_{12} + a_{12}b_{22} \\ a_{21}b_{11} + a_{21}b_{21} & a_{21}b_{12} + a_{22}b_{22} \end{pmatrix},$$

so that, for example,

$$B \circ G = \begin{pmatrix} 0 & -1 \\ 1 & 0 \end{pmatrix} \circ \begin{pmatrix} 1 & 0 \\ 0 & -1 \end{pmatrix} = \begin{pmatrix} 0.1 + [-1].0 & 0.0 + [-1].[-1] \\ 1.1 + 0.0 & 1.0 + 0.[-1] \end{pmatrix}$$
$$= \begin{pmatrix} 0 & 1 \\ 1 & 0 \end{pmatrix} = A.$$

Although this law of combination may seem difficult to remember at first, it soon comes with practice.

(i) Show that the eight patterns are the elements of a group for the operation o specified and write out the group table.

(ii) What is the neutral element?

(iii) Is the group commutative?

(iv) Make a list showing the inverse of each element.

Rectangular patterns of numbers, of which the eight above are special cases, are known as *matrices*. They are of the utmost mathematical importance, as is the operation o, and we shall frequently return to them in increasing detail later (see, especially, the next chapter).

5. Cut out a cardboard square and letter its vertices, on both sides, A, B, C, D. This square can be fitted into a fixed square frame in eight different ways as below

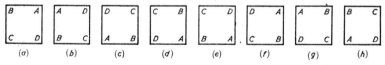

(a)   (b)   (c)   (d)   (e)   (f)   (g)   (h)

As in Exercise 1 of the previous chapter (page 102), we obtain each position from the first position by rotations about axes fixed in the frame as shown below

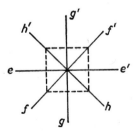

together with an axis 00' through the centre of the frame perpendicular to its plane.

Name and describe each of the eight rotations (including one of 0°) and use the o operation and the = symbol as in Exercise 1 of the previous chapter. Verify that the eight rotations form a group for the o operation and establish an isomorphic correspondence between this group and that of Exercise 4 on page 122.

6. It is of considerable importance to discover the 'reason' for the iso-morphism of the groups in the last two examples. If (x, y) are the coordinates of a point P in a plane with respect to some rectangular coordinates, then we call the pattern $\begin{pmatrix} x \\ y \end{pmatrix}$ the column vector of the point. Such a column vector is just an example of a rectangular matrix. If $\begin{pmatrix} a & b \\ c & d \end{pmatrix}$ is a square matrix (i.e. a square array) of four numbers, then we define

$$\begin{pmatrix} a & b \\ c & d \end{pmatrix} \circ \begin{pmatrix} x \\ y \end{pmatrix}$$

to be

$$\begin{pmatrix} ax + by \\ cx + dy \end{pmatrix},$$

which is again a column vector. For example, if the point P is (3, 4) and the square matrix is $\begin{pmatrix} -1 & 0 \\ 0 & 1 \end{pmatrix}$, then

$$\begin{pmatrix} -1 & 0 \\ 0 & 1 \end{pmatrix} \circ \begin{pmatrix} 3 \\ 4 \end{pmatrix} = \begin{pmatrix} [-1].3 + 0.4 \\ 0.3 + 1.4 \end{pmatrix} = \begin{pmatrix} -3 \\ 4 \end{pmatrix}.$$

Now if $\begin{pmatrix} -3 \\ 4 \end{pmatrix}$ is interpreted as the column vector of a point P', so that the coordinates of P' are $(-3, 4)$, we call P' the *transform* of P under $\begin{pmatrix} -1 & 0 \\ 0 & 1 \end{pmatrix}$.

On graph paper, draw the triangle with vertices $A(2, 2)$, $B(6, 2)$, $C(2, 5)$. Find the transforms A', B' and C' of A, B and C under $\begin{pmatrix} -1 & 0 \\ 0 & 1 \end{pmatrix}$ and draw the triangle of which A', B' and C' are the vertices. Triangle $A'B'C'$ is called the transform of the triangle ABC under $\begin{pmatrix} -1 & 0 \\ 0 & 1 \end{pmatrix}$. It will be seen that if ABC is rotated through 180° about the y-axis it takes up the position $A'B'C'$.

Hence, in this sense, the matrix $\begin{pmatrix} -1 & 0 \\ 0 & 1 \end{pmatrix}$ with the o operation represents a rotation of 180° about the y-axis. Thus, in Exercise 5, a rotation of 180° about gg' corresponds to matrix F in Exercise 4, and one corresponding pair of elements in the isomorphism is established.

The process by which triangle ABC is transformed into triangle $A'B'C'$ is called a *transformation*: it is evident that the particular transformation we have just dealt with may be described in either of two ways:

(i) in 'geometrical' terms, for example as a rotation through 180° about the y-axis (or gg' axis). (There are other 'geometrical' descriptions of the same transformation: e.g. 'a reflection in the y-axis'.)*

(ii) in matrix terms, as the transformation corresponding to $\begin{pmatrix} -1 & 0 \\ 0 & 1 \end{pmatrix}$ under the operation o.

Repeat the above process with each of the other seven matrices of Exercise 4 and describe, in 'geometrical' terms, the transformation corresponding to each. Hence associate each matrix with the corresponding rotation of Exercise 5, thus, once again, establishing the isomorphism between the two groups.

7. Find the matrices which, operating on column vectors by the o operation, correspond to the transformations of Chapter 7, Exercise 1, page 102. The following may be helpful.

Since there are two rotations about OO' it will be convenient to find the matrix corresponding to a rotation through θ about OO', rather than consider the two numerical cases separately.

Let $P'(x', y')$ be the transform of $P(x, y)$ under an anticlockwise rotation through θ about OO'. Then in the diagram below, angle $P'OP$ = angle $N'ON = \theta$. Also angle $MP'N' = \theta$.

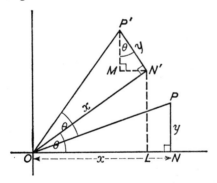

Hence $\qquad x' = OL - MN' = x \cos \theta - y \sin \theta,$
and $\qquad y' = N'L + P'M = x \sin \theta + y \cos \theta.$

In matrix notation this gives

$$\begin{pmatrix} x' \\ y' \end{pmatrix} = \begin{pmatrix} [\cos \theta].x + [-\sin \theta].y \\ [\sin \theta].x + [\cos \theta].y \end{pmatrix}$$

$$= \begin{pmatrix} \cos \theta & -\sin \theta \\ \sin \theta & \cos \theta \end{pmatrix} o \begin{pmatrix} x \\ y \end{pmatrix} \qquad . \qquad . \qquad . \quad (1)$$

* In two-dimensional geometry it is usual to refer to this transformation as a reflection in order to remain in the plane.

so that the matrix $\begin{pmatrix} \cos\theta & -\sin\theta \\ \sin\theta & \cos\theta \end{pmatrix}$ corresponds to a rotation of θ anti-

clockwise about OO', and the two particular matrices required may be found by substitution of numerical values for θ.

Again there are three rotations through $180°$ about axes in the plane (reflections). We therefore consider a rotation of $180°$ about an axis in the plane at θ to the x-axis, as in the diagram below.

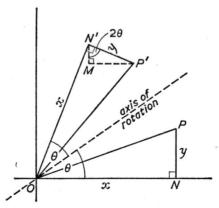

Angle $NON' = 2\theta$ and angle $MN'P' = 2\theta$.

Hence $x' = ON' \cos 2\theta + P'N' \sin 2\theta = x \cos 2\theta + y \sin 2\theta,$

and , $y' = ON' \sin 2\theta - P'N' \cos 2\theta = x \sin 2\theta - y \cos 2\theta.$

That is $\begin{pmatrix} x' \\ y' \end{pmatrix} = \begin{pmatrix} \cos 2\theta & \sin 2\theta \\ \sin 2\theta & -\cos 2\theta \end{pmatrix} \text{ o } \begin{pmatrix} x \\ y \end{pmatrix}$

and the three particular matrices may be found by substitution for θ.

8. Teachers might like to make use of the matrix equation labelled (1) in the previous exercise to verify the standard 'sine sum' and 'cosine sum' formulae, by observing that a rotation through θ about OO' followed by a further rotation through ϕ about OO' plainly produces the same transformation as a rotation of $\theta + \phi$ about OO'. (But note that the mechanics of the verification could be much simplified if a little more matrix technique were developed first, particularly the associativity of the o operation, see Chapter 9, Example E, page 140.)

We have established in equation (1) that the result of a rotation through an angle θ can be written

$$\begin{pmatrix} x' \\ y' \end{pmatrix} = \begin{pmatrix} x \cos\theta - y \sin\theta \\ x \sin\theta + y \cos\theta \end{pmatrix}.$$

Suppose that this is followed by a rotation through an angle ϕ, then if $\begin{pmatrix} x' \\ y' \end{pmatrix}$

transforms into $\begin{pmatrix} x'' \\ y'' \end{pmatrix}$ under this further rotation, we have

(A) $$\begin{pmatrix} x'' \\ y'' \end{pmatrix} = \begin{pmatrix} \cos \phi & -\sin \phi \\ \sin \phi & \cos \phi \end{pmatrix} \circ \begin{pmatrix} x' \\ y' \end{pmatrix} =$$

$$= \begin{pmatrix} x \cos \phi \cos \theta - y \sin \theta \cos \phi - x \sin \theta \sin \phi - y \cos \theta \sin \phi \\ x \cos \theta \sin \phi - y \sin \theta \sin \phi + x \sin \theta \cos \phi + y \cos \theta \cos \phi \end{pmatrix}.$$

If, on the other hand, we regard $\begin{pmatrix} x'' \\ y'' \end{pmatrix}$ as the transform of $\begin{pmatrix} x \\ y \end{pmatrix}$ under a single rotation through $[\theta + \phi]$, we have, using equation (1) again

(B) $$\begin{pmatrix} x'' \\ y'' \end{pmatrix} = \begin{pmatrix} x \cos [\theta + \phi] - y \sin [\theta + \phi] \\ x \sin [\theta + \phi] + y \cos [\theta + \phi] \end{pmatrix}$$

But (A) and (B) must represent the same point for all choices of x and y, so make any particular choice, $x = 1$, $y = 0$ say. Then we get

$$\begin{pmatrix} \cos [\theta + \phi] \\ \sin [\theta + \phi] \end{pmatrix} = \begin{pmatrix} \cos \phi \cos \theta - \sin \theta \sin \phi \\ \cos \theta \sin \phi + \sin \theta \cos \phi \end{pmatrix}.$$

Similarly, if we choose $x = 0$, $y = 1$, we get

$$\begin{pmatrix} -\sin [\theta + \phi] \\ \cos [\theta + \phi] \end{pmatrix} = \begin{pmatrix} -\sin \theta \cos \phi - \cos \theta \sin \phi \\ \cos \theta \cos \phi - \sin \theta \sin \phi \end{pmatrix}$$

which is the same result.

Note that we have made a particular choice for x and y, and it might be supposed that we could get different results if we made other choices. If it is so supposed, the best thing to do at this level is to try it.

9. The expression (A) in the previous exercise can be written

$$\begin{pmatrix} x'' \\ y'' \end{pmatrix} = \begin{pmatrix} \cos \phi \cos \theta - \sin \theta \sin \phi & -\sin \theta \cos \phi - \cos \theta \sin \phi \\ \cos \theta \sin \phi + \sin \theta \cos \phi & \cos \phi \cos \theta - \sin \theta \sin \phi \end{pmatrix} \circ \begin{pmatrix} x \\ y \end{pmatrix}$$

$$= \left[\begin{pmatrix} \cos \phi & -\sin \phi \\ \sin \phi & \cos \phi \end{pmatrix} \circ \begin{pmatrix} \cos \theta & -\sin \theta \\ \sin \theta & \cos \theta \end{pmatrix} \right] \circ \begin{pmatrix} x \\ y \end{pmatrix},$$

and it follows from our investigations that the combination of the two matrices in the square bracket is the same as the matrix

$$\begin{pmatrix} \cos [\theta + \phi] & -\sin [\theta + \phi] \\ \sin [\theta + \phi] & \cos[\theta + \phi] \end{pmatrix}.$$

Consider the set of all matrices corresponding to the set of all such rotations, i.e. all matrices of the form

$$\begin{pmatrix} \cos \theta & -\sin \theta \\ \sin \theta & \cos \theta \end{pmatrix} :$$

we shall denote such a matrix by the capital letter corresponding to the angle involved, i.e. the last matrix will be denoted by Θ. To each rotation about OO' there corresponds a matrix Θ and to each Θ there corresponds a rotation but before we can say that the correspondence is one-to-one we must define what we mean by the equality of two matrices.

DEFINITION: Two matrices are equal if and only if they are identical, i.e. the arrays have exactly the same shape and corresponding elements in the two arrays are the same. Thus, for example

$$\begin{pmatrix} 1 & 0 \\ 0 & 1 \end{pmatrix} = \begin{pmatrix} 1 & 0 \\ 0 & 1 \end{pmatrix} \neq \begin{pmatrix} 1 & 0 \\ 0 & 1 \\ 0 & 0 \end{pmatrix} \neq \begin{pmatrix} -1 & 0 \\ 0 & 1 \\ 0 & 0 \end{pmatrix}.$$

Exercise 9 (*continued*). It now follows that i: rot.$\theta \longrightarrow \Theta$, the correspondence discussed above, is one-one. We can combine rotations by performing them successively, and then i is an isomorphism of the rotations onto the matrices under the o operation, as we have shown at the beginning of this exercise.

The set of all rotations mod 2π (Chapter 3, Exercise 1, page 49) about OO' forms a group and it, therefore, follows that the set of all matrices corresponding to these rotations forms a group (cf. Example C Part (1), page 122 with minor modifications).

(i) What is the identity element for rotations? What is the identity element for rotation matrices? (Note that they must correspond under the isomorphism.)

(ii) What is the inverse element for a rotation through θ? What is the inverse of the matrix Θ? (Note that these must also correspond.)

10. Show that the set of four elements 1, -1, j, $-j$ form a group under multiplication with $j^2 = -1$.

Show also that the subset (B, C, E, H) of the set of matrices in Exercise 4, on page 122, forms a group under the o operation.

Show that these two groups are isomorphic. This is a special case of an isomorphism which will be discussed later in the next chapter, in Exercise 4, page 144.

11. Show that the six matrices

$$\begin{pmatrix} 1 & 0 \\ 0 & 1 \end{pmatrix} \begin{pmatrix} 0 & 1 \\ 1 & 0 \end{pmatrix} \begin{pmatrix} \omega & 0 \\ 0 & \omega^2 \end{pmatrix} \begin{pmatrix} \omega^2 & 0 \\ 0 & \omega \end{pmatrix} \begin{pmatrix} 0 & \omega^2 \\ \omega & 0 \end{pmatrix} \begin{pmatrix} 0 & \omega \\ \omega^2 & 0 \end{pmatrix}$$

form a group under the o operation where $\omega^3 = 1$ ($\omega \neq 1$); show, further, that the group is isomorphic to that of Exercise 1 on page 120.

Example D. Consider a group G with a finite number of elements $(g_1, g_2, \ldots, g_n)$ and operation o. Evidently the set $(\tilde{g}_1, \tilde{g}_2, \tilde{g}_3, \ldots, \tilde{g}_n)$ forms a group under the same operation o (where $\tilde{g}_i$ represents, as usual, the inverse of g_i in G). If the one-one correspondence i, defined by

$$i(g_r) = \tilde{g}_r$$

is an isomorphism, prove that G is commutative.

Example E. The set of n anticlockwise rotations of a regular n-sided plane polygon about an axis through its centre perpendicular to its plane through angles $k.2\pi/n$ for $k = 1, 2, 3, \ldots, n$ plainly form a group where the o operation is successive performance modulo 2π, and this group is isomorphic to a certain group of matrices. Write down the matrix corresponding to the rotation through $k.2\pi/n$. If this matrix is $\begin{pmatrix} a & b \\ c & d \end{pmatrix}$ find the values of x satisfying

$[a - x][d - x] - bc = 0$ (this equation is known as the characteristic equation of the matrix) and put $k = 1, 2, 3, \ldots, n$. What are these values? If X is the set of values of x with the operation of multiplication, and S is the set of rotations under o, are X and S isomorphic structures?

12. Consider R the group of all real numbers, with the operation of addition. Let r, s and t be typical members of this group. Consider also the mapping

$$f: r \longrightarrow a^r$$

where a is a fixed positive real number other than unity.

The domain of this mapping is R. What is the range? The elements of the range form a group H under the operation of multiplication, for

(1) $a^r \times a^s = a^{r+s}$ and $a^{r+s} \in H$ since $r + s \in R$,

(2) $a^r \times [a^s \times a^t] = [a^r \times a^s] \times a^t$,

(3) $a^r \times a^0 = a^0 \times a^r = a^r$ and $a^0 \in H$ since $0 \in R$,

(4) $a^r \times a^{-r} = a^{-r} \times a^r = a^0$ and $a^{-r} \in H$ since $-r \in R$.

Name a non-negative real number which does not belong to H. Note that the neutral element of R corresponds to the neutral element of H.

The groups R and H are isomorphic for if, in R, $r + s = v$, we have in H,

$$a^r \times a^s = a^{r+s} = a^v.$$

But the elements of two isomorphic groups are in one-to-one correspondence and H is a subset of R. Could this occur if either H or R were a finite set?

The isomorphism breaks down if we take $a = 1$ for the set H then becomes finite and an infinite set cannot be in one-to-one correspondence with a finite set. How many members has H in this case?

13. Consider the two equivalence classes, even whole numbers (represented by A), and odd whole numbers (represented by B). Then from the well-known results 'even $\times$ odd = even' and so on, we have the table

System 1

$\times$	A	B
A	A	A
B	A	B

Table 1

On the other hand, using the equally well-known results 'even + odd = odd' and so on, we have the table

System 2

$+$	A	B
A	A	B
B	B	A

Table 2

Now consider the two electric circuits below, each containing a battery, a bulb and two switches (switch 1 and switch 2),

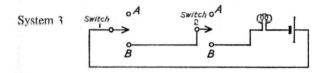

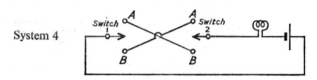

To use one of these circuits to combine, say, B and A (in that order) we set switch 1 to position B and switch 2 to position A. If the bulb lights up we take the result of the combination to be B, while if it does not we take the result to be A. For example, in system 3

$$A \circ A = A,$$

where we use o to represent the operation of combination.

Write out the table for system 3 (call it Table 3) and another table for system 4 (call it Table 4). Compare them with Tables 1 and 2.

Two of the tables represent equivalent structures (not groups). Which are they?

Two of the tables represent equivalent groups.

14. (a) We consider pairs of real numbers (a, b) and define the operations $\oplus$ and $\otimes$ by

$$(a, b) \oplus (c, d) = (a + c, b + d)$$
$$(a, b) \otimes (c, d) = (ac - bd, ad + bc).$$

(i) Show that $\oplus$ and $\otimes$ are commutative.

(ii) Show that $\otimes$ is distributive over $\oplus$.

(iii) We define $q(a, b)$ to be (qa, qb), where q is any real number. Show that
$$(p + q)(a, b) = p(a, b) \oplus q(a, b).$$

(iv) Consider the particular elements $(0, 1)$ and $(1, 0)$, and obtain the following results:

$(1, 0) \otimes (1, 0) = (1, 0)$, $(0, 1) \otimes (1, 0) = (0, 1)$, $(0, 1) \otimes (0, 1) = -1(1, 0)$.

(v) Any element (a, b) can be written as $a(1, 0) \oplus b(0, 1)$. For brevity we write $(1, 0)$ as x and $(0, 1)$ as y. Writing $(a, b) \otimes (a, b)$ as $(a, b)^2$ rewrite (iv) in terms of x and y, e.g. $y^2 = -1.x$.

(vi) Show that the system above is isomorphic under $\oplus$ and $\otimes$ to the system usually known as complex numbers under addition and multiplication respectively.

(b) In an analogous way we can construct other systems, some of which are useful or interesting and some of which are not, by defining combinations of n-tuples of real numbers. We give some examples, all of which are, in fact, in the 'useful or interesting' category.

(i) $(a, b, c) \oplus (d, e, f) = (a + d, b + e, c + f)$
and $(a, b, c) \otimes (d, e, f) = (ad + be + cf, 0, 0)$.
(See Chapter 9, Exercise 6 (iv), page 149.)

(ii) $(a, b) \oplus (c, d) = (a + c, b + d)$
and $(a, b) \otimes (c, d) = (ac, ad + bc)$.
(See Chapter 9, Exercise 4 (c), pages 138 and 145.)

(iii) $(a, b) \oplus (c, d) = (a + c, b + d)$
and $(a, b) \otimes (c, d) = (ac + bd, ad + bc)$.
(See Chapter 9, Exercise 4 (b), pages 138 and 144.)

(iv) $(a, b, c, d) \oplus (e, f, g, h) = (a + e, b + f, c + g, d + h)$
and $(a, b, c, d) \otimes (e, f, g, h) = (ae - bf - cg - dh, af + be + ch - dg, ag + ec + df - bh, ah + de + bg - cf)$.
(See Chapter 9, Exercise 4 (d), pages 139 and 145.)

Investigate these systems as suggested in (a). In particular, define an x and y and show that in (ii) $y^2 = 0.x = (0, 0)$ and in (iii) $y^2 = 1.x = x$: in (iv) one would have to define x, y, z and w in an analogous way.

(c) In each of the above examples we have two operations. This really means that we have a more complicated structure (see Chapter 13). We can, however, investigate each combination operation separately to see if we have group structure. It will generally be found that the n-tuple containing all zeros should be discarded to obtain multiplicative group structure: in some cases not even this will help. For the significance of this see Chapter 13.

(d) The reader might like to set up a different system of his own similar to any one of (a), (b) (ii) or (b) (iii) in particular.

The usual and convenient, but rather obscure, method of definition of such structures as the above is 'backwards'. (We do this ourselves, but only as a convenient form of reference; see the exercises referred to in (b) above.) For instance, one defines the set of complex numbers as the set of numbers of the form $a + by$ where $y^2 = -1$ and a and b are real, with $[a + by] + [c + dy] = [a + c] + [b + d]y$ and $[a + by] \times [c + dy] = [ac - bd] + [ad + bc]y$. One consequence of this approach is the unfortunate temptation, given $y^2 = -1$, to make unjustified deductions about y itself arising from $y \times y = -1$, and falsely treating the last $\times$ sign as identical with that in $a \times b = ab$. At the best this approach is incomplete. (The student engineer is much encouraged, at the cost of subsequent disillusionment, by being told that y (or j to an engineer) has something to do with a phase change of $\pi/2$. The disillusion could be avoided by carefully pointing out the isomorphism: after all one does not have to use the word.) It would seem that for teaching purposes one should mix the two approaches, pointing out the difference between the elements and operations where appropriate, seeking to arrive at a rigorous system, intuitively motivated.

$$* \quad * \quad * \quad * \quad *$$

At the end of the last chapter we gave a topological example from what was once one of the more light-hearted aspects of this subject, but which has led to much serious mathematics. We return now to a little more formal development.

We have already had two examples of the induction (see foot-note, Chapter 3, page 52) of a topology from one set into a related set: the first case was one in which we had an equivalence relation on the set and the second was that of a subset. In the first case we defined the topology on the set of equivalence classes in such a way that the natural mapping of an element onto the equivalence class is continuous. In the second case if U is a subset of S we have a natural (and only apparently trivial) mapping of U into S

$$i : u \in U \longrightarrow u \in S$$

and this is continuous if U has the subset topology:* conversely we could define a topology for U by requiring i to be continuous. It is this idea of defining a topology in order to make a natural mapping continuous which also motivates this section in which we introduce a topology into the direct product of two spaces.

At the end of Chapter 4, (Example S, page 65), we mentioned the idea of a base for a topology. It is useful to see how economically a topology can be specified, and we can define something less than a base. A *sub-base* for a topology is a family of sets F such that the set of all intersections of a finite number of sets of F is a base for the topology.

Example F. A base for the natural topology for the reals R is the set of all intervals of the form $a < x < b$. A sub-base for this topology is the family of all infinite intervals of the form $x < a$ or $x > a$ for any $a \in R$. Thus the interval $0 < x < 1$ is the intersection of the two 'sub-base elements' $x > 0$ and $x < 1$

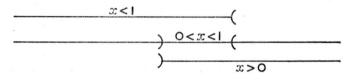

Example G. If $(A, T:A)$ and $(B, T:B)$ are two topological spaces and if F is a sub-base for $T:B$ then a function f of A onto B is continuous if and only if $\tilde{f}(U_F)$ is open in $T:A$ for all $U_F \in F$ (cf. Example S on page 65 at the end of Chapter 4).

* Note that we must define $\tilde{i} : V \longrightarrow V \cap U$, $V \in T:S$.

Now consider two sets A and B with topologies $T : A$ and $T : B$. There are two natural mappings of the direct product $A \triangledown B$ onto the original sets, viz. $p_1 : A \triangledown B \rightarrow A$ defined by $p_1 : (a, b) \rightarrow a$ and $p_2 : A \triangledown B \rightarrow B$ defined by $p_2 : (a, b) \rightarrow b$. By obvious analogy with our more common experience A and B are called *coordinate spaces* and p_1 and p_2 are called the *projections* into the coordinate spaces. We shall try to induce a topology into $A \triangledown B$ by requiring that each of the two projections be continuous. Let U be an open set in $T : A$ then $\tilde{p}_1(U) = U \triangledown B$ will have to be open in $T : A \triangledown B$ to satisfy our requirement. Similarly if V is open in $T : B$ then $\tilde{p}_2(V) = A \triangledown V$ must be open in $T : A \triangledown B$. So the projections will be continuous if we admit as open sets of $T : A \triangledown B$ all sets of the form $U \triangledown B$ and $A \triangledown V$ where U is open in $T : A$ and V is open in $T : B$. But these sets do not themselves constitute a topology nor even a base: consider, for example,

$$[U \triangledown B] \cap [A \triangledown V] = U \triangledown V,$$

and $U \triangledown V$ is not necessarily a set of the type $U \triangledown B$ or $A \triangledown V$. Before we resolve this difficulty in a simple way we consider a more familiar example.

Example H. The normal Cartesian coordinate system for the Euclidean plane is the set $R \triangledown R$ and the images of the projections are the coordinates of the points of the plane. The sets defined above are then infinite strips as illustrated, where U is the interval $a < x < b$ and V is the interval $d < y < c$. The union of these two sets is rather difficult to describe, and the intersection (the cross-hatched section) is $U \triangledown V$. The natural topology for the real plane is defined analogously to that of the real line: a base is the set of all interiors of rectangles. We see that the sets $U \triangledown R$ and $R \triangledown V$ form a sub-base for the topology of the plane.

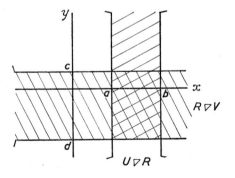

Example I. In Chapter 6, page 95, we said that a cube within a cube is topologically equivalent to two cubes next to each other. Now that we have described a topology for the plane the reader might like to consider the corresponding two dimensional configurations below and show that they are homeomorphic, where each configuration is regarded as a subset of the plane in which it lies and is given subset topology.

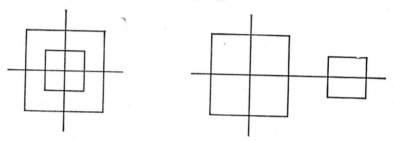

In general, consider the sets $U \bigtriangledown B$ and $A \bigtriangledown V$. These will define a sub-base for the topology of $A \bigtriangledown B$, if the set of all sets of the form $U \bigtriangledown V$ (where U is open in $T:A$ and V is open in $T:B$) is a base. To prove this we have to show that the intersection of any two of these sets is another one of these sets, i.e. that

$$[U \bigtriangledown V] \cap [U_1 \bigtriangledown V_1] = X \bigtriangledown Y$$

where U, U_1 and X are open in $T:A$ and V, V_1 and Y are open in $T:B$. In fact

$$[U \bigtriangledown V] \cap [U_1 \bigtriangledown V_1] = [U \cap U_1] \bigtriangledown [V \cap V_1]$$

We leave this to the reader to consider and it is suggested that he take the case of the Euclidean plane as an illustration.

The topology we have here constructed is called the *product topology* and the space and its topology is called the *product space*.

Example J. A subset X of $A \bigtriangledown B$ is open in the product topology if and only if for each $(a, b) \in X$ there are open sets $U \in T:A$ and $V \in T:B$ such that $a \in U$ and $b \in V$ and $[U \bigtriangledown V] \subset X$.

Example K. An interesting result is the following: a many-one mapping f of a topological space $(X, T:X)$ into a product space $(A \bigtriangledown B, T:A \bigtriangledown B)$ is continuous if and only if the two mappings $p_1 \circ f$ and $p_2 \circ f$ are continuous where p_1 and p_2 are the projections, as on the previous page.

If f is continuous then $p_1 \circ f$ and $p_2 \circ f$ are also continuous because p_1 and p_2 are designed to be continuous and a continuous function of a continuous function is continuous, as we proved at the end of Chapter 6. On the other hand if $p_1 \circ f$ is continuous, then if U is open in $T:A$ we have

$$\widetilde{[p_1 \circ f]}(U) = \tilde{f}(\tilde{p}_1(U)) = \tilde{f}(W), \text{ say,}$$

is open in $T:X$. But $W = \tilde{p}_1(U)$ is open in $T:A \triangledown B$ because p_1 is always continuous and all such W together with all $\tilde{p}_2(V)$ form a sub-base for $T:A \triangledown B$. Therefore, by Example G above, f is continuous.

As an application of this consider the idea of a curve. At an elementary level we assume that everyone knows what we are talking about, but we can give a precise and general definition. A curve in any topological space $(A, T:A)$ is the image of a continuous many-one mapping of some interval $a \leqslant t \leqslant b$ of the real line with the natural topology into $(A, T:A)$. We shall consider this in more detail in the next chapter: here we shall just consider how this agrees with the definition of a plane curve given in analysis. By our definition a plane curve is the image of a continuous many-one mapping of, say, the interval T, $a \leqslant t \leqslant b$, of R into $R \triangledown R$ with the natural topologies understood. Now $p_1 \circ f$ is a mapping of the interval T into R which, by our result above, must be continuous. But the image of $p_1 \circ f$ is just the set of x-coordinates of the points of the curve so we may write $p_1 \circ f(t) = x(t)$ and so '$x(t)$ is a continuous function of t' (in the terminology of analysis). Similarly $p_2 \circ f(t) = y(t)$ is continuous and we have the more usual definition of a plane curve given in analysis (see Phillips, *A Course of Analysis*, (Cambridge)).

CHAPTER 9

MATRICES

WE introduced the idea of a matrix by a geometrical application in the earlier exercises in the last chapter. Matrix algebra is an important enough topic in mathematics today to warrant our spending some time on it. We shall, therefore, develop some of the simple ideas here, confining ourselves in the main to the square two-by-two matrices and the two-by-one column vectors, with which the reader is already familiar. Although this course may seem somewhat restrictive we choose it for a number of reasons:

(1) The methods involved will be quite general and the reader should have no difficulty with larger matrices introduced subsequently.

(2) The technical manipulation remains simple and does not obscure the principles.

(3) There are many interesting isomorphisms of sets of 2×2 (two-by-two) matrices onto known mathematical structures which afford interesting teaching possibilities—we shall give some of these.

(4) Partially by way of reason (3) and also for other reasons, the statement that the theory of 2×2 matrices contains much of mathematics, although imprecise, is evocative of the vast scope of this small topic. We will allow ourselves one major departure from the above scheme and that is that we shall, whenever possible, give general definitions. This will avoid the necessity of undue repetition.

DEFINITION: A matrix is a rectangular array of elements for which 'multiplication and addition' are defined (usually elements of a field, see Chapter 13) arranged in rows and columns. If there are r rows and s columns, the matrix is said to be an r by s (written $r \times s$) matrix.

DEFINITION: Two matrices are equal if they are both $r \times s$ for the same r and s and have identical entries in corresponding positions.

DEFINITION: The 'sum' of two $r \times s$ matrices, the corresponding operation being denoted by $\oplus$ (later by $+$), is the $r \times s$ matrix obtained by adding the corresponding elements of the two matrices. Thus if the element in the ith row and the jth column of an $r \times s$ matrix A is denoted by a_{ij}, so that we can abbreviate the whole matrix to $A = (a_{ij})$, then we have

$$A \oplus B = (a_{ij}) \oplus (b_{ij}) = (a_{ij} + b_{ij}),$$

where B is a matrix of the same shape as A. The operation is known as *matrix addition*. Note that we cannot add a matrix to a matrix of a different shape.

Example A.
$$\begin{pmatrix} 1 & 0 \\ 2 & 1 \end{pmatrix} \oplus \begin{pmatrix} 2 & 3 \\ 1 & -1 \end{pmatrix} = \begin{pmatrix} 3 & 3 \\ 3 & 0 \end{pmatrix}$$

and
$$\begin{pmatrix} 1 & 0 \\ 2 & 1 \end{pmatrix} \oplus \begin{pmatrix} 1 \\ 0 \end{pmatrix} \text{ is undefined.}$$

Exercises

It is assumed that pupils have been given a motivated introduction to matrices such as those given in

(i) Mansfield and Thompson, *Mathematics: A New Approach*, Book 3 (Chatto and Windus), 1964.

(ii) G. Matthews, *Matrices 1* (Edward Arnold), 1964.

1. Matrix addition is commutative. Matrix addition is associative.

2. The set of all 2×2 matrices form a group for the operation $\oplus$. What is the identity element?

3. The set of all 2×1 matrices form a group for the operation $\oplus$. What is the identity element?

4. There are a number of sets of matrices which form groups for matrix addition and which are isomorphic to other common mathematical structures. (There are, in general, several sets isomorphic to each structure. The reason for our particular choice is given at the end of this exercise.)

(a) Consider the set of all 2×2 matrices of the form $\begin{pmatrix} a & b \\ -b & a \end{pmatrix}$ where a and b are real. This set is a group for the operation $\oplus$. There is a one-one correspondence between this set and the set of complex numbers

$$f: \begin{pmatrix} a & b \\ -b & a \end{pmatrix} \longrightarrow a + bi, \text{ where } i^2 = -1.$$

f is an isomorphism of this set of matrices under matrix addition onto the set of complex numbers under addition.

(b) Consider the set of all 2×2 matrices of the form $\begin{pmatrix} a & b \\ b & a \end{pmatrix}$ where a and b are real. This set is a group for matrix addition. There is a one-one correspondence between this set and the set of numbers of the form $a + bi$, where $i^2 = 1$ and a and b are real (cf. Chapter 8, Exercise 14 (b) (iii), page 131). This is not of great interest from our point of view and so we will modify the system slightly.

Consider the set of all matrices of the form $\begin{pmatrix} a & b \\ b & a \end{pmatrix}$ where a, b are positive real numbers. (This set is not a group for matrix addition.) Let f be the mapping

$$f: \begin{pmatrix} a & b \\ b & a \end{pmatrix} \longrightarrow a + [-b]$$

of this set of matrices onto the set of real numbers. It is not one-one; for example

$$f: \begin{pmatrix} 2 & 1 \\ 1 & 2 \end{pmatrix} \longrightarrow 2 + [-1] = 1 \text{ and } f: \begin{pmatrix} 3 & 2 \\ 2 & 3 \end{pmatrix} \longrightarrow 3 + [-2] = 1.$$

We can make it one-one by providing the appropriate equivalence relation: that is $\begin{pmatrix} a & b \\ b & a \end{pmatrix}$ is equivalent to $\begin{pmatrix} c & d \\ d & c \end{pmatrix}$ if $a + [-b] = c + [-d]$.

(i)   Check that this is a proper equivalence relation.
(ii) Show that matrix addition is compatible with the equivalence relation.
(iii) Show that the set of equivalence classes with induced matrix addition forms a group.
(iv) Show that this group is isomorphic to the set of all real numbers under addition.

(c) The set of all matrices of the form $\begin{pmatrix} a & b \\ 0 & a \end{pmatrix}$, where a and b are real, forms a group under the operation $\oplus$. This group is isomorphic to the so-called dual numbers under addition. A *dual number* is an expression of the form $a + bi$, where $i^2 = 0$ and a and b are real (cf. Chapter 8, Exercise 14 (b) (ii), page 131).

(d) The set of all matrices of the form $\begin{pmatrix} \alpha & \beta \\ -\bar{\beta} & \bar{\alpha} \end{pmatrix}$, where α and β are complex and $\bar{\alpha}$ is the conjugate of α, forms a group under matrix addition. This group is isomorphic to the set of quaternions under addition. A *quaternion* may also be regarded as an expression of the form $a + bi + cj + dk$, where

$$i^2 = j^2 = k^2 = -1, \quad ij = -ji = k, \quad jk = -kj = i, \quad ki = -ik = j$$

(cf. Chapter 8, Exercise 14 (b) (iv), page 131).
The isomorphism is given by the correspondence

$$\begin{pmatrix} \alpha & \beta \\ -\bar{\beta} & \bar{\alpha} \end{pmatrix} \longrightarrow a + bi + cj + dk,$$

where $\alpha = a + bl$, $\beta = c + dl$, $l^2 = -1$.

(e) The set of matrices in section (d) can be put into one-one correspondence with a set of 4 × 4 matrices with real entries. Suppose that

$$\alpha = a + bl, \ \beta = c + dl,$$

then

$$\begin{pmatrix} \alpha & \beta \\ -\bar{\beta} & \bar{\alpha} \end{pmatrix} \longrightarrow \begin{pmatrix} a & b & c & d \\ -b & a & -d & c \\ -c & d & a & -b \\ -d & -c & b & a \end{pmatrix}$$

is an isomorphism between the two sets of matrices under matrix addition.

The isomorphisms exhibited in this exercise are in themselves trivial and if this were all, they would be of little interest, but, as we shall show later (except for case (e) because it is too tedious), the mapping given in each case is also an isomorphism of the multiplicative structure of the sets involved. This means that we can study these complete structures by studying certain subsets of 2 × 2 matrices.

The sum of two $r \times s$ matrices A and B will now be denoted by $A + B$.

DEFINITION: Let X be the $n \times 1$ column vector $\begin{pmatrix} x_1 \\ x_2 \\ \vdots \\ x_n \end{pmatrix}$ and let Y

be the $1 \times n$ row vector $(y_1 \ y_2 \ \ldots \ y_n)$. Then the 'product', denoted by $Y \circ X$, of Y and X is defined to be the element

$$y_1 x_1 + y_2 x_2 + \ldots + y_n x_n.$$

Note that $X \circ Y$ is not yet defined (see Example D below).

Example B. $(1 \ 3) \circ \begin{pmatrix} 2 \\ -1 \end{pmatrix} = 2 + [-3] = -1,$

and $\begin{pmatrix} 2 \\ -1 \end{pmatrix} \circ (1 \ 3)$ is not yet defined.

DEFINITION: Let A be a matrix with n columns and B a matrix with n rows, then the product, denoted by $A \circ B$, of A and B is the matrix C whose element in the ith row and jth column is the product of the ith row of A and jth column of B in the sense of the word 'product' in the above definition. Thus, with the usual notation

$$c_{ij} = a_{i1} b_{1j} + a_{i2}b_{2j} + \ldots + a_{in}b_{nj}.$$

The operation o is known as *matrix multiplication*.
If A is an $r \times n$ matrix and B is an $n \times s$ matrix, then $A \circ B$ is an $r \times s$ matrix. Note that $B \circ A$ may not be defined and even when it is defined $A \circ B$ is not necessarily the same as $B \circ A$.

Example C. $(1\ 3) \circ \begin{pmatrix} 2 & 1 \\ -1 & 0 \end{pmatrix} = (1 \times 2 + 3 \times [-1] \quad 1 \times 1 + 3 \times 0)$

$$= (-1\ 1)$$

and $\begin{pmatrix} 2 & 1 \\ -1 & 0 \end{pmatrix} \circ (1\ 3)$ is not defined. The first matrix in the case for which the operation is defined is a 1×2 matrix, the second is 2×2 and the product is 1×2.

Example D.
$$\begin{pmatrix} 1 & 3 \\ 2 & 1 \end{pmatrix} \circ \begin{pmatrix} 2 & 1 \\ -1 & 0 \end{pmatrix} = \begin{pmatrix} -1 & 1 \\ 3 & 2 \end{pmatrix}$$

and
$$\begin{pmatrix} 2 & 1 \\ -1 & 0 \end{pmatrix} \circ \begin{pmatrix} 1 & 3 \\ 2 & 1 \end{pmatrix} = \begin{pmatrix} 4 & 7 \\ -1 & -3 \end{pmatrix}.$$

Thus multiplication of matrices is not commutative.

Note also that in Example B above we now have $\begin{pmatrix} 2 \\ -1 \end{pmatrix} \circ (1\ 3)$ defined as

$$\begin{pmatrix} 2 \times 1 & 2 \times 3 \\ -1 \times 1 & -1 \times 3 \end{pmatrix} = \begin{pmatrix} 2 & 6 \\ -1 & -3 \end{pmatrix}$$ so that $(1\ 3) \circ \begin{pmatrix} 2 \\ -1 \end{pmatrix}$ is a single element

and $\begin{pmatrix} 2 \\ -1 \end{pmatrix} \circ (1\ 3)$ is a 2×2 matrix.

Example E. Multiplication of matrices is associative provided it is defined. Matrix multiplication is distributive (from the left and right) over matrix addition. Verify this for 2×2 matrices $\begin{pmatrix} a & b \\ c & d \end{pmatrix}$.

Exercises

1. The identity element in the set M of all 2×2 matrices under multiplication is $\begin{pmatrix} 1 & 0 \\ 0 & 1 \end{pmatrix}$. The set M is closed under multiplication, and multi-

plication is associative. But M is not a group. For instance, $\begin{pmatrix} 0 & 0 \\ 0 & 0 \end{pmatrix} \in M$, but

there is no matrix $A = \begin{pmatrix} a & b \\ c & d \end{pmatrix}$ such that

$$\begin{pmatrix} 0 & 0 \\ 0 & 0 \end{pmatrix} \circ \begin{pmatrix} a & b \\ c & d \end{pmatrix} = \begin{pmatrix} 1 & 0 \\ 0 & 1 \end{pmatrix}.$$

We shall look for the subset M' of M which does form a group under multi-plication. The method used is quite general and can be used for any square matrix, whatever the size. A modification of this general method appears in Mansfield and Thompson: *Mathematics: A New Approach*, Books 3 and 5. Other methods of finding the inverse of a 2×2 matrix exist but the reader should note that some of them do not readily extend to larger matrices.*

Consider the equation

$$\begin{pmatrix} 1 & 0 \\ 0 & 1 \end{pmatrix} \circ \begin{pmatrix} a & b \\ c & d \end{pmatrix} = \begin{pmatrix} a & b \\ c & d \end{pmatrix} . \qquad . \qquad . \qquad . \qquad (1)$$

and suppose that we can find a matrix X which is such that

$$X \circ \begin{pmatrix} a & b \\ c & d \end{pmatrix} = \begin{pmatrix} 1 & 0 \\ 0 & 1 \end{pmatrix}.$$

Then X is, of course, the inverse of $\begin{pmatrix} a & b \\ c & d \end{pmatrix}$. If we premultiply equation (1) by

X then, since matrix multiplication is associative we have

$$\left[X \circ \begin{pmatrix} 1 & 0 \\ 0 & 1 \end{pmatrix} \right] \circ \begin{pmatrix} a & b \\ c & d \end{pmatrix} = X \circ \begin{pmatrix} a & b \\ c & d \end{pmatrix} = \begin{pmatrix} 1 & 0 \\ 0 & 1 \end{pmatrix}.$$

In fact, we do not go straight to the inverse X, but we shall premultiply both sides of equation (1) by a series of matrices $X_1, X_2, \ldots, X_n$ which are con-structed in such a way that the right-hand side is transformed step-by-step

into $\begin{pmatrix} 1 & 0 \\ 0 & 1 \end{pmatrix}$, i.e. $\left[X_n \circ \ldots \circ X_2 \circ X_1 \circ \begin{pmatrix} 1 & 0 \\ 0 & 1 \end{pmatrix} \right] \circ \begin{pmatrix} a & b \\ c & d \end{pmatrix}$

$$= X_n \circ \ldots X_2 \circ X_1 \circ \begin{pmatrix} a & b \\ c & d \end{pmatrix} = \begin{pmatrix} 1 & 0 \\ 0 & 1 \end{pmatrix}.$$

It follows that the term enclosed in the square brackets on the left-hand side is the X we are looking for.

In the first place let us transform the first entry a into 1. We shall suppose $a \neq 0$ (if $a = 0$, see later) and premultiply both sides of equation (1) by

* The following description of a procedure for finding the inverse of a matrix is too brief and rather obscure. It should be preceded by a discussion of those matrices which effect elementary row transformations.

$\begin{pmatrix} \frac{1}{a} & 0 \\ 0 & 1 \end{pmatrix}$.* Then using the associativity of matrix multiplication, we have

$$\begin{pmatrix} \frac{1}{a} & 0 \\ 0 & 1 \end{pmatrix} \circ \begin{pmatrix} a & b \\ c & d \end{pmatrix} = \begin{pmatrix} 1 & \frac{b}{a} \\ c & d \end{pmatrix} \qquad . \qquad . \qquad . \quad (2)$$

Premultiply both sides of equation (2) by $\begin{pmatrix} 1 & 0 \\ -c & 1 \end{pmatrix}$ so that the bottom left-hand element of the matrix on the right-hand side of the equation becomes 0. Thus

$$\left[\begin{pmatrix} 1 & 0 \\ -c & 1 \end{pmatrix} \circ \begin{pmatrix} \frac{1}{a} & 0 \\ 0 & 1 \end{pmatrix} \right] \circ \begin{pmatrix} a & b \\ c & d \end{pmatrix} = \begin{pmatrix} 1 & 0 \\ -c & 1 \end{pmatrix} \circ \begin{pmatrix} 1 & \frac{b}{a} \\ c & d \end{pmatrix}$$

i.e.

$$\begin{pmatrix} \frac{1}{a} & 0 \\ -\frac{c}{a} & 1 \end{pmatrix} \circ \begin{pmatrix} a & b \\ c & d \end{pmatrix} = \begin{pmatrix} 1 & \frac{b}{a} \\ 0 & d - \frac{cb}{a} \end{pmatrix}. \qquad . \qquad . \quad (3)$$

The next step is to produce a 1 in the bottom right-hand corner on the right-hand side without spoiling the 1 and 0 already achieved. We can do this, if, and only if, $ad - bc \neq 0$. Then premultiplying equation (3) by $\begin{pmatrix} 1 & 0 \\ 0 & \frac{a}{ad-bc} \end{pmatrix}$ we obtain

$$\begin{pmatrix} \frac{1}{a} & 0 \\ \frac{-c}{ad-bc} & \frac{a}{ad-bc} \end{pmatrix} \circ \begin{pmatrix} a & b \\ c & d \end{pmatrix} = \begin{pmatrix} 1 & \frac{b}{a} \\ 0 & 1 \end{pmatrix}. \qquad . \qquad . \quad (4)$$

* The reader might object that there is a simpler matrix which achieves our stated object, viz. $\begin{pmatrix} \frac{1}{a} & 0 \\ 0 & 0 \end{pmatrix}$, but this has a disastrous effect on future steps, for

$$\begin{pmatrix} \frac{1}{a} & 0 \\ 0 & 0 \end{pmatrix} \circ \begin{pmatrix} a & b \\ c & d \end{pmatrix} = \begin{pmatrix} 1 & \frac{b}{a} \\ 0 & 0 \end{pmatrix}$$

and there is no matrix which can transform this into $\begin{pmatrix} 1 & 0 \\ 0 & 1 \end{pmatrix}$. 'Simpler' has to be qualified. Roughly, for our purpose, a matrix is simple if it causes a minimum of irrelevant disturbance to the matrix which it premultiplies: above all it should have an inverse so that we can retrace our steps. In this sense $\begin{pmatrix} \frac{1}{a} & 0 \\ 0 & 1 \end{pmatrix}$ is simpler than $\begin{pmatrix} \frac{1}{a} & 0 \\ 0 & 0 \end{pmatrix}$.

Finally, premultiply equation (4) by $\begin{pmatrix} 1 & -\dfrac{b}{a} \\ 0 & 1 \end{pmatrix}$ giving

$$\begin{pmatrix} \dfrac{d}{ad-bc} & \dfrac{-b}{ad-bc} \\ \dfrac{-c}{ad-bc} & \dfrac{a}{ad-bc} \end{pmatrix} \circ \begin{pmatrix} a & b \\ c & d \end{pmatrix} = \begin{pmatrix} 1 & 0 \\ 0 & 1 \end{pmatrix}.$$

It follows from this last equation that the inverse of $\begin{pmatrix} a & b \\ c & d \end{pmatrix}$ is

$$\begin{pmatrix} \dfrac{d}{ad-bc} & \dfrac{-b}{ad-bc} \\ \dfrac{-c}{ad-bc} & \dfrac{a}{ad-bc} \end{pmatrix} \qquad . \quad . \quad . \quad . \quad (5)$$

subject, so far, to the conditions $a \neq 0$, $ad-bc \neq 0$.

Suppose now that $a = 0$, then if $c = 0$, $ad-bc = 0$ and the matrix $\begin{pmatrix} 0 & b \\ 0 & d \end{pmatrix}$ has no inverse, for if $\begin{pmatrix} u & v \\ w & x \end{pmatrix}$ is any matrix

$$\begin{pmatrix} 0 & b \\ 0 & d \end{pmatrix} \circ \begin{pmatrix} u & v \\ w & x \end{pmatrix} = \begin{pmatrix} bw & bx \\ dw & dx \end{pmatrix}$$

and there is no choice of u, v, x and w which makes the last matrix the identity matrix.

If $a = 0$, and $c \neq 0$, then equation (1) becomes

$$\begin{pmatrix} 1 & 0 \\ 0 & 1 \end{pmatrix} \circ \begin{pmatrix} 0 & b \\ c & d \end{pmatrix} = \begin{pmatrix} 0 & b \\ c & d \end{pmatrix}.$$

Premultiplying both sides by $\begin{pmatrix} 0 & 1 \\ 1 & 0 \end{pmatrix}$ brings c into the leading position, i.e.

$$\begin{pmatrix} 0 & 1 \\ 1 & 0 \end{pmatrix} \circ \begin{pmatrix} 0 & b \\ c & d \end{pmatrix} = \begin{pmatrix} c & d \\ 0 & b \end{pmatrix}$$

and the steps can now continue as above provided that $bc \neq 0$.

Summing up it follows that the matrix $\begin{pmatrix} a & b \\ c & d \end{pmatrix}$ has an inverse given by (5)

if, and only if, $ad-bc \neq 0$. This defines the set M' for which we are looking, where we leave the reader to show that M' is closed under o. The expression $ad-bc$ is called the *determinant* of the matrix $\begin{pmatrix} a & b \\ c & d \end{pmatrix}$. Since M' is a group, left inverses are also right inverses although the operation is not commutative.

2. Use the method, but not the result, of the last exercise to construct the inverse of $\begin{pmatrix} -1 & 2 \\ 3 & 1 \end{pmatrix}$.

3. The more able pupil should be able to devise a corresponding method to find the inverse of say $\begin{pmatrix} 2 & 0 & 3 \\ 1 & 2 & -1 \\ 0 & 1 & -2 \end{pmatrix}$.

4. In this exercise we refer back section by section to Exercise 4 in the last set of exercises on page 137 et seq.

(a) The set of complex numbers (excluding zero) forms a group under multiplication. The one-one correspondence f

$$f: \begin{pmatrix} a & b \\ -b & a \end{pmatrix} \longrightarrow a + bi \qquad \text{where } i^2 = -1$$

is an isomorphism of the multiplicative structures of the two sets, for

$$f: \begin{pmatrix} a & b \\ -b & a \end{pmatrix} \circ \begin{pmatrix} c & d \\ -d & c \end{pmatrix} = f: \begin{pmatrix} ac-bd & ad + bc \\ -bc-ad & -bd + ac \end{pmatrix} \longrightarrow [ac-bd] + [ad + bc]i,$$

but the last expression is equal to $[a + bi][c + di]$ which is equal to

$$f\left[\begin{pmatrix} a & b \\ -b & a \end{pmatrix}\right] \times f\left[\begin{pmatrix} c & d \\ -d & c \end{pmatrix}\right].$$

It follows that we can study the structure of the complex numbers by studying the set of 2×2 matrices of the form $\begin{pmatrix} a & b \\ -b & a \end{pmatrix}$ with real elements a and b, $a^2 + b^2 \neq 0$.

Note that although, in general, matrix multiplication is not commutative, it is commutative for this subset. Prove this directly.

(b) Matrix multiplication is compatible with the equivalence relation introduced in Exercise 4 (b) above, i.e. if $\begin{pmatrix} a & b \\ b & a \end{pmatrix}$ is equivalent to $\begin{pmatrix} c & d \\ d & c \end{pmatrix}$ and $\begin{pmatrix} a' & b' \\ b' & a' \end{pmatrix}$ is equivalent to $\begin{pmatrix} c' & d' \\ d' & c' \end{pmatrix}$, then $\begin{pmatrix} a & b \\ b & a \end{pmatrix} \circ \begin{pmatrix} a' & b' \\ b' & a' \end{pmatrix}$ is equivalent to $\begin{pmatrix} c & d \\ d & c \end{pmatrix} \circ \begin{pmatrix} c' & d' \\ d' & c' \end{pmatrix}$.

The equivalence class $\left\{ \begin{pmatrix} k & k \\ k & k \end{pmatrix} \right\}$ corresponds to zero, and if this is excluded, the remaining set of equivalence classes forms a group under matrix multiplication which is isomorphic to the set of all real numbers (without zero) under multiplication.* It follows that we can study the structure of the real numbers by studying the structure of the set of matrices of the form $\begin{pmatrix} a & b \\ b & a \end{pmatrix}$ where a and b are positive.

Note that this subset of M is also commutative under matrix multiplication. Any negative number $-a$ corresponds to a class with representative $\begin{pmatrix} 1 & a+1 \\ a+1 & 1 \end{pmatrix}$ and any positive number a corresponds to a class with representative $\begin{pmatrix} a+1 & 1 \\ 1 & a+1 \end{pmatrix}$. Verify the rule of signs (i.e. positive $\times$ negative $=$ negative, etc.) using these matrix representations.

(c) The dual numbers, with $a \neq 0$, form a group under multiplication. The inverse of $a + bi$ $(i^2 = 0)$ is $\dfrac{1}{a} - \dfrac{b}{a^2}i$. The mapping

$$f: \begin{pmatrix} a & b \\ 0 & a \end{pmatrix} \longrightarrow a + bi$$

is an isomorphism of the multiplicative structures, and, in particular, of the two subsets which form groups. So, once again, we can study the structure of dual numbers by studying the structure of the corresponding subset of M. The subset is commutative under multiplication, matrix multiplication is associative and distributive over matrix addition. It follows that corresponding results hold for the dual numbers. Solve the equation $[1 + 2i]x = 3 - 4i$ using the equivalent matrix representation.

(d) Show that the multiplicative structure of the quaternions is isomorphic to the set of matrices of the form $\begin{pmatrix} \alpha & \beta \\ -\beta & \bar{\alpha} \end{pmatrix}$ under multiplication, where α and β are complex. It follows that quaternion multiplication is associative and distributive over quaternion addition.

By considering this matrix representation show that quaternion multiplication is not commutative. Also find under what conditions the quaternion $a + bi + cj + dk$ has a multiplicative inverse. (Answer: Not all of a, b, c, d zero.)

A pure quaternion is a quaternion for which $a = 0$. Show, by considering the corresponding matrix, that the square of a pure quaternion is a negative real number.

Much of what we have discussed in the two exercises 4 of this chapter (and for that matter the whole of matrix theory itself) finds its proper mathematical

---

* If we include zero and the equivalence class $\left\{ \begin{pmatrix} k & k \\ k & k \end{pmatrix} \right\}$ in the two sets, then we still have an isomorphism, but we no longer have a group structure because these elements have no multiplicative inverse. The same remark applies in other examples in which we have left out the neutral element for addition when dealing with multiplicative isomorphisms (see Chapter 13).

setting in the theory of rings, fields and vector spaces. We cannot, however, within the compass of this book discuss these topics (except in a limited way in Chapter 13), so we have fitted them as best we can within our existing framework.

5. There are other isomorphisms which use the multiplicative structure of matrices only. These can be used, as those of the previous exercise, to improve the manipulative skill of pupils in a novel way. This has the double advantage of avoiding tedious repetition and of introducing worthwhile mathematical concepts.

(a) The mapping f, of the set of all matrices of the form $\begin{pmatrix} a & 0 \\ 0 & b \end{pmatrix}$, where a and b are integers, onto the set of rationals, defined by

$$f: \begin{pmatrix} a & 0 \\ 0 & b \end{pmatrix} \longrightarrow \frac{a}{b} \qquad ab \neq 0$$

is not one-one, but preserves their respective multiplicative structures (it does not preserve their additive structures). To make the mapping an isomorphism we put an obvious equivalence relation on the set of matrices, viz.

$$\begin{pmatrix} a & 0 \\ 0 & b \end{pmatrix} \text{ is equivalent to } \begin{pmatrix} c & 0 \\ 0 & d \end{pmatrix} \text{ if } ad = bc,$$

and show that matrix multiplication is compatible with the equivalence relation.

Note that the set of matrices does not form a group, but the set of equivalance classes does. If a and b are rationals, however, the set of matrices does form a group. The same remarks apply to the next example, where, in fact, in the application, we have rational entries in our matrices. But, if one wants to use these matrices to improve or investigate the combination of rationals, one must, of course, only allow integral elements in our matrices.

(b) Consider the set of all matrices of the form $\begin{pmatrix} b & a \\ 0 & b \end{pmatrix}$, a and b integers, with the same equivalence relation as in part (a). The equivalence relation is compatible with matrix multiplication and the mapping f

$$f: \left\{ \begin{pmatrix} b & a \\ 0 & b \end{pmatrix} \right\} \longrightarrow \frac{a}{b} \qquad b \neq 0$$

is an isomorphism of the multiplicative structure of the matrices onto the set of rationals under addition.

One can avoid the use of equivalence classes by considering homomorphisms instead of isomorphisms—we shall develop homomorphisms in the next chapter.

A useless application of this isomorphism, which may take the fancy of somebody, is to the process of finding partial fractions—it has no advantage over the usual method except novelty. Consider the problem of finding the

partial fractions of $\dfrac{2x + 3}{[x + 2][x^2 - 1]}$ in the form $\dfrac{A}{x + 2} + \dfrac{B}{x + 1} + \dfrac{C}{x - 1}.$

This is equivalent to finding A, B, C in the matrix equation

$$\begin{pmatrix} [x+2][x^2-1] & 2x+3 \\ 0 & [x+2][x^2-1] \end{pmatrix}$$
$$= \begin{pmatrix} x+2 & A \\ 0 & x+2 \end{pmatrix} \circ \begin{pmatrix} x+1 & B \\ 0 & x+1 \end{pmatrix} \circ \begin{pmatrix} x-1 & C \\ 0 & x-1 \end{pmatrix}.$$

Now a matrix of the type $\begin{pmatrix} 0 & y \\ 0 & 0 \end{pmatrix}$ is very little affected when multiplied (pre

or post) by another matrix—in fact, it retains its general form. We can produce three of these on the right-hand side: for example put $x = -1$, then

$$\begin{pmatrix} 0 & 1 \\ 0 & 0 \end{pmatrix} = \begin{pmatrix} 1 & A \\ 0 & 1 \end{pmatrix} \circ \begin{pmatrix} 0 & B \\ 0 & 0 \end{pmatrix} \circ \begin{pmatrix} -2 & C \\ 0 & -2 \end{pmatrix} = \begin{pmatrix} 0 & -2B \\ 0 & 0 \end{pmatrix},$$

whence $B = -\frac{1}{2}$, etc.

Many standard examination questions can be cast in this form—but it is doubtful, as we have said, whether the actual solution by matrices has any advantage except novelty.

6. Consider the set of all (free) vectors V in three dimensions, i.e. the set discussed in Chapter 3, Exercise 3(g), page 47 and page 50. We first introduce two operations not discussed there.

(i) *Scalar multiplication:* let k be any real number and PQ any line segment, then we define kPQ to be the line-segment beginning at P, $\mid k \mid$* times as long as PQ, and in the direction PQ if k is positive, in the opposite direction if k is negative.

This definition of scalar multiplication is compatible with the equivalence relation of Exercise 3(g), page 47, i.e. if

$$PQ \ R \ ST \text{ then } kPQ \ R \ kST,$$

and so we can talk of multiplying a (free) vector by a scalar.

(ii) If OP and PQ are two line-segments, then we define the *addition* of OP and PQ by

$$OP \circ PQ = OQ.$$

(a) Show that scalar multiplication is distributive over addition, i.e. that

$$k[OP \circ PQ] = kOP \circ kPQ.$$

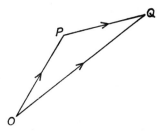

* $\mid k \mid$ means the absolute value of k, e.g. $\mid 2 \mid = \mid -2 \mid = 2$.

(b) According to our definition commutativity has no meaning for addition of line segments.

(c) Show that addition is compatible with the equivalence relation. Notice that we can add any two (free) vectors, because every vector contains a line-segment starting from any point of space (the localized vector).

(d) Show that the addition of (free) vectors is commutative and compare Example L, Chapter 3, page 49 and (b) above.

(e) By definition $\{PQ\} \circ \{QP\} = \{PP\}$ and this needs interpretation. We shall add to our set of vectors a so-called zero vector, i.e. a vector of zero length. It is rather difficult to talk of the direction of such a vector and so we say it has no direction.

Why bother with such a vector? To answer this show that without the zero vector V is not a group for addition, and that with this 'fictional' addition we have a group structure. The difficulty with the zero vector is an intuitive one and we shall see that a simple isomorphism overcomes this difficulty. We shall now establish this isomorphism.

(iii) Suppose that we have a set of (right-handed) mutually perpendicular axes in three-dimensional space with the usual Cartesian coordinate system. Let OX, OY, OZ be the line-segments shown in the diagram, each line segment being of unit length.

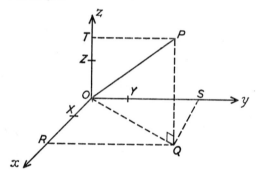

We then have three vectors $\{OX\}$, $\{OY\}$ and $\{OZ\}$ which are usually denoted by $\underline{i}, \underline{j}, \underline{k}$ respectively, in vector analysis. Using the two operations introduced above we can express any vector $v \in V$ in terms of these three 'orthogonal unit vectors'. Let OP be the localized vector starting at the origin which is a member of the vector $\underline{v}$, and let the projection of OP on the x, y-plane be OQ. Also let the projection of P onto the z-axis be T, and the projection of Q onto the x- and y-axes be R and S respectively. Then

$$OR = a\,OX, \quad OS = b\,OY, \quad OT = c\,OZ$$

for some real numbers a, b and c. Now

$$\{OQ\} = \{OR \circ RQ\} = \{OR\} \circ \{OS\} = a\{OX\} \circ b\{OY\}$$

and

$$\{OP\} = \{OQ \circ QP\} = \{OQ\} \circ \{OT\} = [a\{OX\} \circ b\{OY\}] \circ c\{OZ\}$$
$$= a\{OX\} \circ b\{OY\} \circ c\{OZ\},$$

since o is associative. (a, b and c are, of course, the coordinates of P.) We thus have a one-one correspondence between all non-zero vectors $\underline{v}$ and the set of 3×1 matrices

$$f: \underline{v} = \{OP\} \longrightarrow \begin{pmatrix} a \\ b \\ c \end{pmatrix}.$$

(We could, of course, establish this correspondence more quickly by the series

of one-one mappings $\underline{v} \longrightarrow OP \longrightarrow$ coordinates of $P \longrightarrow \begin{pmatrix} a \\ b \\ c \end{pmatrix}$; the sophistica-

tion of the reader will decide which he prefers.)

(a) The mapping f is an isomorphism of the additive structure of the non-zero vectors onto the additive structure of the set of all 3×1 matrices

excluding the one matrix $\begin{pmatrix} 0 \\ 0 \\ 0 \end{pmatrix}$. There is nothing unusual or intuitively difficult

about this matrix, so we admit it to our set and in order to maintain the isomorphism we add the so-called *zero vector* to our set of vectors. In this way the intuitive difficulty of the zero vector is overcome by the absence of such a difficulty for the matrix. (Show that the isomorphism is so maintained.)

(b) We introduce *scalar multiplication* for matrices to correspond to scalar multiplication for vectors, i.e. we define

$$k \begin{pmatrix} a \\ b \\ c \end{pmatrix} = \begin{pmatrix} ka \\ kb \\ kc \end{pmatrix}$$

for any real number k. (In general, if A is any matrix, we define kA to be that matrix whose elements are k times the corresponding elements in A.)

(c) Note that $k\underline{o}$ (where $\underline{o}$ is the zero vector) $= \underline{o}$ and that $0\underline{a} = \underline{o}$.

NOTE: So far we have denoted matrix multiplication by o; matrices are usually written next to each other to denote matrix multiplication (i.e. $A \circ B = AB$) and from now on we shall do the same.

(iv) Using the idea of the correspondence f we can express the inner product of two vectors (see Chapter 3, page 50) as the product of two matrices. If we denote the inner product operation by a dot, then

$$\underline{v}.\underline{v}' = (a\ b\ c) \begin{pmatrix} a' \\ b' \\ c' \end{pmatrix} \qquad . \qquad . \qquad . \qquad . \qquad (1)$$

where
$$\underline{v} \longrightarrow \begin{pmatrix} a \\ b \\ c \end{pmatrix} \text{ and } \underline{v}' \longrightarrow \begin{pmatrix} a' \\ b' \\ c' \end{pmatrix}.$$

The validity of (1) can be demonstrated by the following steps.

(a) Denote addition of vectors by $+$ and the inner product of two vectors by a dot. (These are the usual notations.) Then show that the inner product is distributive over addition, i.e. if $\underline{a}$, $\underline{b}$ and $\underline{c}$ are vectors, that

$$\underline{a} . [\underline{b} + \underline{c}] = \underline{a} . \underline{b} + \underline{a} . \underline{c}.$$

This can be done by choosing suitable representative localized vectors for the free vectors.

(b) Show that $\underline{a} . [k\underline{b}] = k[\underline{a} . \underline{b}]$, where k is any real number.

(c) Denote $\{OX\}$, $\{OY\}$, $\{OZ\}$ by $\underline{i}$, $\underline{j}$, $\underline{k}$ respectively, and show that

$$\underline{i} . \underline{i} = \underline{j} . \underline{j} = \underline{k} . \underline{k} = 1, \quad \underline{i} . \underline{j} = \underline{j} . \underline{k} = \underline{k} . \underline{i} = 0.$$

(d) Then, finally, if $\underline{v} = a\underline{i} + b\underline{j} + c\underline{k}$ and $\underline{v}' = a'\underline{i} + b'\underline{j} + c'\underline{k}$, we can use (a), (b) and (c) to evaluate

$$\underline{v} . \underline{v}' = [a\underline{i} + b\underline{j} + c\underline{k}] . [a'\underline{i} + b'\underline{j} + c'\underline{k}]$$
$$= aa' + bb' + cc'$$
$$= (a\ b\ c) \begin{pmatrix} a' \\ b' \\ c' \end{pmatrix} = (a'\ b'\ c') \begin{pmatrix} a \\ b \\ c \end{pmatrix}.$$

7. Although this is not the right place we wish to mention some other common cases in which one-one correspondences are used to overcome the intuitive difficulties. We have, in the previous example, met one case where the zero vector is rather a difficult concept, but where the 3×1 column matrix with three zero entries is quite natural.

In Chapter 7, page 106, we introduced the point at infinity in the complex plane as the image of $z = 0$ under the mapping $z \longrightarrow \dfrac{1}{z}$. This in itself was a one-one correspondence used to define the non-intuitive concept. There is another interesting way of looking at this. Suppose that we have a complex plane with a sphere in contact with it at the origin say. Let P be the point on the sphere at the opposite pole to the point of contact. Then we set up a correspondence between the points of the complex plane and the points of the sphere as follows: let Z be any point in the plane, then the point in which PZ meets the sphere is the point corresponding to Z. The correspondence is one-to-one except for P itself which has no image point in the plane; therefore we adjoin the point at infinity to the plane.

In Chapter 12, we shall discuss the projective plane and there introduce the 'line at infinity' in the plane. This can also be motivated from a 'finitely' situated model by a one-one correspondence.

$(a\ b\ c)$ is usually called the transpose of $\begin{pmatrix} a \\ b \\ c \end{pmatrix}$. In general, if A is any matrix, the *transpose* of A is the matrix obtained by interchanging rows and columns, e.g.

$$\text{transpose } \begin{pmatrix} 1 & 2 \\ 0 & 3 \\ 1 & 6 \end{pmatrix} = \begin{pmatrix} 1 & 0 & 1 \\ 2 & 3 & 6 \end{pmatrix}$$

Note that the first row, read left to right, becomes the first column, read top to bottom.

8. An interesting subset of the set of all 2×2 matrices is the set of matrices such as A where A multiplied by its transpose is the unit matrix I, i.e.

$$AA' = I = \begin{pmatrix} 1 & 0 \\ 0 & 1 \end{pmatrix}, \text{ where } A' \text{ is the transpose of } A.$$

(In general, any square matrix A with the property $AA' = I$, where I is the unit matrix of the correct size, is called *orthogonal*.)

(a) The equation $AA' = I$, means that A' is the right-inverse of A, i.e. A belongs to the group of all 2×2 matrices M' of Exercise 1, page 143. Since in a group, right-inverses are also left-inverses, we have

$$A'A = I.$$

(b) Show that the transpose of the transpose of any matrix A is A. Show also that, for 2×2 matrices A and B,

$$(AB)' = B'A'.$$

This result holds for square matrices of any order.

(c) We shall denote the set of orthogonal 2×2 matrices by O_2. From (a) and the fact that the transpose of A' is A it follows that if $A \in O_2$, then A' is also orthogonal.

(d) O_2 is a group under matrix multiplication. It is clear that $I \in O_2$ and is the unit element, that the inverse of A is A' and that matrix multiplication is associative. It remains to show that O_2 is closed, i.e. that if A and $B \in O_2$, then $AB \in O_2$. Consider

$$[AB][AB]' = [AB][B'A'] = A[BB']A' = AIA'$$
$$= AA' = I.$$

(e) Suppose that $A = \begin{pmatrix} a & b \\ c & d \end{pmatrix} \in O_2$, then

$$\begin{pmatrix} a & b \\ c & d \end{pmatrix}\begin{pmatrix} a & c \\ b & d \end{pmatrix} = \begin{pmatrix} 1 & 0 \\ 0 & 1 \end{pmatrix},$$

i.e.
$$\begin{pmatrix} a^2 + b^2 & ac + bd \\ ac + bd & c^2 + d^2 \end{pmatrix} = \begin{pmatrix} 1 & 0 \\ 0 & 1 \end{pmatrix},$$

whence $\qquad a^2 + b^2 = 1, c^2 + d^2 = 1$ and $ac + bd = 0.$

From $a^2 + b^2 = 1$, it follows that we can write $a = \cos\theta, b = \sin\theta$. Similarly we can write $c = \sin\phi, d = \cos\phi$. The last relation then reads

$$\cos\theta \sin\phi + \sin\theta \cos\phi = 0,$$

whence $\sin[\theta + \phi] = 0$ and $\theta = -\phi$ is one solution of this. Thus some of the matrices of O_2 are of the form

$$\begin{pmatrix} \cos\phi & -\sin\phi \\ \sin\phi & \cos\phi \end{pmatrix}$$

and we have met these matrices before (see Chapter 8, Exercise 7, page 125). We could, however, make other choices, e.g.

$$a = \cos\theta, b = \sin\theta, c = \sin\phi, d = -\cos\phi$$

whence the last relation is

$$\cos\theta \sin\theta - \sin\theta \cos\phi = 0, \text{ i.e. } \theta = \phi$$

and we have the matrices of the form $\begin{pmatrix} \cos\phi & \sin\phi \\ \sin\phi & -\cos\phi \end{pmatrix}$, which we have again met (see Chapter 8, Exercise 7, page 126).

These two types of matrices are in fact the only possible types and so we see the significance of the group O_2. Show that the rotation matrices form a subgroup of O_2 and the reflection matrices do not.

(f) Note that the set of rotation matrices $\begin{pmatrix} \cos\phi & -\sin\phi \\ \sin\phi & \cos\phi \end{pmatrix}$ are a subset of the set of matrices $\begin{pmatrix} a & b \\ -b & a \end{pmatrix}$ which we found were isomorphic to the complex numbers (Exercise 4 (a), page 144). Under that isomorphism

$$\begin{pmatrix} \cos\phi & -\sin\phi \\ \sin\phi & \cos\phi \end{pmatrix} \rightarrow \cos\phi + i\sin\phi = e^{i\phi}.$$

and, as is well known, the effect of multiplying a complex number by $e^{i\phi}$ is to rotate its representation in the complex plane through an angle ϕ.

9. In Chapter 7, page 108, we mentioned the bilinear mapping

$$f: z \rightarrow \frac{az + b}{cz + d} \qquad ad - bc \neq 0$$

of the complex plane onto the complex plane. Consider the correspondence

$$\begin{pmatrix} a & b \\ c & d \end{pmatrix} \rightarrow f \qquad ad - bc \neq 0.$$

It is not one-one, because $\begin{pmatrix} ka & kb \\ kc & kd \end{pmatrix} = k\begin{pmatrix} a & b \\ c & d \end{pmatrix}$ where k is any non-zero (complex) number, also maps onto f.

(i) Put the appropriate equivalence relation on the set of 2×2 matrices with complex elements, so that the correspondence is one-one.

(ii) Show that the equivalence relation is compatible with matrix multiplication.

(iii) Show that the one-one correspondence is an isomorphism of the *group* of equivalence classes of matrices under multiplication onto the group of bilinear functions under their usual combination.

An excellent book on matrices in the teaching field is *Introduction to Matrix Algebra* published by Yale University Press for the School Mathematics Study Group. There is a students' and a teachers' text.

*   *   *   *   *

In this section we shall lead up to a description of another group occurring in topology which we shall finally describe at the end of the next chapter. Our approach will be a mixture of the intuitive and the precise: to prove all our statements rigorously in an introductory account serves only to obscure the ideas. On the other hand, it is instructive to see how the ideas can be given a precise mathematical formulation, and we shall therefore prove a few results and indicate the gaps.

It is intuitively obvious that a hyperboloid of two sheets is not homeomorphic to, say, the surface of a sphere (see the remark on the natural topology for three dimensional space, Chapter 6, page 95); equally it is intuitive, though perhaps not quite so obvious, that a torus is not homeomorphic to either. The hyperboloid is in two pieces, whereas the sphere and torus are in one: the torus has a hole in it and the sphere has not. We can put this in topological terms by using the definition of a curve introduced in the previous chapter. There we defined a curve as the image of a many-one continuous mapping of any interval of the form $a \leqslant x \leqslant b$ of the reals R with the natural topology into the space under consideration. Since any such interval of R is homeomorphic to any other such interval, we always choose the interval to be $0 \leqslant x \leqslant 1$ which we shall denote by R_1. To return to our examples; given any point P on one sheet of the hyperboloid and any point P_1 on the other sheet it is intuitively obvious that there is no curve which joins P to P_1, whereas for any two points on a sphere or a torus there is always a curve joining them. Hence the hyperboloid cannot be homeomorphic to the sphere or the torus, because the homeomorphic image of a curve is a curve.

The difference between the sphere and the torus can also be expressed in terms of curves, as at the end of Chapter 6. If f is the function defining a curve in a topological space then the curve is closed if $f(0) = f(1)$. Using our intuition we can see that any closed curve on a sphere can be continuously deformed into a point—drop a stone into a calm sea: further any curve, closed or not, can be deformed into any other on the sphere in a continuous way. This is not true on a torus. None of the curves a, b, or c, it would seem, can be continuously deformed into each other, and only one can be continuously deformed into a point.

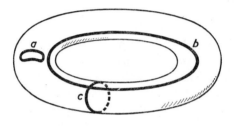

Example F. Are there any further curves on a torus which are not deformable into each other or into a, b or c? (See end of Chapter 11.)

So we see that the idea of a curve and its continuous deformation are useful topological concepts in highlighting the difference between topological spaces. We shall, therefore, try to make the concept of a continuous deformation more precise. Let f be a continuous many-one mapping of $(R_1, T: R_1)^*$ into a topological space $(X, T: X)$: if $s \in R_1$ then $f(s)$ is a point of the curve and $f(0)$ and $f(1)$ are its end points. We shall restrict ourselves to the continuous deformation of curves with the same end points, this being sufficient for our purpose at the end of the next chapter: the restriction is also applied to the intermediate curves of the deformation, i.e. they also have the same end points as the original and final curves.

Let $f_0(R_1)$ and $f_1(R_1)$ be two such curves then a continuous deformation of $f_0(R_1)$ into $f_1(R_1)$ would seem to involve a series of intermediate curves. In other words if we regard all the functions

---

* $T: R_1$ is the subset topology for R_1 induced by the natural topology for R.

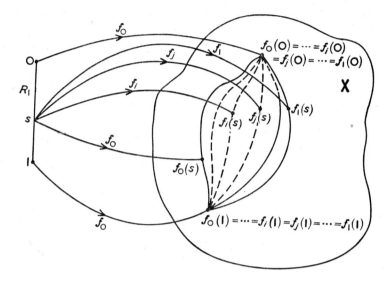

of R_1 into X, whose images are these curves, as themselves points of another space Y, then the sort of continuous series of curves we are looking for can be envisaged as associated with a curve in Y.

NOTE: The last statement may be sufficiently evocative to be excusable, but it is precisely meaningless. What is the topology for Y? Before one can speak of a curve in Y one must have a topology. The reader might like to define a topology in Y. With this topology is our last statement above valid?

Having beaten about the bush for long enough, let us now come to the final definition. We are looking for a family of curves the first of which is $f_0(R_1)$ and the last of which is $f_1(R_1)$ and such that they all have the same end points. Since they are to vary continuously, we can denote the family of curves by a continuous function F of $(R_1 \triangledown R_1, T: R_1 \triangledown R_1)$ into $(X, T: X)$ such that for any fixed $t \in R_1$, $F(R_1, t)$ is one of the corresponding system of curves and in particular that

$$F(s, 0) = f_0(s), \qquad F(s, 1) = f_1(s)$$
$$\text{and} \qquad F(0, t) = f_0(0) = f_1(0), \qquad F(1, t) = f_0(1) = f_1(1).$$

(Note the tenuous conceptual connection between this precise statement and the meaningless one above.)

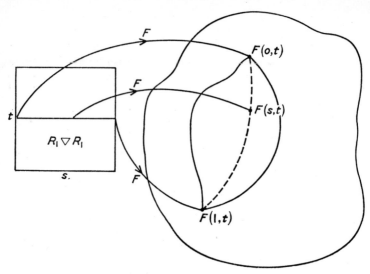

NOTE: If we remove the second set of conditions, i.e. we have a general set of paths without fixed end points (and $f_0(R_1)$ and $f_1(R_1)$ need not necessarily have the same end points either), then we may have a more general continuous deformation. A simple example of this type is given by the function F of $R_1 \triangledown R_1$ into $R \triangledown R$ (with their natural topologies) defined by

$$F: (s, t) \longrightarrow (s, [1 - t]s + te^s).$$

$F(s, 0) = (s, s)$ and $F(s, 1) = (s, e^s)$ which shows that the segment of the straight line (in the usual diagrammatic representation using (s, v) coordinates) $v = s$ is deformable in the plane, with the natural topology, into a segment of the exponential curve $v = e^s$. The reader might like to sketch some of the intermediate curves.

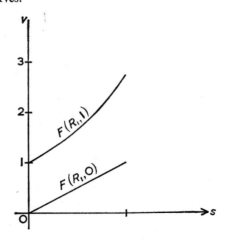

Example G. As an example of deformation with fixed end points consider deforming (in the plane, with the natural topology) the upper half of the unit circle shown in the diagram into the lower half.

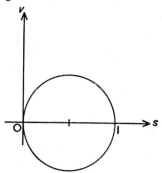

The equations for the two halves are $v = \pm\sqrt{[s - s^2]}$ and the function F given by

$$F: (s, t) \longrightarrow (s, [1 - 2t]\sqrt{[s - s^2]})$$

achieves the required deformation:

$$F(s, 0) = (s, \sqrt{[s - s^2]}), \quad F(s, 1) = (s, -\sqrt{[s - s^2]})$$

and $F(0, t) = (0, 0)$, $F(1, t) = (1, 0)$ as required. What are the intermediate curves? This problem is particularly simple because we chose our fixed points conveniently. Find a mapping F which deforms the upper half of the ellipse

$$s^2 + 4v^2 = 1$$

into the lower half. Remember that according to our definition of a curve $0 \leqslant s \leqslant 1$.

It is a much more difficult problem to discuss analytically deformations on a sphere or torus, because we have no convenient coordinate system: we, therefore, rely on intuition to a great extent.

CHAPTER 10

HOMOMORPHISMS

WE defined homomorphism in Chapter 4, but as with isomorphisms in Chapter 8, we shall repeat ourselves briefly. A homomorphism preserves structure as does an isomorphism, but unlike an isomorphism it is not necessarily a one-one mapping. From the examples of homomorphisms already given (see the list in the next example) it is clear that the idea of homomorphic images is an important one. We found that two isomorphic structures are essentially and mathematically equivalent, their only difference being that the corresponding objects of the two sets have (perhaps) acquired different names. With a homomorphism the situation is somewhat different: if f is a homomorphism of the set A onto the set B then

(i) in the technical aspect of mathematics we solve our problem in the more convenient set and then find the corresponding solution in the other set if required by using the homomorphism f,

(ii) in the theoretical aspect of mathematics we use one set and the homomorphism f to throw light on the structure of the other, as we shall show.

The formal definition of a homomorphism (for groups) is as follows: Let G and H be two groups, with elements $(g_1, g_2, g_3, \ldots)$ and $(h_1, h_2, h_3, \ldots)$ respectively, and operations symbolized by o and □ respectively. H is said to be a homomorphic image of G if a many-one (onto) mapping can be established from G to H so that if any two elements g_i and g_j of G map onto h_p and h_q respectively, and if

$$g_i \text{ o } g_j = g_k$$
$$\downarrow \quad \downarrow$$

and $\qquad h_p \text{ o } h_q = h_r,$

and g_k maps onto h_r. We can put this in other words. Let f be the many-one mapping of G onto H, then f is a homomorphism if

$$f(g \text{ o } g') = f(g) \square f(g'),$$

where g and g' belong to G. (In this chapter all our theory will be devoted to groups, although we may sometimes give examples of sets which do not form groups.)

Note that if f is a homomorphism of G onto H, $\tilde{f}$ is not necessarily a homomorphism of H onto G (cf. isomorphisms) and G is
not necessarily a homomorphic image of H at all. This means that
'homomorphic' does not provide us with an equivalence relation
between sets.

Example A. We have introduced a number of homomorphisms (not necessarily of groups) throughout the text and we list them here to remind the
reader. The chapter and page numbers in brackets refer to the first mention
of these homomorphisms.

(1) A set S with operation o and an equivalence relation R compatible
with o. Let S' be the set of equivalence classes and a be an element of S, then

$$f: a \longrightarrow \{a\} \in S'$$

is a homomorphism of S onto S' with the induced operation o (Chapter 4,
page 61).

(2) The mapping of the natural numbers onto the classes E and O of the
even and odd numbers respectively, is a particular example of case (1)
(Chapter 4; page 61).

(3) The slide-rule (Chapter 4, page 62).

(4) The mapping of the matrices $\begin{pmatrix} a & b \\ b & a \end{pmatrix}$, (where a and b are positive real

numbers) onto the real numbers given by $\begin{pmatrix} a & b \\ b & a \end{pmatrix} \longrightarrow a + [-b]$ is a homo-

morphism of the multiplicative structure of the matrices* onto the additive
structure of the reals (Chapter 9, pages 138 and 144).

(5) The mapping of the matrices $\begin{pmatrix} a & 0 \\ 0 & b \end{pmatrix}$, (where a and b are non-zero

integers) given by $\begin{pmatrix} a & 0 \\ 0 & b \end{pmatrix} \longrightarrow \dfrac{a}{b}$ onto the rationals, is a homomorphism of one

multiplicative structure onto the other (Chapter 9, page 146).

(6) The mapping of the matrices $\begin{pmatrix} b & a \\ 0 & b \end{pmatrix}$, (where a and b are integers and

$b \neq 0$) onto the rationals given by $\begin{pmatrix} b & a \\ a & b \end{pmatrix} \longrightarrow \dfrac{a}{b}$ is a homomorphism of the

multiplicative structure of matrices onto the additive structure of the rationals
(Chapter 9, page 146).

(7) The mapping h which maps the matrix $\begin{pmatrix} a & b \\ c & d \end{pmatrix}$ onto the function

$$f: z \longrightarrow \frac{az + b}{cz + d} \qquad ad - bc \neq 0$$

* See the footnote on page 145.

is a homomorphism of the multiplicative structure of these 2×2 matrices onto the set of functions with their usual law of combination (Chapter 9, page 152).

We shall adopt the following notation throughout the rest of this chapter unless otherwise stated: G and H are two groups, where H is the homomorphic image of G under the mapping f; the elements of G will be denoted by small g's with subscripts and dashes (primes) as necessary, with the exception of the neutral element which will be denoted by e_G to distinguish it from e_H, the neutral element in H. The binary operation in G will be denoted by o, and in H by $\square$.

We noted that for two isomorphic groups the image of the neutral element for one group is the neutral element for the other group. Now this is still true when we only have a homomorphism, for

$$f(g \circ e_G) = f(g) \,\square\, f(e_G)$$

because f is a homomorphism, but $f(g \circ e_G) = f(g)$, therefore

$$f(g) = f(g) \,\square\, f(e_G),$$

i.e. $f(e_G) = e_H$. But e_G may not be the only element of G which maps onto e_H under f, since f is many-one. Let K be the subset of G of all those elements whose image is e_H: thus if $g_K \in K$, then

$$f(g_K) = e_H.$$

This subset K is of particular importance: it is called the *kernel* of the homomorphism.

Example B. In the previous example we gave seven homomorphisms: find the kernel of each. For example, the kernel of the fifth homomorphism is the set of matrices of the form $\begin{pmatrix} a & 0 \\ 0 & a \end{pmatrix}$.

Note that although not all the sets in the seven examples form groups we can still say that the kernel of the homomorphism is the set of all those elements which map onto the identity element whenever the image set contains an identity element. In (4) to (7) we turned the homomorphisms into isomorphisms by introducing new sets using equivalence relations which can be found in the previous chapter. What do you notice about the kernel of the homomorphism and the neutral equivalence class in the new sets in each case?

Example C. Any set which is a homomorphic image of a group is a group. For, let G be the group and let H be the homomorphic image. Then $\square$ is associative because o is; H contains an element e_H, the image of e_G, which acts as neutral element; the inverse of an element $h = f(g) \in H$ is $\tilde{h} = f(\tilde{g}) \in H$. Finally H is closed because if $h = f(g)$ and $h' = f(g')$ belong to H, then

$$h \,\square\, h' = f(g) \,\square\, f(g') = f(g \circ g') = f(g'')$$

for some $g'' \in G$. Note, however, that if H is a group and f is a homomorphic mapping of G onto H, then it does not follow that G is a group. We have had some examples of this.

We shall now prove that the kernel K of a homomorphism of a group G onto a group H is a subgroup of G, i.e. a subset of G which forms a group for o.

Example D. Before embarking on the formal proof the reader might like to verify the accuracy of the statement for some of the kernels of those homomorphisms found in Example C in which both sets are groups.

We have to show that K is a group under o.

(1) The operation o is associative in G and since $K \subseteq G$ it is also associative in K.

(2) If g and $g' \in K$, i.e. $f(g) = f(g') = e_H$, then since f is a homomorphism it follows that

$$f(g \circ g') = f(g) \,\square\, f(g') = e_H \,\square\, e_H = e_H,$$

i.e. $g \circ g' \in K$, so that K is closed under o.

(3) $e_G \in K$, as we have shown above.

(4) $g \circ \tilde{g} = \tilde{g} \circ g = e_G$ (where, as usual, $\tilde{g}$ is the inverse of g in G), and since the mapping is a homomorphism, it follows that

$$f(g) \,\square\, f(\tilde{g}) = f(\tilde{g}) \,\square\, f(g) = e_H.$$

Now if $g \in K$, $f(g) = e_H$, therefore, we have

$$e_H \,\square\, f(\tilde{g}) = f(\tilde{g}) \,\square\, e_H = e_H,$$

i.e. $f(\tilde{g}) = \tilde{e}_H = e_H$, and so $\tilde{g} \in K$ if $g \in K$.
Hence K is a group under o.

We have thus proved that the kernel of any homomorphism of a group G is a subgroup of G, and, given a sufficient degree of sophistication, we might suppose that all subgroups of G are kernels of some homomorphism. This is, however, not true and we shall investigate it later (Example E illustrates this remark).

Example E. Consider the group G with six elements (see Chapter 8, page 120) whose group table is

o	e_G	g_1	g_2	g_3	g_4	g_5
e_G	e_G	g_1	g_2	g_3	g_4	g_5
g_1	g_1	g_2	e_G	g_5	g_3	g_4
g_2	g_2	e_G	g_1	g_4	g_5	g_3
g_3	g_3	g_4	g_5	e_G	g_1	g_2
g_4	g_4	g_5	g_3	g_2	e_G	g_1
g_5	g_5	g_3	g_4	g_1	g_2	e_G

The pair (e_G, g_3) form a subgroup and we shall suppose that there exists a homomorphism f onto a group H with these elements as kernel. So the homomorphic image of G can have at most five elements and we shall write

$$f(e_G) = e_H = f(g_3), f(g_1) = h_1, f(g_2) = h_2, f(g_4) = h_4, f(g_5) = h_5.$$

Using the hypothesis that f is a homomorphism we have

$$f(g_3 \circ g_1) = f(g_3) \,\square\, f(g_1) = e_H \,\square\, h_1 = h_1.$$

But from the group table $g_3 \circ g_1 = g_4$, therefore

$$h_1 = h_4.$$

Similarly, considering $g_3 \circ g_2 = g_5$, we get $h_5 = h_2$. Hence H can have at most three elements e_H, h_1, h_2, say. Now, using the same argument we have further that

$$f(g_1 \circ g_2) = f(g_1) \,\square\, f(g_2) = h_1 \,\square\, h_2$$

and since $g_1 \circ g_2 = e_G, h_1 \,\square\, h_2 = e_H.$

But $f(g_4 \circ g_5) = f(g_4) \,\square\, f(g_5) = h_1 \,\square\, h_2$ and $g_4 \circ g_5 = g_1$.

Therefore

$$h_1 \,\square\, h_2 = h_1 = e_H,$$

which contradicts our assumption that the kernel is (e_G, g_3). (It also follows that h_2 must be the same as e_H, so that H consists of e_H only. It is true that for any group G there exists a homomorphism which maps G onto the single element $e_H = H$, i.e. the kernel of the homomorphism is G. Such a homomorphism is too trivial and will not be admitted.)

Consider the same problem for any other subgroup of our original group.

Example F. Let U be a *finite* subset of G closed under o, so that if g and g' are members of U then $(g \circ g') \in U$. Prove that U is a subgroup of G. (Hints: Since G is a group, o is associative. It is given that U is closed. It remains to prove that the neutral element e_G is necessarily a member of U and that if $g \in U$ then $\tilde{g} \in U$. Let U have n distinct members g_i $(i = 1, 2, 3, .., n)$ and let g_j be any one of them. Consider the n combinations $g_j \circ g_i, i = 1, 2, 3, .., n$).

Exercises

1. Consider the group R of all rational numbers (excluding zero) under the operation of multiplication and the group $S = (p, n)$ where the operation □ is defined by the table

□	p	n
p	p	n
n	n	p

Establish the homomorphism of $(R, \times)$ onto $(S, \square)$. What is the kernel?

2. Consider the group I of all integers under addition and the set

$$M = (0, 1, 2, 3, 4, 5, 6)$$

under the operation symbolized by $\oplus$ where the result of combining any two elements is defined to be the remainder left after dividing their sum by 7. Verify that M is a group. Use the equivalence classes set out in Chapter 7, page 104, to establish a homomorphism of $(I, +)$ onto $(M, \oplus)$. What is the kernel of this homomorphism? Verify that the kernel is a group under addition.

Note that a homomorphic image group arises in a similar way from the set of residue classes to any modulus n, where n is a natural number, $M = (0, 1, 2, \ldots, [n - 1])$ and 7 is replaced by n in the definition of $\oplus$.

3. Let M be the set of all 2×2 matrices (where the elements are real numbers) with the operation of matrix multiplication. Let R be the set of all real numbers under multiplication.

(i) Prove that the mapping of any matrix $\begin{pmatrix} a & b \\ c & d \end{pmatrix} \in M$ onto the real number $(ad - bc) \in R$, i.e. the determinant of the matrix, establishes a homomorphism of the multiplicative structure of the matrices onto $(R, \times)$. Use this result to show that an orthogonal 2×2 matrix has determinant ± 1.

(ii) As we noticed in Chapter 9, page 141, the set M under multiplication is not a group; nor is the structure $(R, \times)$ a group. The removal of one element from $(R, \times)$ gives $(R, \times)$ group structure. Which element?

(iii) Which class of elements must then be removed from M to regain the homomorphism? The remainder of M then forms a group.

(iv) What is the kernel of the homomorphism? Verify that the kernel is a group.

4. The A, B, C, D scales of a standard slide rule represent homomorphic images of the positive real numbers. Discuss the operations in the two groups.

The kernel for the C, D scales homomorphism differs from that for the A, B scales. In what way? What practical significance has this difference?

5. Some of the mappings which are in 'common mathematical use' are homomorphisms. Which of the following mappings of the multiplicative group of all non-zero real numbers onto a subset of itself are homomorphisms? Are any isomorphisms?

(i) $x \longrightarrow |x|$; (ii) $x \longrightarrow x^2$; (iii) $x \longrightarrow \dfrac{1}{x}$; (iv) $x \longrightarrow 2x$; (v) $x \longrightarrow [x + 1]^2$;

(vi) $x \longrightarrow -\dfrac{1}{x}$; (vii) $x \longrightarrow e^x$; (viii) $x \longrightarrow 1$ if $x > 0$ and $x \longrightarrow -1$ if $x < 0$;

(ix) $x \longrightarrow \log x$; (x) $x \longrightarrow$ integral part of x.

As proved in Example C on page 160, the homomorphic image of a group is a group: find the homomorphic image groups in those of the examples above which are homomorphisms. Also, find the kernels of the homomorphisms.

6. Exactly as the last example, except that the mappings are considered to be mappings of the additive group of all real numbers onto a subset of itself.

(i) $x \longrightarrow |x|$; (ii) $x \longrightarrow x^2$; (iii) $x \longrightarrow 2x$; (iv) $x \longrightarrow x + 3$; (v) $x \longrightarrow e^x$;

(vi) $x \longrightarrow$ integral part of x; (vii) $x \longrightarrow 0$ if $x \leqslant 0$ and $x \longrightarrow x$ if $x \geqslant 0$;

(vii) $x \longrightarrow \sin x$.

7. Consider the set of all differentiable functions F which map the reals into the reals. Let the combination be addition, then the mapping of F onto a set F' defined by

$$f \longrightarrow \text{derivative of } f \qquad f \in F$$

is a homomorphism, since

$$f + g \longrightarrow \text{derivative of } f + \text{derivative of } g \qquad f, g \in F.$$

What is the kernel? Compare this result with the equivalence relation in Chapter 3, Exercise 3 (d), page 47.

8. The set of all 2×1 matrices with real elements is a group G under matrix addition. Let $A = \begin{pmatrix} a & b \\ c & d \end{pmatrix}$ be any fixed 2×2 matrix with real elements, then the mapping of G into itself defined by

$$\begin{pmatrix} x \\ y \end{pmatrix} \longrightarrow \begin{pmatrix} a & b \\ c & d \end{pmatrix} \begin{pmatrix} x \\ y \end{pmatrix} \qquad \begin{pmatrix} x \\ y \end{pmatrix} \in G$$

is a homomorphism of G onto a subgroup of itself. Under what conditions on A is it an isomorphism?

Determine the subgroup (and consider its geometric representation) and the kernel of the homomorphism in each of the following cases.

(i) $A = \begin{pmatrix} 1 & 1 \\ 1 & 1 \end{pmatrix}$; (ii) $A = \begin{pmatrix} 1 & 0 \\ 0 & 0 \end{pmatrix}$; (iii) $A = \begin{pmatrix} 1 & 0 \\ 0 & 1 \end{pmatrix}$;

(iv) $A = \begin{pmatrix} 1 & 1 \\ 2 & 2 \end{pmatrix}$; (v) $A = \begin{pmatrix} 0 & 1 \\ 0 & 0 \end{pmatrix}$; (vi) $A = \begin{pmatrix} 1 & 2 \\ 2 & 1 \end{pmatrix}$.

We return to our general investigation of homomorphisms of groups. We have indicated vaguely in some of the various examples and exercises that there is some connection between the kernel of a homomorphism and the equivalence relation which turns the homomorphism into an isomorphism. This connection will be the object of our next investigation; in order to simplify the subsequent abstract argument we begin by considering an example.* The reader should check the statements made.

The mapping f of any matrix $\begin{pmatrix} a & b \\ c & d \end{pmatrix}$ with non-zero determinant

(and real elements) onto the function $x \rightarrow \dfrac{ax + b}{cx + d}$ is a homo-

morphism of the multiplicative group G of these 2×2 matrices onto the group H of such functions with the combination of sub-stitution. The kernel K of the homomorphism is the group of

elements of the form $\begin{pmatrix} k & 0 \\ 0 & k \end{pmatrix}$. We can put an equivalence relation on

G to obtain a group G' of equivalence classes, so that the homo-morphism induces an isomorphism of G' onto H, where the opera-tion and mapping are induced from G to G'. The equivalence relation R is

$$\begin{pmatrix} a & b \\ c & d \end{pmatrix} R \begin{pmatrix} a' & b' \\ c' & d' \end{pmatrix} \text{ if } \begin{pmatrix} a' & b' \\ c' & d' \end{pmatrix} = k \begin{pmatrix} a & b \\ c & d \end{pmatrix}$$

for some non-zero real number k. Now what is the connection between the kernel of this homomorphism and the equivalence relation? In the first place we notice that the set of elements of K forms one equivalence class (i.e. one element) of G', and that this element is the neutral element, for

$$\left\{ \begin{pmatrix} a & b \\ c & d \end{pmatrix} \right\} \left\{ \begin{pmatrix} k & 0 \\ 0 & k \end{pmatrix} \right\} = \left\{ \begin{pmatrix} ka & kb \\ kc & kd \end{pmatrix} \right\} = \left\{ \begin{pmatrix} a & b \\ c & d \end{pmatrix} \right\}.$$

Secondly, if $\begin{pmatrix} a & b \\ c & d \end{pmatrix} R \begin{pmatrix} a' & b' \\ c' & d' \end{pmatrix}$ then $\begin{pmatrix} a' & b' \\ c' & d' \end{pmatrix} = \begin{pmatrix} a & b \\ c & d \end{pmatrix} \begin{pmatrix} k & 0 \\ 0 & k \end{pmatrix}$ for

* In the following example, if complex numbers were used instead of real numbers, we would have the situation discussed on page 152. We do not refer directly to this in deference to the reader unfamiliar with complex numbers.

some non-zero k. Thus the elements of any one equivalence class $\left\{\begin{pmatrix} a & b \\ c & d \end{pmatrix}\right\}$ are the elements of K premultiplied by any one particular element of the class. For instance, the class $\left\{\begin{pmatrix} 1 & 0 \\ -1 & -1 \end{pmatrix}\right\}$ contains all the elements of the form $\begin{pmatrix} 1 & 0 \\ -1 & -1 \end{pmatrix}\begin{pmatrix} k & 0 \\ 0 & k \end{pmatrix}$ and we write this class $\begin{pmatrix} 1 & 0 \\ -1 & -1 \end{pmatrix}K$. Equally, if we had chosen say $\begin{pmatrix} -2 & 0 \\ 2 & 2 \end{pmatrix}$ to represent this class we could write $\begin{pmatrix} -2 & 0 \\ 2 & 2 \end{pmatrix}K$ to express the same class.

Further we could post-multiply the elements of K by the chosen representative matrix and still obtain the same equivalence class.

We can investigate the general case in a precisely similar way. Let f be a homomorphic mapping of a group G onto a group H and let the kernel be K. Then in our usual notation, and with the previous example in mind, we define a relation on the elements of G by

$$g \, R \, g' \quad \text{if} \quad f(g) = f(g'),$$

i.e. two elements are related if they map to the same element of H. This is clearly an equivalence relation, and the kernel K is the equivalence class of elements which maps onto e_H. We thus now have a set G' of equivalence classes which is in one-one correspondence with the group H. We next show that the equivalence relation is compatible with the operation o in G, i.e. that

$$\text{if } g \, R \, g' \text{ and } g_1 \, R \, g_1' \text{ then } [g \circ g_1] \, R \, [g' \circ g_1'].$$

This follows because f is a homomorphism, for

$$f(g \circ g_1) = f(g) \,\square\, f(g_1) = f(g') \,\square\, f(g_1') = f(g' \circ g_1').$$

We can thus combine the equivalence classes by the operation o, i.e. the definition $\{g\} \circ \{g'\} = \{g \circ g'\}$ is proper.

We could now show that G' is a group for the induced operation, but choose instead to show the stronger result, i.e. that G' is isomorphic to H. We have already seen that G' is in one-one correspondence with H, the correspondence being

$$f' : \{g\} \rightarrow f(g)$$

and we show that f' sets up a homomorphism from G' to H by

$$\{g \circ g'\} \rightarrow f(g \circ g') = f(g) \ \square \ f(g')$$
$$= f'(\{g\}) \ \square \ f'(\{g'\}).$$

Thus f' represents a one-one homomorphism, that is, an iso-morphism.

Further if $\{g\} \in G'$, then we can show that $\{g\} = gK$, where gK means the set of elements of K premultiplied by g. For if $g' \ R \ g$ then $\tilde{g}$ exists since we are in a group and

$$f(\tilde{g} \circ g') = f(\tilde{g}) \ \square \ f(g').$$

But under a homomorphism f, $\tilde{g}$ maps to the inverse of $f(g)$ which is the same as the inverse of $f(g')$, since $f(g) = f(g')$, and so

$$f(\tilde{g} \circ g') = e_H.$$

Therefore $\tilde{g} \circ g' \in K$, i.e. $\tilde{g} \circ g' = k$, for some $k \in K$, whence

$$g' = g \circ k,$$

which proves that $\{g\} \subseteq gK$. But every element of the form $g \circ k$, for some $k \in K$, maps to $f(g)$ and so is equivalent to g. Thus $gK \subseteq \{g\}$ and our statement is proved.

Let us summarize what we have proved. If f is a homomorphism of G onto H then

(i)   the kernel K is a subgroup of G;

(ii) $g \ R \ g'$ if $f(g) = f(g')$ is an equivalence relation on G com-patible with $\circ$ and we obtain a group of equivalence classes G' isomorphic with H. K is the identity element of G';

(iii) the equivalence classes are of the form gK. It follows, by the definition of $\circ$ in G' and G, that

$$[gK] \circ [g_1 K] = [g \circ g_1]K;$$

(iv) see Example G below.

It is usual to write G/K instead of G' and to call this group a *factor group* of G. The sets gK are called the *left cosets* of K in G. The word left is used because the elements of K are premultiplied, or multiplied on the left, by g. (See, however, the following example.)

Example G. The above abstract analysis is simple, in fact, so simple that it is difficult to follow. The only way to get on is to prove some results oneself. It is, therefore, suggested that the reader prove the following.

(iv) $gK = Kg$, where Kg means the set of all the elements of the form $k \circ g$ for any fixed g and all $k \in K$. Note that this does not mean that

k o $g = g$ o k necessarily, but that k o $g = g$ o k' for some k, $k' \in K$. In words, this result states that the left and *right cosets*, for the same g, of K in G are equal sets.

Exercises

1. The set $R^3 = \nabla RRR$ of all triples of real numbers (x, y, z) forms a group under vector addition defined by

$$(x, y, z) + (x'\ y', z') = (x + x', y + y', z + z')$$

and the set $R^2 = R \nabla R$ of all pairs of reals (x', y') forms a group under the same operation. R^3 is homomorphically mapped onto R^2 by the equations

$$x + y + z = x'$$
$$5x - y + z = y'$$

Describe the infinite set of triples which form the kernel of this homomorphism and use it to obtain the complete set of solutions of

$$x + y + z = 3$$
$$5x - y + z = 5.$$

Note that, by what we have proved above, if K is the kernel of a homomorphism and $g \in G$ maps onto $h \in H$, then the complete set of elements which maps onto h is gK. Note also that the equations can be written in the matrix form

$$\begin{pmatrix} x' \\ y' \end{pmatrix} = \begin{pmatrix} 1 & 1 & 1 \\ 5 & -1 & 1 \end{pmatrix} \begin{pmatrix} x \\ y \\ z \end{pmatrix}$$

if desired. The homomorphic property of the mapping is then immediately evident.

2. In Exercise 7 above the reader (or pupil) was asked to find the kernel of the homomorphism of the group of differentiable real functions F onto a group F'. This kernel is clearly all the constant functions $c_a : x \longrightarrow a$, for all $x \in R$, the set of reals, and where a is a real number.

Thus if the function f is a particular solution of $\dfrac{dy}{dx} = h$ where h is a known function of the reals into the reals, the complete solution is the coset $fK =$ the set of functions of the form $f + c_a$ for all real a, where

$$f + c_a : x \longrightarrow f(x) + a.$$

Investigate similarly the complete solution of

$$\frac{dy}{dx} + y.f = h.$$

An important class of differential equations is the set of second order linear differential equations with constant coefficients, i.e. the equations of the form

$$a \frac{d^2y}{dx^2} + b \frac{dy}{dx} + cy = h,$$

where a, b and c are real or complex constants. We may consider the problem of their solution in this context and then the usual expression

$$y = \text{complementary function} + \text{particular integral}$$

becomes

$$y = \text{kernel} + \text{particular integral}$$

where 'kernel' is the kernel of the homomorphism

$$y \longrightarrow a\,\frac{d^2y}{dx^2} + b\,\frac{dy}{dx} + cy.$$

3. Let G be the group of non-zero complex numbers z with the operation of multiplication. If we map z onto z^6 we obtain a homomorphic mapping of G onto G. What is the kernel?

Given that $z = 1 - i\sqrt{3}$ is one of the sixth roots of 64, find the other five. Find the value of $[2 + 2i\sqrt{3}]^6$.

4. Let V_2 be the group of all (free) vectors in a given plane under vector addition and show that if $\underline{a} \in V_2$ ($\underline{a} \neq \underline{o}$) is a given vector, then the mapping of a vector onto its inner product with $\underline{a}$ is a homomorphism of V_2 onto the real numbers under addition.

Find the complete solution of $\underline{a}.\underline{x} = b$ where b is a given real number and $\underline{a}.\underline{x}$ represents the inner product of $\underline{a}$ and $\underline{x}$.

5. Referring to Exercise 8 above (page 164), find the cosets corresponding to the kernel of the homomorphism $A = \begin{pmatrix} 1 & 0 \\ 0 & 0 \end{pmatrix}$ and interpret them geometrically. Do the same for $A = \begin{pmatrix} 1 & 1 \\ 2 & 2 \end{pmatrix}$.

6. The mapping $z \longrightarrow |z|$, where z is a complex number, is a homomorphism of the multiplicative group of non-zero complex numbers onto the multiplicative group of non-zero reals. What is the geometrical representation in the complex plane of the kernel and the cosets of the kernel?

The mapping $z \longrightarrow \arg z$ is a homomorphism of the multiplicative group of non-zero complex numbers onto the additive group of equivalence classes of real numbers modulo 2π. What is the geometrical representation of the kernel and the cosets of the kernel?

So far we have shown that if a homomorphic mapping exists from a group G onto a group H, then the kernel K of the homomorphism is a subgroup of G with certain properties ((ii) to (iv) on page 167, and the group H is isomorphic to the factor group G/K. We now look for the possible homomorphisms of a group G. We know the rather weak result that there cannot be more homomorphisms than subgroups, and as we already discovered in Example E on page 162 there are subgroups which are not the kernels of homomorphisms.

Let G be any group and F any subgroup of G, then (ii) to (iv) imply that F will be subject to certain restrictions if it is the kernel

of some homomorphism. We ask the reader to bear the properties
(ii) to (iv) in mind in the following discussion: we shall refer to
them explicitly from time to time.

Consider the left cosets of F in G, i.e. the cosets gF where g is
any element of G. Let gF and $g'F$ be any two cosets $g \neq g'$. Then
we shall show that they are either equal or distinct, i.e.

$$gF \cap g'F = gF = g'F \quad \text{or} \quad gF \cap g'F = \emptyset.$$

Suppose that the two cosets have some element in common, i.e.

$$g \circ f = g' \circ f'$$

for some $f, f' \in F$. Then any other element of gF, say $g \circ f_1$, can be
written

$$g \circ f_1 = g \circ [f \circ \tilde{f}] \circ f_1 = g' \circ [f' \circ \tilde{f} \circ f_1].$$

But F is a group, so $f' \circ \tilde{f} \circ f_1 = f_2$ say, where $f_2 \in F$, and so every
element of gF is a member of $g'F$. Similarly every element of
$g'F$ is an element of gF and our statement is proved.

It follows that we have a partition of G into left cosets of F
(since $e_G \in F$, $g \in gF$ and so every element of G is in some left coset),
and therefore we have an equivalence relation on G defined by the
partition. This corresponds to the first part of property (iii) of the
kernel K above and we see that we have not had to impose any
restrictions on F as yet. We can state the equivalence relation
explicitly: $g \mathrel{R} g'$ if g and g' belong to the same left coset of F, i.e. if

$$g' = g \circ f \quad . \quad . \quad . \quad . \quad (1)$$

for some $f \in F$, or, what is the same thing, if $\tilde{g} \circ g' \in F$.

Example H. Using the definition $g \mathrel{R} g'$ if $\tilde{g} \circ g' \in F$, show directly that this
is an equivalence relation and that the equivalence classes are the left cosets
of F in G.

Our next point is clearly to investigate the compatibility of the
equivalence relation and the binary operation. We wish to show
that if

$$g \mathrel{R} g' \text{ and } g_1 \mathrel{R} g_1' \text{ then } [g \circ g_1] \mathrel{R} [g' \circ g_1'].$$

Now from equation (1) above this becomes 'if

$$g' = g \circ f \text{ and } g_1' = g_1 \circ f_1 \text{ then } g' \circ g_1' = [g \circ g_1] \circ f_1'',$$

for some $f_1' \in F$. Now

$$g' \circ g_1' = [g \circ f] \circ [g_1 \circ f_1]$$

and we see that there is no reason to suppose it always true that

$$[g \circ f] \circ [g_1 \circ f_1] = [g \circ g_1] \circ f_1'. \qquad . \qquad . \qquad (2)$$

Example I. In Example E on page 162 we chose the subgroup (e_G, g_3). The corresponding left cosets are

$$(e_G, g_3), (g_1, g_5), (g_2, g_4)$$

as the reader may easily satisfy himself. Hence

$$g_1 \, R \, g_5 \text{ and } g_2 \, R \, g_4,$$

but $g_1 \circ g_2 = e_G$ and $g_5 \circ g_4 = g_2$ and e_G is not equivalent to g_2. Thus it is impossible to define $(g_1, g_5) \circ (g_2, g_4)$ as the class whose representative is obtained by combining any element of the one with any element of the other, since the resulting class here depends on the choice of elements.

It follows that we must impose some condition on the subgroup F at this stage in order to obtain the required compatibility. We must somehow be able to get the g_1 on the left-hand side of equation (2) onto the other side of the f. To require that the g_1 should commute with the f is unnecessarily restrictive; all we need is that

$$f \circ g_1 = g_1 \circ f' \qquad . \qquad . \qquad . \qquad . \qquad (3)$$

for some $f' \in F$. Then equation (2) will be satisfied and our operation will be compatible with the equivalence relation. Now we require that equation (3) shall be satisfied for all $f \in F$ and $g_1 \in G$: this means that we must have

$$Fg_1 = g_1F \text{ for all } g_1 \text{ in } G \qquad . \qquad . \qquad (4)$$

which is our property (iv) for the kernel K. If a group G has a subgroup F which has this property then F is said to be an *invariant** subgroup. For such a subgroup the left coset for any element is the same as the right coset.

If F is an invariant subgroup, equation (2) is satisfied and we can then define the combination of two left cosets by

$$gF \circ g_1F = [g \circ g_1]F.$$

It remains to show that with this definition the set of left cosets forms a group which is a homomorphic image of G. This is left as a simple exercise to the reader. (Note that $F = e_GF$ is the identity element of the group.)

We have now proved the following fundamental theorem:
Theorem: If F is any invariant subgroup of G then the factor group

---

* There are various names in use beside 'invariant', e.g. normal, self-conjugate.

G/F is a homomorphic image of G and the kernel of the homomorphism is F. Further, if H is any homomorphic image of the group G, then H is isomorphic to the factor group G/K, where K is the kernel of the homomorphism.

This theorem shows that by listing the invariant subgroups of G and forming the corresponding factor groups we can completely investigate all possible homomorphisms of G: also, given any arbitrary homomorphism of G we can identify it structurally with the factor group corresponding to its kernel. There is just one point here: before we can find the invariant subgroups of a group G we must be able to find the subgroups of a group G. Suppose G has n elements (we say, G is of *order n*) then there are 2^n subsets. For a subset to be a subgroup it must at least contain the neutral element of G, so there seems to be at most something like 2^{n-1} subsets which might possibly be subgroups. But even this number is rather large: for the group of order 6 in the last example we would have to examine 32 subsets. So it would seem advisable to find some further restriction on subsets, i.e. a further necessary condition which any subset must satisfy if it is a subgroup. In fact, we have passed over an almost ready made condition in our previous working without noticing it.

Let G be any finite group of order n and F be any subgroup (invariant or not) of G. Then we have shown that the left cosets of F in G form a partition of G. Let w be the number of distinct cosets; w is known as the *index* of F in G. Each coset contains exactly the same number of elements, for if g is any fixed element of G and f runs through all the elements of F, then

$$g' = g \circ f$$

takes a different value for each value of f (because if $g \circ f = g \circ f_1$ it follows that $f = f_1$) and so a one-one correspondence can be established between the elements of F and the elements of each coset. Let m be the number of elements in F, then the number of elements in all the distinct cosets is mw. But F contains e_G, therefore $g \circ F$ contains g and the distinct cosets together contain all the elements of G, thus

$$mw = n.$$

It follows that m divides n. We have thus proved *Lagrange's Theorem*: The order of a subgroup divides the order of the group.

In our example of the group of order 6, we can now have subgroups of order 1, 2 and 3 only. The subgroup of order 1 is e_G and we discount this since every group has this subgroup. Since e_G must belong to every subgroup, we have now at most 15 subgroups. We shall investigate this case completely at the beginning of the next chapter.

NOTE: It should be unnecessary to point out that the left coset of F in G which contains the neutral element is the group F itself. Since the neutral element occurs in no other coset (for the cosets are non-overlapping), no other coset can be a group for the o operation.

We have covered a little more theory than usual in this chapter so we will devote the next chapter to some miscellanea: examples, exercises, applications and extensions of the ideas introduced in this chapter. Many of the examples are suitable for more advanced pupils, although we shall list them all as examples. Lagrange's theorem in particular, with its many beautiful consequences, is easy to prove and can be done with most classes of 15-year-old pupils of average ability.

*   *   *   *   *

We conclude this chapter by continuing the note at the end of the previous chapter, obtaining a particular topological group, the fundamental homotopy group. This group is a topological invariant (see Chapter 11, Example R, page 200) and hence in theory provides us with a possible means of distinguishing between different topological spaces in the sense that any two spaces with different fundamental groups cannot be homomorphic. The discussion which follows is fairly technical and the reader who wishes may omit, in particular, details of the construction of the homotopy functions F. He should, at least, read pages 176 to 177 and understand the terms used. (Incidentally, it should be borne in mind that not all closed curves are deformable into one another in any arbitrarily given topological space or even in such a physical case as the surface of a torus: one tends to lose sight of this in the technical trivia.)

In the first place we reorientate our discussion slightly. It is the usual practice in this theory to discuss the continuous functions of f on R_1 (the closed unit interval of the real line) with the natural subset topology into the topological space $(X, T : X)$ rather than the images of these functions, the curves in X. The reason for this is that this approach allows of immediate generalization: we too will talk about the functions, although we shall not go into the generalizations. The continuous function f we shall call a *path* into X: because the word 'path' has an everyday meaning somewhat similar to that of 'curve' we emphasize the technical use we are here making of these words: the image under f is not the path; the image is a curve, the path is the mapping itself. A path f will be said to be closed if $f(0) = f(1)$. For the motivation of our subsequent remarks we rely implicitly on the idea of a curve: the reader is asked to bear this in mind.*

A path f_0 is said to be *homotopic* to a path f_1 if there exists a continuous function F on $(R_1 \triangledown R_1, T: R_1 \triangledown R_1)$ into $(X, T: X)$ such that $F(s, 0) = f_0(s)$ and $F(s, 1) = f_1(s)$ for all $s \in R_1$. (This will imply that we can continuously deform the curve $f_0(R_1)$ into the curve $f_1(R_1)$.) If x_0 and x_1 belong to X, and if F exists satisfying, not only the previous conditions, but also

$$F(0, t) = f_0(0) = f_1(0) = x_0,$$
$$F(1, t) = f_0(1) = f_1(1) = x_1,$$

for all $t \in R_1$, then we shall say that f_0 is homotopic to f_1 relative to x_0 and x_1.

Let f and g be paths into a topological space $(X, T: X)$ such that $f(1) = g(0)$. Then it is intuitively reasonable that we can combine these two paths into a new path $h = g \circ f$. (Consider the corresponding curves.) To do this analytically we must so combine them that h is a continuous mapping of $(R_1, T: R_1)$ into $(X, T: X)$. Consider the function h defined by

$$h(s) = \begin{cases} f(2s) & , \quad 0 \leqslant s < \tfrac{1}{2} \\ g(2s - 1) & , \quad \tfrac{1}{2} \leqslant s \leqslant 1. \end{cases}$$

We notice that $h(0) = f(0), h(1) = g(1)$ and that $h(\tfrac{1}{2}) = f(1) = g(0)$, which expresses our intuitive ideas exactly. It would remain to show that h is continuous: we shall not do this, but the reader might like to try; it is not difficult.

Having described the combination of two particular paths and remembering that we are, in the end, looking for a group, our next step would be to look for something that might act as a sort of identity element. For any point $x \in X$ we can define a special path e_x which is such that it maps the whole of R_1 onto x, i.e.

$$e_x(s) = x \quad , \quad 0 \leqslant s \leqslant 1.$$

---

* The reader can of course draw pictures: these are helpful to focus attention on the problem in hand but he should remember that he would be drawing curves and not paths.

We can combine this with a path f if either $f(0) = x$ or $f(1) = x$.
In the first case we would have $h = f \circ e_x$, where

$$h(s) = \begin{cases} e_x(2s) = x & , \quad 0 \leqslant s \leqslant \frac{1}{2} \\ f(2s - 1) & , \quad \frac{1}{2} \leqslant s \leqslant 1, \end{cases}$$

but this is not the same as f, although the image set of h and f are
the same. It would seem likely, however, that h is homotopic to
f relative to x and $f(1)$. We can make the homotopy explicit by
finding the function F on $R_1 \triangledown R_1$ into X: consider, as a first
attempt

$$F(s, t) = \begin{cases} x & , \quad 0 \leqslant s \leqslant t/2 \\ f\left([t + 1]\left[s - \dfrac{t}{2}\right]\right) & , \quad t/2 \leqslant s \leqslant 1. \end{cases}$$

Then $\qquad F(s, 0) = \begin{cases} x & , \quad 0 \leqslant s \leqslant 0 \\ f(s) & , \quad 0 \leqslant s \leqslant 1 \end{cases} = f(s)$

and $\qquad F(s, 1) = \begin{cases} x & , \quad 0 \leqslant s \leqslant \frac{1}{2} \\ f(2s - 1) & , \quad \frac{1}{2} \leqslant s \leqslant 1 \end{cases} = h(s).$

Also $F(0, t) = x$, but $F(1, t) = f([t + 1][1 - t/2])$ which is not
necessarily the same as $f(1)$. Therefore, F is not the required
function. Before we give a satisfactory function we point out two
further requirements of the function F which are somewhat
obscured in the technicalities. These requirements are both associated with the continuity of F:

(i) We must ensure that for all values of (s, t) the function F
is properly defined on R_1: for instance, for the F above $F(1, \frac{1}{4})$
$= f(35/32)$ which is not defined.

(ii) Where F is defined 'in bits' over $R_1 \triangledown R_1$ we must ensure that
on any overlap the bits have the same image in X: for instance,
in our example, the bits overlap at $s = t/2$, and here

$$F(t/2, t) = \begin{cases} x \\ f(0) = x, \end{cases}$$

so we see that this condition is satisfied.

A satisfactory function F (which meets all six requirements) is

$$F(s, t) = \begin{cases} x & , \quad 0 \leqslant s \leqslant \dfrac{1 - t}{2} \\ f\left(\dfrac{2(s - 1)}{t + 1} + 1\right) & , \quad \dfrac{1 - t}{2} \leqslant s \leqslant 1. \end{cases}$$

That the first four conditions are satisfied we leave the reader to
check: the value $(1 - t)/2$ for splitting the interval R_1 has been

chosen to ensure continuity (as well as from the requirement $F(s, 0) = h(s)$): it remains to show that

$$0 \leqslant \frac{2[s-1]}{t+1} + 1 \leqslant 1 \text{ for } \frac{1-t}{2} \leqslant s \leqslant 1.$$

Since
$$s \geqslant \frac{1-t}{2} \text{ and } \frac{2[s-1]}{t+1} \leqslant 0$$

we have
$$\frac{2[s-1]}{t+1} \geqslant \frac{2\left[\dfrac{1-t}{2}-1\right]}{t+1} = -1,$$

which satisfies the left-hand inequality: the right-hand inequality is a consequence of the fact that $\dfrac{2[s-1]}{t+1} \leqslant 0$.

Example J. We have spent rather a long time over this one case in order to try to illustrate the methods and snags, but the only way to pursue this topic is for the reader to struggle for himself. We suggest, therefore, that he try the other half of the problem (before reading any further in this section): that is, suppose that $f(1) = x$ and that we form $h = e_x \circ f$; then show that h is homotopic to f by finding a relevant homotopy function F.

Example K. As we shall see later the relation of being homotopic is an equivalence relation in a set of paths. It follows that f is homotopic to h in the case discussed in the text and in Example J. Find the corresponding homotopy functions F. Can you suggest a general result?

Let us now see how far we have got. It would seem that we must introduce the idea of homotopy classes, i.e. classes of homotopic paths, and with luck these will be equivalence classes. It then follows that we must show that the combination that we have defined is compatible with the equivalence relation. Further it looks as if the class containing the path e_x will act as the identity element, but we know that in a group the left identity is the same as the right identity and at the moment $e_x \circ f$ may be defined (i.e. if $x = f(1)$) and $f \circ e_x$ may not be defined (i.e. if $x \neq f(0)$), hence we shall require

$$f(0) = f(1) = x,$$

i.e. the set of paths we shall consider are all the closed paths to a point $x \in X$. The combination of any two such paths belongs to the set so the closure requirement for a group is satisfied. It remains to discover whether the combination of classes is associative and to find an inverse. If we can do all this we shall have a group. We shall prove some of the results and leave the rest explicitly to the reader: there is only one point at each stage of our investigation, to find the relevant homotopy function F. We shall take the continuity of each function that we construct for granted, merely adopting the safeguards mentioned above: in general it is not difficult to prove the continuity and a generally applicable result can be obtained.

(1) Denote the set of closed paths to $x \in X$ such that $f(0) = f(1) = x$ by P_x. If f and g belong to P_x and f is homotopic to g relative to x (i.e. $f(0) = g(0) = f(1) = g(1) = x$ and there exists a function F such that $F(0, t) = F(1, t) = x$, etc.) then we shall write $f \sim g$. We wish to show that $\sim$ is an equivalence relation.

(a) $\sim$ is symmetric. Suppose that $f \sim g$ then there exists a function F such that

$$F(s, 0) = f(s), \quad F(s, 1) = g(s), \quad F(0, t) = F(1, t) = x.$$

Consider $F_1(s, t) = F(s, 1 - t)$, then

$$F_1(s, 0) = F(s, 1) = g(s), \quad F_1(s, 1) = f(s),$$

and
$$F_1(0, t) = F_1(1, t) = x.$$

Hence $g \sim f$.

(b) $\sim$ is reflexive. Define $F(s, t) = f(s)$ for all t, which proves the result. (Incidentally, this function can be seen to be continuous because the topology for any direct product is so chosen that the projections are continuous, and we can decompose F into two continuous functions, i.e.

$$F: (s, t) \rightarrow s \rightarrow f(s).)$$

(c) $\sim$ is transitive. Suppose that $f \sim g$ and $g \sim h$ then there exist functions F and G of the required type. We wish to define a function H which shows that $f \sim h$. Consider

$$H(s, t) = \begin{cases} F(s, 2t) & , \quad 0 \leqslant t \leqslant \frac{1}{2} \\ G(s, 2t - 1) & , \quad \frac{1}{2} \leqslant t \leqslant 1. \end{cases}$$

Note the similarity between this function and that obtained for the combination of two paths. We leave the reader to check the details.

(2) Denote the set of equivalence classes defined in P_x (by the relation $\sim$) by P'_x. We wish to show that the combination defined

in P_x is compatible with $\sim$ and can, therefore, be defined in P'_x, i.e. if $f \sim g$ and $f_1 \sim g_1$ then we shall prove that $[f \circ f_1] \sim [g \circ g_1]$. (Note that since we are dealing with closed paths, combination is always defined, and the result is always a closed path in P_x.) Since $f \sim g$ and $f_1 \sim g_1$, there exist functions F and F_1 of the required type: define

$$H(s, t) = \begin{cases} F(2s, t) & , \quad 0 \leqslant s \leqslant \tfrac{1}{2} \\ F_1(2s - 1, t) & , \quad \tfrac{1}{2} \leqslant s \leqslant 1. \end{cases}$$

Then $H(s, 0) = \begin{cases} F(2s, 0) \\ F_1(2s - 1, 0) \end{cases}$

$$= \left\{ \begin{matrix} f(2s) & , & 0 \leqslant s \leqslant \tfrac{1}{2} \\ f_1(2s - 1) & , & \tfrac{1}{2} \leqslant s \leqslant 1 \end{matrix} \right\} = [f \circ f_1](s),$$

and we leave the reader to check the rest of the conditions. Again note the way that the function H was formed.

(3) We now have a combination in P'_x, which is closed and contains an identity element $\{e_x\}$. It remains to show that combination is associative and that there exists an inverse for each element in P'_x. We shall consider the latter point first: let f be any path belonging to P_x so that $\{f\} \in P'_x$: as $s \in R_1$ goes from 0 to 1 we have a sense for the description of the curve $f(R_1)$ and it would seem reasonable that if we reverse the sense we shall undo the curve: to be more precise define a new path f_1 by

$$f_1(s) = f(1 - s),$$

whence $f_1(0) = f(1) = f(0) = f_1(1) = x$, therefore $f_1 \in P_x$. We wish to show that

$$\{f \circ f_1\} = \{e_x\},$$

i.e. that $[f \circ f_1] \sim e_x$. Let $f \circ f_1 = h$, then

$$h(s) = \begin{cases} f(1 - 2s) & , \quad 0 \leqslant s \leqslant \tfrac{1}{2} \\ f(2s - 1) & , \quad \tfrac{1}{2} \leqslant s \leqslant 1. \end{cases}$$

The function F we are looking for must be e_x when $t = 1$, i.e. $f(0)$ or $f(1)$: this suggests that we might introduce a factor $1 - t$ somewhere, so we try

$$F(s, t) = \begin{cases} f([1 - t][1 - 2s]) & , \quad 0 \leqslant s \leqslant \tfrac{1}{2} \\ f([1 - t][2s - 1]) & , \quad \tfrac{1}{2} \leqslant s \leqslant 1. \end{cases}$$

Then $F(s, 0) = h(s)$, but $F(0, t) = f(1 - t)$ and $F(1, t) = f(1 - t)$ which will not do. (Incidentally, the two continuity conditions are satisfied.) We leave the reader to modify the function suitably.

Lastly we must show that if f, g and h belong to P_x that

$$[f \circ g] \circ h \sim f \circ [g \circ h].$$

If $k = [f \circ g] \circ h$ then

$$k(s) = \begin{cases} h(2s) & , \quad 0 \leqslant s \leqslant \frac{1}{2} \\ g(4s - 2) & , \quad \frac{1}{2} \leqslant s \leqslant \frac{3}{4} \\ f(4s - 3) & , \quad \frac{3}{4} \leqslant s \leqslant 1 \end{cases}$$

and a similar expression for $f \circ [g \circ h]$. It is clearly going to require considerable ingenuity to produce a function F: the reader might like to try: we shall be satisfied that intuitively such a function must exist. (Consider combining the corresponding curves.)

Thus, finally, we have produced our group P'_x at any point $x \in X$. This is the *fundamental group* at x: we shall consider some examples and some of its properties at the end of the next chapter. In particular, we shall prove that the fundamental group is a topological invariant, i.e. that if X_1 is homeomorphic to X_2 under a homeomorphism q then P'_x, $x \in X_1$, is isomorphic to $P'_{q(x)}$: we would like to think, however, that this again is an intuitive result since the whole definition of P'_x has been in topological terms.

CHAPTER 11

CONSEQUENCES

Example A. We shall first find all the subgroups of the group of order 6 which we considered in the previous chapter (see page 172). Its combination table is

o	e_G	g_1	g_2	g_3	g_4	g_5
e_G	e_G	g_1	g_2	g_3	g_4	g_5
g_1	g_1	g_2	e_G	g_5	g_3	g_4
g_2	g_2	e_G	g_1	g_4	g_5	g_3
g_3	g_3	g_4	g_5	e_G	g_1	g_2
g_4	g_4	g_5	g_3	g_2	e_G	g_1
g_5	g_5	g_3	g_4	g_1	g_2	e_G

Since the order of a subgroup divides the order of the group we can only have proper subgroups of order 2 and 3. A subgroup of order 2 must contain e_G and one other element g_i which is such that

$$g_i \text{ o } g_i = e_G$$

Hence from the combination table we find that there are three subgroups of order 2, i.e.

$$(e_G, g_3), \quad (e_G, g_4), \quad (e_G, g_5).$$

Any subgroup of order 3 contains e_G and two other elements g_i, g_j. But a group is closed, therefore $g_i \text{ o } g_j$ must be one of these three elements: it is easily seen that it cannot be g_i or g_j, so $g_i \text{ o } g_j = g_j \text{ o } g_i = e_G$. If we now write out the combination table for this group, remembering that no element may be repeated in any row or column (why?), we find that the subgroup is completely determined.

o	e_G	g_i	g_j
e_G	e_G	g_i	g_j
g_i	g_i		e_G
g_j	g_j	e_G	

From the above group table, this is only satisfied by $i = 1$ or $j = 2$ (or vice versa). Hence there is one subgroup of order 3.

The three groups of order 2 are isomorphic. There is, of course, only one abstract group of order two, i.e. every combination table is of the form

o	e	a
e	e	a
u	a	e

These three particular subgroups are not invariant and so do not give rise to a homomorphism.

The discussion we gave above for the subgroup of order 3 shows that there is only one abstract group of order 3, i.e. any group of order three has a combination table of the form

o	e	a	b
e	e	a	b
a	a	b	e
b	b	e	a

The fact that there is only one abstract group of order 2 and one of order 3 is a particular result of the general statement in Example E (iv).

Returning to our group of order 6 and its subgroup of order 3, we notice that the subgroup is invariant: we show the left cosets explicitly.

$$e_G (e_G, g_1, g_2) = (e_G, g_1, g_2); \quad g_1 (e_G, g_1, g_2) = (g_1, g_2, e_G);$$
$$g_2 (e_G, g_1, g_2) = (g_2, e_G, g_1); \quad g_3 (e_G, g_1, g_2) = (g_3, g_4, g_5);$$
$$g_4 (e_G, g_1, g_2) = (g_4, g_5, g_3); \quad g_5 (e_G, g_1, g_2) = (g_5, g_3, g_4).$$

The two distinct cosets are (e_G, g_1, g_2) and (g_3, g_4, g_5). They form a group under the induced operation o. This factor group is, of course, isomorphic to the abstract group of order 2.

So this group of order 6 considered has

(1) 3 subgroups of order 2 and 1 of order 3,

(2) 1 invariant subgroup of order 3, and hence

(3) a homomorphism onto the abstract group of order 2.

Example B. If f is a homomorphism of G onto H, show that the order of H divides the order of G.

(Hint: if K is the kernel of f, [order K] $\times$ [order H] = [order G].)

Example C. Any subgroup of an Abelian group is invariant.

Example D. It is an immediate corollary of Lagrange's Theorem that a group of prime order has no subgroups: in consequence, it also admits no homomorphic images.

Example E. The *order n* of an element g of a group G is defined as the least positive integer n for which $g^n = e_G$, where $g^n = g \circ g \circ \ldots \circ g$, i.e. g combined with itself n times. In a group of infinite order there is no reason why n should be finite, but in a group of finite order n must be finite, for consider the sequence

$$e_G, g, g^2, g^3, \ldots$$

These are all elements of G (G is closed), but since G is finite we must get repetition at some stage, i.e. we must have

$$g^t = g^s \qquad s > t$$

and so, since $g^t \circ [\tilde{g}]^t = e_G$ and $g^s \circ [\tilde{g}]^t = g^{s-t}$, we have

$$e_G = g^{s-t}$$

and the order n of g is such that $n \leqslant s - t$.

If $g \in G$ and g is of order n, then the elements

$$g, g^2, \ldots g^{n-1}, g^n = e_G$$

form an Abelian subgroup of G. Hence, by Lagrange's theorem, the order of any element of a finite group, divides the order of the group. (Note that if g is of order n, the inverse of g^r is g^{n-r}, $r < n$.)

A group *generated* in this way by one element is called a *cyclic group*. The choice of name is easily explained. All cyclic groups of the same order are clearly isomorphic and for any given order n, say, rotations in a plane about a fixed point through an angle of $2\pi/n$ form a cyclic group of order n. Any point in the plane is transformed into itself after n applications of this rotation operation: on its way it describes n points equally spaced on the circumference of a circle centre the fixed point. (In general, if all the elements of a group may be represented as powers or combinations of powers of the elements of some subset, then the elements in this subset are called the generating elements of the group (e.g. the note on braids, Chapter 7, page 116).)

Clearly we have a cyclic group C_n of any order n. It follows that the group of order 3 is a cyclic group of the form e_G, g, g^2. This is a special case of the general result (iv) below.

(i)   There are isomorphic representations of the cyclic group other than the geometric one given above.

(ii)   Find a 2×2 matrix representation of the cyclic group of order six. (Hint: use the geometric representation.)

(iii) Consider the group of elements 1, 2, 3, 4 with multiplication modulo 5. Find the order of each of the elements and show that the group is cyclic. Which of these elements generates the whole group? Consider other 'modulo' groups.

(iv)   Use Lagrange's theorem to show that there is only one abstract group of each prime order, i.e. the cyclic group of that order. (Hint: consider the order of an element g.)

(v)   Show that any homomorphic image of a cyclic group is cyclic.

(vi)   Show that any subgroup of a cyclic group is cyclic. (Hint: if g generates G and g^r and g^s belong to the subgroup then g^d belongs to the subgroup where d is the highest common factor of r and s.)

Example F. Lagrange's theorem, together with the fact that the order of any element divides the order of the group, can be used to investigate the number of possible abstract, non-isomorphic groups of any given order. For orders with a small number of factors this is a relatively easy problem, but with increasing number of factors it usually becomes more difficult.

Of the groups of order less than 8, the only ones we have not settled are the groups of order 4 and 6. Consider the problem for groups of order 4. We gave two non-isomorphic group tables in Chapter 8, Exercise 2, page 121: in fact, these are the only two abstract groups of order 4. We leave the proof to the reader with the following hints. The elements of the group can either be of order 4 or 2. If there is one element of order 4 it generates the group, which is therefore cyclic (see the first table and notice the cyclic arrangement). Otherwise the three non-neutral elements must be of order 2. It remains to show that there can be only one such group: this can be done directly by trying to fill in the gaps in the combination table given below. It will be found that there is only one possibility for each empty place.

o	e	a	b	c
e	e	a	b	c
a	a	e		
b	b		e	
c	c			e

There are two groups of order 6: one is certainly cyclic. Except for this case the elements of a group of order 6 can be only of order 2 or 3. Show that not all elements can be of order 2: hence there must be at least one element g of order three, whence three elements of the group are e_G, g, g^2. Let g_1 be any further element then g_1, $g_1 \circ g$ and $g_1 \circ g^2$ must be the other three elements, whence g_1^2 must be already listed: show that g_1^2 must be equal to e_G, etc. See the reference below.

If we consider the number of possible abstract groups of order 8 we see immediately that the problem becomes more involved. We have, of course, the cyclic group of order 8 generated by one element of order 8. But then we can have elements of order 4 or 2 and possible combinations of these must be considered. In fact there are five groups and the reader can find a survey of such groups in Ledermann, *Introduction to the Theory of Finite Groups* (Oliver and Boyd).

The reader who is interested can pursue the problem to groups of higher order: it is not always more difficult. For instance, there are only two groups of order 9.

Example G. In order to grasp the ideas of the previous chapter, especially the idea of an invariant subgroup and the multiplication of cosets, it is advisable to work an example in full as we did for the group of order 6 in

Example A. For this purpose we suggest that the reader find and investigate all the subgroups of the group of order 8 whose table is given below.

o	e	f	g	h	i	j	k	l
e	e	f	g	h	i	j	k	l
f	f	g	h	e	j	k	l	i
g	g	h	e	f	k	l	i	j
h	h	e	f	g	l	i	j	k
i	i	l	k	j	e	h	g	f
j	j	i	l	k	f	e	h	g
k	k	j	i	l	g	f	e	h
l	l	k	j	i	h	g	f	e

This group, known as the *dihedral group of order 8*, is isomorphic to the group of symmetries of the square considered in Chapter 8, page 123. As a typical result we mention that the group has five subgroups of order two, of which only one is invariant. This means that the factor group for this invariant subgroup is of order 4: it remains to discover with which of the two abstract groups of order 4 it is isomorphic. To do this latter part, the reader is advised to calculate the cosets as in Example A of this chapter and then to set up the combination table for the distinct cosets. It would also be useful to show directly, as in Chapter 10, Example E, page 162, that any one of the other subgroups of order two is not the kernel of a homomorphism.

Example H. Let H be an invariant subgroup of a group G then $gH = Hg$ for all $g \in G$. This means that for any element $h \in H$ there must be an $h_1 \in H$ such that

$$g \circ h = h_1 \circ g,$$

i.e. $g \circ h \circ \tilde{g} = h_1.$

Conversely, if $g \circ h \circ \tilde{g} \in H$, for all $g \in G$ and $h \in H$, $gH = Hg$. Thus we can rephrase our definition of an invariant subgroup in the following form: H is an invariant subgroup of the group G if $g \circ h \circ \tilde{g}$ belongs to H for all $g \in G$ and $h \in H$, or briefly if $gH\tilde{g} = H$ for all $g \in G$. Note that replacing g by $\tilde{g}'$ we get the equivalent statement: H is an invariant subgroup of G if $\tilde{g}'Hg' = H$ for all $g' \in G$.

Example I. So far in this chapter we have confined our examples to finite groups: we shall now give a few examples of infinite groups with invariant subgroups.

1. As we shall see in the next chapter certain groups of square matrices with real elements play an important role in geometry. Among these groups are the orthogonal group and the similarity group. We have already met the orthogonal group O_2 of 2×2 matrices: it is the set of all matrices A such that

$$AA' = I, \qquad . \qquad . \qquad . \qquad . \qquad . \qquad (1)$$

where A' is the transpose of A and I is the unit 2×2 matrix $\begin{pmatrix} 1 & 0 \\ 0 & 1 \end{pmatrix}$. The *similarity group* S_2 is the set of 2×2 matrices B such that

$$BB' = \lambda I, \quad . \quad . \quad . \quad . \quad . \quad (2)$$

where λ is any non-zero positive real number. We leave the reader to verify that this is a group along the lines indicated for O_2. (Why must λ be non-zero?)

Clearly O_2 is a subgroup of S_2. We will show that it is an invariant sub-group. To do this we must show that (cf. equation (4) of Chapter 10, page 171)

$$O_2 B = B O_2 \quad \text{for all } B \text{ in } S_2.$$

This is the same as showing that

$$\text{for all } A \in O_2 \ AB = BA_1 \quad \text{for some } A_1 \in O_2,$$

i.e. that

$$[\tilde{B} A B] \in O_2, \text{ i.e. that } [\tilde{B} A B][\tilde{B} A B]' = I.$$

Now $\tilde{B} = \dfrac{1}{\lambda} B'$ by the definition of S_2.   Consider

$$\left[\frac{1}{\lambda} B'AB\right]\left[\frac{1}{\lambda} B'AB\right]' = \left[\frac{1}{\lambda} B'AB\right]\left[\frac{1}{\lambda} B'A'B\right]^{*}$$

$$= \left[\frac{1}{\lambda} B'A\right] I \, [A'B] \quad \text{by equation (2)}$$

$$= \left[\frac{1}{\lambda} B'\right] I \, B \quad\quad \text{by equation (1)}$$

$$= I,$$

by equation (2) and the fact that a right-inverse in a group is also the left inverse. It follows that $\tilde{B}AB \in O_2$. Thus S_2/O_2 is the homomorphic image of S_2 with kernel O_2.

This latter group is rather difficult to visualize, so we shall investigate the cosets which are its elements in an attempt to establish an isomorphism with a more well-known group. Let B be any element of S_2 such that $BB' = kI$. Consider the elements of the coset BO_2 and let BA, $A \in O_2$, be any one. Then

$$[BA][BA]' = BAA'B' = BIB' = kI,$$

i.e. every element of the coset BO_2 satisfies an equation of the form (2) for a fixed scalar λ $(= k$, in this case). But perhaps there are two cosets BO_2 and

---

* There are two points here which we have not explicitly mentioned:

(i) $A[\lambda B] = [\lambda A]B = \lambda[AB]$, for any matrices A and B.

(ii) The extension of the transpose operation to the product of any number of matrices. The reader was asked to prove that for 2×2 matrices A and B

$$[AB]' = B'A'$$

(see Chapter 9, Exercise 8 (b), page 151) and it follows from this and the associativity of matrix multiplication that for any 2×2 matrices A, B, C

$$[ABC]' = C'B'A',$$

etc. In fact the results are quite general and apply equally to $n \times n$ matrices.

CO_2, say, whose elements satisfy the equation $XX' = kI$ for the same k. To see whether this is the case or not we shall try to find some relation between B and C. Now we can always find a matrix $Y \in S_2$ such that $C = BY$ (we are working in a group) and if $CC' = kI$, we have

$$[BY][BY]' = BYY'B' = kI,$$

where premultiplying by the inverse of B, viz. $\frac{1}{k}B'$, and postmultiplying by $\frac{1}{k}B$, the inverse of B', we have

$$\left[\frac{1}{k}B'\right]B[YY']B'\frac{1}{k}B = \left[\frac{1}{k}B'\right]kI\left[\frac{1}{k}B\right],$$

and this simplifies to

$$YY' = \frac{1}{k}B'B = I,$$

which shows that $Y \in O_2$ and, therefore, $BO_2 = CO_2$. Thus, to summarize: matrices B and C, belonging to S_2, belong to the same coset of O_2 in S_2 if, and only if, they both satisfy the equation of the form (2) for the same value of λ, i.e. there is a one-one correspondence between the cosets and the positive real numbers. We leave the reader to complete the isomorphism.

We could have obtained the result more directly by showing that the mapping of the multiplicative group of S_2 onto the positive reals under multiplication defined by

$$B \longrightarrow \lambda$$

where B satisfies $BB' = \lambda I$, is a homomorphism with kernel O_2. Then, subsequently, we could have investigated the cosets. The reader should remember that the method which most appeals to him may not be the best method to teach. Most of our mathematical teaching still remains unmotivated either from within or from without mathematics. A series of theorems or problems of the type 'Show that O_2 is an invariant subgroup of S_2 and that S_2/O_2 is isomorphic to the multiplicative group of positive reals', may be stimulating to the sophisticated but is more likely, at all levels, to yield the muttered reaction of 'So what?' If possible one should not begin with the result and then provide the investigation. If one wishes one's students to react then one should present them with a reasonable problem suitably motivated depending on their level, and not with the answer. This cannot, of course, always be done; time, energy and, in the case of books, space is lacking; but it ought to be one of our aims.

To continue with our problem. The reader might like to consider its generalization to larger square matrices. He might also like to consider analogous problems for other groups of 2×2 matrices of which we give a few below. All the groups are multiplicative.

The largest multiplicative group of 2×2 matrices is, of course, the group M' of all non-singular matrices, i.e. the group of matrices which possess multiplicative inverses. So far in this example we have met the two subgroups S_2 and O_2. We suggest for consideration the sets of matrices of the following form also.

(i) $\begin{pmatrix} a & b \\ 0 & 1 \end{pmatrix}, a \neq 0;$ (ii) $\begin{pmatrix} 1 & b \\ 0 & 1 \end{pmatrix};$ (iii) $\begin{pmatrix} \pm 1 & b \\ 0 & 1 \end{pmatrix};$ (iv) $\begin{pmatrix} a & 0 \\ 0 & 1 \end{pmatrix}$

2. We have come across many other subgroups of 2×2 matrices in Chapter 9 and one can consider these in their matrix form or in their isomorphic numerical form. For instance, consider the additive groups of matrices. M, the set of all 2×2 matrices, is our main group and it is Abelian. Therefore all the subgroups are invariant. It only remains to recognize the factor groups.

On the other hand, the multiplicative group M' is not Abelian and, therefore, the corresponding subgroups of the multiplicative structure given in Chapter 9 may not be invariant.

Of all these possible combinations of groups and subgroups we consider a final example, the complex numbers as a subgroup of the quaternions. The additive group of quaternions is Abelian, therefore the complex numbers form an invariant additive subgroup. The factor group is the set of cosets of the form $qC^* = \{q + c\}$, where q is a fixed quaternion and $c \in C$, the set of complex numbers. Using our matrix representation of these sets we suppose that

$$q \leftrightarrow \begin{pmatrix} \alpha & \beta \\ -\bar{\beta} & \bar{\alpha} \end{pmatrix} \text{ and } c \leftrightarrow \begin{pmatrix} a & b \\ -b & a \end{pmatrix},$$

where a, b are real and α, β are complex. Thus

$$q + c \leftrightarrow \begin{pmatrix} \alpha + a & \beta + b \\ -\bar{\beta} - b & \bar{\alpha} + a \end{pmatrix}$$

and the matrix representation of the coset qC is obtained by letting a and b take all real values. All the matrices in the representation of qC, therefore, are such that the complex part of each entry is the same, i.e. if $\alpha = r + sj$ and $\beta = t + uj$, $j^2 = -1$, then each matrix in the representation of qC can be written

$$c_1 + j \begin{pmatrix} s & u \\ u & -s \end{pmatrix},$$

where c_1 is a real matrix depending on c. Thus there is a one-one correspondence between the cosets qC and the matrices of the form $\begin{pmatrix} s & u \\ u & -s \end{pmatrix}$.

This form of matrix is not directly recognizable as one of those given in Chapter 9 but we can establish a further one-one correspondence of the form

$$\begin{pmatrix} s & u \\ u & -s \end{pmatrix} \leftrightarrow \begin{pmatrix} u & s \\ -s & u \end{pmatrix}$$

which is recognizable as the matrix corresponding to the complex number $u + js$. We leave the reader to show that

$$qC \leftrightarrow \begin{pmatrix} u & s \\ -s & u \end{pmatrix}$$

is an isomorphism.

---

* The reader is reminded that qC signifies the set obtained by combining (under the group operation, and here this is addition) the element q with every element in C.

Now consider the multiplicative structures. The multiplicative group of non-zero quaternions is not Abelian, therefore, the subgroup of non-zero complex numbers is not necessarily invariant. To investigate whether it is or not we will consider the quaternions and complex numbers in their 'standard' form and not their isomorphic matrix forms. Let $q = a + bi + cj + dk$ be a quaternion and $\alpha = u + vl$ be a complex number, $l^2 = -1$. Then α, considered as a quaternion element, is written as $\alpha = u + 0i + vj + 0.k$ (see Chapter 9, Exercise 4 (d), page 138), and we leave the reader to verify that $\tilde{q} \alpha q$ is not a complex number where

$$\tilde{q} = \frac{1}{a^2 + b^2 + c^2 + d^2} [a - bi - cj - dk]$$

is the inverse of q. Hence the complex numbers are not an invariant subgroup of the quaternions under multiplication and there is no corresponding factor group.

Example J. Suppose that H is any subgroup of G, then if H is not invariant $gH\tilde{g}$ for some $g \in G$ is not H (see Example H, page 184) but some other subset H_1 of G. In fact, H_1 is a group isomorphic to H; we leave this to the reader to prove. H_1 is said to be *conjugate* to H and this is why an invariant subgroup is often called self-conjugate.

The type of transformation g [something] $\tilde{g}$ is important in certain applications of group theory, so we shall consider it a little further. Let G be a group and g, g' any two elements of G and suppose that there exists some element $g_1 \in G$, such that

$$g_1 \circ g \circ \tilde{g}_1 = g',$$

then g' is said to be a *conjugate* of g. Clearly every element is *self-conjugate*, i.e. is a conjugate of itself, for

$$e \circ g \circ \tilde{e} = g \qquad (\text{also } g \circ g \circ \tilde{g} = g)$$

and if g' is a conjugate of g then g is a conjugate of g', for if $g_1 \circ g \circ \tilde{g}_1 = g'$ then $\tilde{g}_1 \circ g' \circ g_1 = g_1$ and g_1 is, of course, the inverse of $\tilde{g}_1$. Thus the relation 'g conjugate of g'' is reflexive and symmetric; it is an equivalence relation if it is also transitive, i.e. if 'g conjugate of g'' and 'g' conjugate of g''' imply 'g conjugate of g'''. Now 'g conjugate of g'' implies that there is an element $g_1 \in G$ such that $g_1 \circ g \circ \tilde{g}_1 = g'$ and similarly we have for some $g_2 \in G$,

$$g_2 \circ g' \circ \tilde{g}_2 = g''.$$

Hence

$$[g_2 \circ g_1] \circ g \circ [\tilde{g}_1 \circ \tilde{g}_2] = g''$$

and $\overline{[g_2 \circ g_1]} = \tilde{g}_1 \circ \tilde{g}_2$, thus '$g$ conjugate of g'''.

Since the relation of being conjugate is an equivalence relation it divides the elements of G into non-overlapping classes, the elements in each class being conjugate to each other. To construct these classes for any given group G (we shall immediately consider an example) we begin with any element g and form the expressions of the form $g_1 \circ g \circ \tilde{g}_1$ for all $g_1 \in G$ and so find all the elements conjugate to g: then we take any element g', not belonging to this class, and proceed similarly, and so on till all the elements of the group are exhausted.

As an example we choose the symmetry group of the square (the dihedral group D_8 of order 8) which we have already considered in Chapter 8, Exercise 5, page 123 and on page 184 in this chapter. To save the reader continually referring back we reproduce the figure and the group table here, using a slightly different notation. a, b, c, d will refer to rotations through 180° about

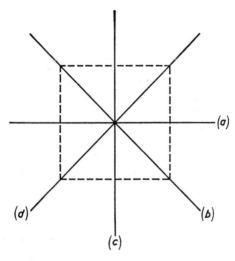

the axes marked (a), (b), (c) and (d) respectively. e will refer to a rotation through 0° about an axis through the centre of the frame and perpendicular to its plane; f, g, h will refer to rotations of 90°, 180° and 270° respectively about this axis. The group table then is

o	e	a	b	c	d	f	g	h
e	e	a	b	c	d	f	g	h
a	a	e	h	g	f	d	c	b
b	b	f	e	h	g	a	d	c
c	c	g	f	e	h	b	a	d
d	d	h	g	f	e	c	b	a
f	f	b	c	d	a	g	h	e
g	g	c	d	a	b	h	e	f
h	h	d	a	b	c	e	f	g

Clearly e is in a class by itself since $x \circ e \circ \tilde{x} = e$ for all x belonging to D_8.

(The reader might like to show that any element of a group which commutes with every other element of the group is in a class by itself. Also, he might like to show that the set of all elements which commute with every element of the group form a subgroup. This subgroup is called the *centre* of the group. Is it an invariant subgroup? In an Abelian group each element is conjugate to itself only.)

Now consider the next element a and form all the expressions of the form $x \circ a \circ \tilde{x}, x \in D_8$.

$$b \circ a \circ \tilde{b} = b \circ a \circ b = c; \quad c \circ a \circ \tilde{c} = c \circ a \circ c = a; \text{ etc.}$$

It will be found that we get either a or c in every case. So our second class is $\{a, c\}$. Continuing in this way we obtain the following set of classes:

$$\{e\}, \{a, c\}, \{b, d\}, \{f, h\}, \{g\}.$$

(The element g commutes with every element of the group. This can be seen in the group table by noting that each entry g has a mirror image in the main diagonal from top left to bottom right.)

We can give these classes an interesting geometrical significance by considering the elements of D_8 as mappings of the points of the square (in general, the whole plane: cf. Chapter 8, Exercises 6 and 7, page 124). This is best described using a conventional coordinate system, i.e. the x-axis along the axis marked (a) and the y-axis along the axis marked (c). If P is a point with coordinates (x, y), then $a(P)$, the reflection of P in the (a)-axis (or x-axis) has coordinates $(x, -y)$; similarly the reader may find the new coordinates for each of the other seven symmetry operations. (Note that they correspond to the eight possible combinations of $\pm x$ and $\pm y$.)

Now consider the relation $c = f \circ a \circ \tilde{f}$ and let P be any point and $a(P) = Q$, say. Then

$$c(f(P)) = [c \circ f](P) = [f \circ a \circ \tilde{f} \circ f](P) = [f \circ a](P) = f(a(P)) = f(Q).$$

Thus, if a maps P to Q, c maps $f(P)$ to $f(Q)$, or to put it otherwise the effect of a on P is the same as c on $f(P)$. A similar sort of relation clearly holds for all conjugate transformations. One might say, very naïvely, that conjugate elements must be elements of the same 'kind', where the word 'kind' is left imprecise. (But it does not necessarily follow that elements of the same 'kind' are conjugate: see later.) For example, a and c are both rotations of 180°, but about different axes; the element $\tilde{f}$ (where we call f the auxiliary element) puts along the (a)-axis those points of the square which would otherwise have lain along the (c)-axis: the operation a then achieves the same result as operation c would have done, except, of course, that to achieve the same final position the operation $\tilde{f}$ must be undone, that is, $\tilde{\tilde{f}} = f$ must be applied. Hence one can easily see, from the diagram, that a is conjugate to c using as auxiliary operation any one of f, d, b, h (for each one of these maps the points of the square which lie along the (c)-axis onto the (a)-axis: more simply, these operations applied to the axes map the one into the other).

In a similar way, b and d plainly could be (and are) conjugate: again they are both rotations of 180°. The auxiliary operation here could evidently be a, for instance, but could not be g, for g does not map the points lying along the (d)-axis onto the (b)-axis.

On the other hand, a and b are also elements of the same 'kind', but the auxiliary operation required is a rotation of 45° or 135° or a reflection in the line bisecting either of the angles between the (a) and (b)-axis; no such operation exists in this group so that a and b are not conjugate.

We leave the reader to consider f, g and h, which certainly cannot be conjugate to a, b, c or d. Notice that g maps every one of the other axes into itself.

In considering the transformations of three dimensional space the same type of reasoning holds: for example, rotations of the same magnitude and sense about different axes will be conjugate if an operation exists in the group which would map one axis onto the other; on the other hand, a plane of reflection evidently cannot be conjugate to an axis of rotation, since they are of different 'kinds'. (In two dimensions an axis of reflection may be regarded as an axis of 180° rotation: the corresponding result fails in three dimensions.)

(It does not necessarily follow that if $g_1 \circ g \circ \tilde{g}_1 = g'$ then $g_1 \circ g' \circ \tilde{g}_1 = g$, i.e. that g and g' are mutually conjugate for the same auxiliary element g_1. The reader may discover the condition that this should be so.)

The symmetry groups and their conjugacy classes are of considerable importance in quantum mechanics and various chemical theories. There one is interested in what are known as *matrix representations* of the symmetry groups: in our terms a matrix representation of a symmetry group is a homomorphic image whose elements are matrices. An isomorphic image whose elements are matrices is called a *faithful representation*. One group can, of course, have many representations. A faithful representation of the group D_8 is the set of eight matrices given in Chapter 8, Exercise 4, page 122. Since this group of matrices, M_8 say, is isomorphic to D_8, the classes of conjugate elements of M_8 are the images of the classes of D_8; the same applies for other faithful representations of D_8 and, of course, for the faithful representations of any group. Another faithful representation of D_8 could be obtained by 'bordering' each 2×2 matrix $\begin{pmatrix} a & b \\ c & d \end{pmatrix}$ of M_8 obtaining $\begin{pmatrix} a & b & 0 \\ c & d & 0 \\ 0 & 0 & 1 \end{pmatrix}$.

In the application of this theory not all matrix representations are of interest: the so-called irreducible representations are the important ones. It is not our purpose to explain this specialized theory here (for those interested see, for instance, Cotton, *Chemical Applications of Group Theory* (Wiley) 1963), but we can prove one quite simple and elegant result requiring the following definition. The *character* (*trace, spur*) of a square matrix A is the sum of the elements in its leading diagonal.

We denote the character of A by the Greek letter chi $\chi(A)$. Now although matrices do not, in general, commute under multiplication, it is true that if

A and B are $n \times n$ matrices and $AB = C$ and $BA = D$, then the characters of C and D are equal, that is

$$\chi(C) = \chi(D) \qquad . \qquad . \qquad . \qquad . \qquad . \qquad (1)$$

We leave the reader to prove this in the 2×2 case, and more generally if he wishes. If, then, we have two matrices X and Y which belong to the same conjugacy class of a matrix representation of a group, there must be a third matrix Z, say, in the matrix group such that

$$X = ZY\tilde{Z}.$$

Consider $\chi(X) = \chi(ZY\tilde{Z}) = \chi([ZY]\tilde{Z}) = \chi(\tilde{Z}[ZY])$, by equation (1)
$$= \chi([\tilde{Z}Z]Y) = \chi(Y),$$

i.e. the characters of matrices representing conjugate elements of a group are the same. This is why in the so-called character tables of the symmetry groups, the elements can be grouped in *conjugacy classes*, i.e. equivalence classes of conjugate elements.

Referring back to our representation M_8 of D_8 we see that E, which has character 2, and H, which has character -2, must be in classes by themselves; E corresponds to e and H to g in D_8. All the other elements of M_8 have character zero; this shows, incidentally, that the converse of our result is not true; two matrices with the same character do not necessarily belong to the same class.

The reader might like to consider some examples of his own along lines similar to those used in this example. The symmetry group of an equilateral triangle (Chapter 7, page 103) is a group of order 6 and another much larger group is provided by the group of symmetries of the cube which is of order 48. (If one restricts oneself to three dimensions and will not turn the cube inside out the order reduces to 24.)

Example K. Lagrange's theorem states that for any finite group the order of a subgroup divides the order of the group. A similar result holds for conjugacy classes as defined in the last example: the number of elements in a class of conjugate elements divides the order of the group.

We prove this by considering a given element g of a group G. Now, it is clear that if $n \in G$ commutes with g then $n \circ g \circ \tilde{n} = g$ and so produces no new element. Let N be the subset of G of all those elements which commute with g, then N is a subgroup, for

  (i) N contains e_G and the operation in N is associative;

  (ii) N is closed, for if $n_1, n_2 \in N$ then

$$[n_1 \circ n_2] \circ g = n_1 \circ g \circ n_2 = g \circ [n_1 \circ n_2];$$

  (iii) if $n_1 \in N$ then $n_1 \circ g = g \circ n_1$ and hence pre- and post-multiplying by $\tilde{n}_1$ we have $g \circ \tilde{n}_1 = \tilde{n}_1 \circ g$.

Therefore, the order h_N of N divides the order h_G of G. Now consider the decomposition of G into left-cosets of N and let $g_1 N$ be any such coset, then if $n \in N$ we have

$$[g_1 \circ n] \circ g \circ [\tilde{n} \circ \tilde{g}_1] = g_1 \circ g \circ \tilde{g}_1 = g', \text{ say,}$$

and we see that every element of g_1N gives the same element g' conjugate to g. But if g_2N is distinct from g_1N, do the elements of g_2N give an element g'' conjugate to g and $g'' \neq g'$ (i.e. do two distinct cosets give different conjugates for g)? Suppose that

$$g_2 \circ g \circ \tilde{g}_2 = g_1 \circ g \circ \tilde{g}_1,$$

then, premultiplying by $\tilde{g}_1$ and postmultiplying by g_2, we have

$$[\tilde{g}_1 \circ g_2] \circ g = g \circ [\tilde{g}_1 \circ g_2],$$

i.e. $\tilde{g}_1 \circ g_2 \in N$, therefore $g_2 = g_1 \circ n$ for some $n \in N$. Thus g_1N and g_2N cannot be distinct. Hence there are as many elements conjugate to g as there are distinct cosets; but the number of distinct cosets is h_G/h_N which proves our stated result that the number of elements in a conjugacy class decides the order of the group.

In our decomposition of D_8 into conjugacy classes we had classes of 1 and of 2 elements: we had no classes with 4 elements, i.e. not every factor of the order of the group need be represented, the extreme case being an Abelian group in which every element is conjugate to itself only, whatever the order of the group.

Equally, of course, there need not be a subgroup corresponding to every factor of the order of the group.

The following two examples are in the form of references or brief indications for the reader who would like to pursue certain topics further.

Example L. An interesting application of the concept of cosets, etc., to coding and circuitry can be found in the second chapter of *Some Lessons in Mathematics*, ed. Fletcher (C.U.P.), 1964.

Example M. We have nowhere in this book mentioned groups of permutations, and although a first mention is certainly appropriate in the isomorphisms chapter, we indicate the theory here because some of the points to be made are only now meaningful.

Consider a set of n objects in some order and give the objects labels 1, 2, ..., n in that order. Any rearrangement of the objects is called a *permutation*; we describe the permutation by the corresponding rearrangement of 1, 2, ... n. If the new arrangement is say, $x_1, x_2, \ldots, x_n$ then we denote the permutation by

$$\begin{pmatrix} 1 & 2 & \ldots & n \\ x_1 & x_2 & \ldots & x_n \end{pmatrix}$$

For example, all the permutations of three objects are represented by

$$\begin{pmatrix} 1 & 2 & 3 \\ 1 & 2 & 3 \end{pmatrix}, \begin{pmatrix} 1 & 2 & 3 \\ 3 & 1 & 2 \end{pmatrix}, \begin{pmatrix} 1 & 2 & 3 \\ 2 & 3 & 1 \end{pmatrix}, \begin{pmatrix} 1 & 2 & 3 \\ 2 & 1 & 3 \end{pmatrix}, \begin{pmatrix} 1 & 2 & 3 \\ 3 & 2 & 1 \end{pmatrix}, \begin{pmatrix} 1 & 2 & 3 \\ 1 & 3 & 2 \end{pmatrix}.$$

The number of permutations of n objects is $n!$.

We can combine permutations: e.g.

$$\begin{pmatrix} 1 & 2 & 3 \\ 3 & 2 & 1 \end{pmatrix} \circ \begin{pmatrix} 1 & 2 & 3 \\ 2 & 3 & 1 \end{pmatrix} = \begin{pmatrix} 1 & 2 & 3 \\ 2 & 1 & 3 \end{pmatrix}$$

i.e. $1 \rightarrow 2 \rightarrow 2$, 1 goes to 2 in the first permutation (reading from the right as usual) and 2 goes to 2 in the second permutation, thus 1 goes to 2 in the combination; etc. We can, of course, write a permutation in a number of equivalent ways, e.g.

$$\begin{pmatrix} 1 & 2 & 3 \\ 3 & 2 & 1 \end{pmatrix} = \begin{pmatrix} 3 & 1 & 2 \\ 1 & 3 & 2 \end{pmatrix} = \ldots,$$

but it makes no difference to the resulting rearrangement of any objects to which the permutation is applied. Thus an alternative way of combining two permutations would be to write

$$\begin{pmatrix} 1 & 2 & 3 \\ 3 & 2 & 1 \end{pmatrix} \circ \begin{pmatrix} 1 & 2 & 3 \\ 2 & 3 & 1 \end{pmatrix} = \begin{pmatrix} 2 & 3 & 1 \\ 2 & 1 & 3 \end{pmatrix} \circ \begin{pmatrix} 1 & 2 & 3 \\ 2 & 3 & 1 \end{pmatrix} = \begin{pmatrix} 1 & 2 & 3 \\ 2 & 1 & 3 \end{pmatrix}$$

i.e. to rearrange the order of the columns in the left-hand bracket so that the top row of that bracket is the same as the bottom row in the right-hand bracket, then whatever the way in which the permutations are written the result of the combination is

$$\begin{pmatrix} \text{top row in right-hand bracket} \\ \text{bottom row in left-hand bracket} \end{pmatrix}.$$

This method of performing the combination of two permutations has advantages in theoretical work, for instance, in proving that combination is associative and in proving Cayley's theorem (see below).

It can be proved that the set of $n!$ permutations of n things forms a group with this law of combination. In the first place the reader might like to show this for the set of 6 permutations above. Is the group so obtained Abelian? To which of the two abstract groups of order 6 is this group isomorphic? (The proof of the general result can be found in Ledermann; *The Theory of Finite Groups* (Oliver and Boyd), as can many of the other results mentioned here without proof.) The complete group of permutations of n elements (of order $n!$) is called the *symmetric group of degree n* and denoted by P_n.

Now let G be any finite group with elements $g_1, g_2, \ldots, g_r$ and let g be any one of these elements and consider the correspondence

$$g \rightarrow \begin{pmatrix} g_1 & g_2 & \ldots & g_r \\ g \circ g_1 & g \circ g_2 & \ldots & g \circ g_r \end{pmatrix}$$

Certainly all the $g \circ g_i$ are distinct and therefore, as g runs through all elements in G, we have a mapping of the group G onto a set of permutations. This can be shown to be an isomorphism and then we have the celebrated theorem of Cayley: *Cayley's Theorem*: Any finite group G of order h is isomorphic to a group of permutations which is a subgroup of P_h.

So we have another type of representation for a group: in Example J we saw how some groups can be represented by multiplicative groups of matrices and now Cayley's theorem shows that every group can be represented by a group of permutations.

Consider the example of the group of order 4 whose combination table is

o	b_1	b_2	b_3	b_4
b_1	b_1	b_2	b_3	b_4
b_2	b_2	b_1	b_4	b_3
b_3	b_3	b_4	b_1	b_2
b_4	b_4	b_3	b_2	b_1

Then b_1, which is the identity element, corresponds to the identity permutation $\begin{pmatrix} 1 & 2 & 3 & 4 \\ 1 & 2 & 3 & 4 \end{pmatrix}$. Consider b_2:

$$\begin{pmatrix} b_1 & b_2 & b_3 & b_4 \\ b_2 \circ b_1 & b_2 \circ b_2 & b_2 \circ b_3 & b_2 \circ b_4 \end{pmatrix} = \begin{pmatrix} b_1 & b_2 & b_3 & b_4 \\ b_2 & b_1 & b_4 & b_3 \end{pmatrix}.$$

Therefore, b_2 corresponds to the permutation $\begin{pmatrix} 1 & 2 & 3 & 4 \\ 2 & 1 & 4 & 3 \end{pmatrix}$, etc. The group of permutations is a subgroup of the symmetric group P_4 of order 24.

It should be fairly evident that just as the matrix representation of a group is not unique so the representation of a group as a subgroup of P_n for some particular n is not unique. For instance, if we consider the group D_8 and apply the method of the foregoing example, then we get a representation which is a subgroup of P_8. On the other hand, we can regard the symmetry operations as permutations of the vertices of the square and obtain a representation which is a subgroup of P_4.

We can divide permutations into two classes called, for a reason which will become evident, even and odd. We consider a particular case: let P denote the polynomial

$$[x_1 - x_2][x_1 - x_3][x_2 - x_3] \text{ for any fixed unequal } x_1, x_2, x_3$$

and consider the effect of permuting the subscripts. The set of all permutations is, of course, P_3: any one permutation of the subscripts has the effect of either changing the sign of P or not. Separate P_3 into two classes:

(i) *even permutations* which do not change the sign of P,

(ii) *odd permutations* which change the sign of P.

Then the even permutations are

$$\begin{pmatrix} 1 & 2 & 3 \\ 1 & 2 & 3 \end{pmatrix}, \begin{pmatrix} 1 & 2 & 3 \\ 3 & 1 & 2 \end{pmatrix} \text{ and } \begin{pmatrix} 1 & 2 & 3 \\ 2 & 3 & 1 \end{pmatrix}$$

and the odd permutations are

$$\begin{pmatrix} 1 & 2 & 3 \\ 2 & 1 & 3 \end{pmatrix}, \begin{pmatrix} 1 & 2 & 3 \\ 3 & 2 & 1 \end{pmatrix} \text{ and } \begin{pmatrix} 1 & 2 & 3 \\ 1 & 3 & 2 \end{pmatrix}.$$

It is clear that if we consider the combination of two permutations then if both are even the result is even, if both are odd then the result is even, etc. It follows that the mapping of an even permutation onto $+1$ and an odd permutation onto -1 is a homomorphism of the group P_3 onto the multiplicative group with elements $(+1, -1)$ (or the additive group of elements 0, 1 modulo 2 —hence, perhaps, the names even and odd). The kernel of this homomorphism is the group A_3 of all the even permutations in P_3 which is, therefore, an invariant subgroup of P_3. A_3 is called the *alternating group* of degree 3.

In general we can divide P_n into odd and even permutations (the reader might like to consider ways of doing this which do not depend upon the change of sign of a polynomial) and the even permutations form an invariant subgroup A_n of order $\frac{1}{2}[n!]$, the alternating group of degree n.

Incidentally, we can give the definition of a *symmetric polynomial*. Polynomials like $x_1 + x_2 + x_3$ or $x_1^2 - 2x_1 x_2 + x_2^2$ are called symmetric because they are unaltered by any permutation of their subscripts, i.e. they are invariant under the appropriate symmetric groups. On the other hand, $x_1 - x_2 + x_3$ is not symmetric. In general a polynomial involving n subscripts is symmetric if it is invariant under the symmetric group P_n of permutation of the subscripts. But even if a polynomial is not symmetric one can find all those permutations of the subscripts under which the polynomial is invariant: this set forms a group, called the *group of the polynomial*. For instance, the group of $x_1 - x_2 + x_3$ is the pair

$$\begin{pmatrix} 1 & 2 & 3 \\ 1 & 2 & 3 \end{pmatrix} \text{ and } \begin{pmatrix} 1 & 2 & 3 \\ 3 & 2 & 1 \end{pmatrix}.$$

(Find the group of $x_1^2 + x_1 x_2 + x_2^2 + x_2 x_3 + x_3^2 + x_3 x_4 + x_4^2$.)

So far the results mentioned in this example have been fairly simple to prove and the reader would be well advised to try to prove them for himself without consulting texts, but the last result we give (there are, of course, many more significant results in this theory) is far from elementary and we do not suggest that the reader try to prove it without help. A group which possesses no invariant subgroups is called a *simple group*. The following theorem is due to Galois:

A_n is a simple group when $n > 4$. (It is this result which is used to prove that no general algebraic method exists for the solution of algebraic equations of degree greater than 4.) The reader might like to find an invariant subgroup of A_4.

* * * * *

We continue the topological note at the end of Chapter 10 by considering some examples.

Example N. Consider any point x on a sphere. Every closed curve at x can be continuously deformed to x, hence every closed path to x is homotopic to e_x. Therefore the fundamental group at x is $\{e_x\}$ for all points x on the sphere.

Example O. Consider any point x on the torus: there are three simple non-homotopic paths to x corresponding to the three curves a, b and c in the figure on page 197; denote the paths by e_x, f and g respectively. But these are

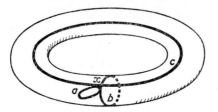

not the only non-homotopic paths: $f^2 = f \circ f, f^3, f^4, \ldots$ are all non-homo-topic: similarly $g^2, g^3, \ldots$ are all non-homotopic. The fundamental group P'_x has generators $\{f\}$ and $\{g\}$: it would seem, however, that possibly

$$\{f\} \circ \{g\} = \{g\} \circ \{f\}.$$

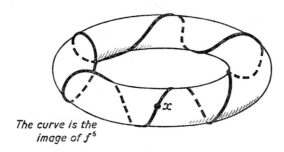

*The curve is the
image of f^5*

This is in fact the case although not very easy to see: intuitively, one must try to deform the curve corresponding to $f \circ g$ into the curve corresponding to $g \circ f$, i.e. the combination of the curve b with c into the combination of c with b, remembering that there is a definite sense in which these curves are traversed. One really requires more general methods: this once again brings us up against the difficulty in topology, the paucity of elementary examples which have a relatively simple solution. Mathematically, integration theory is probably harder than elementary topology, but one can give a great number of examples.

Example P. What is the fundamental group at any point of the curved surface of a cylinder?

In the above examples the fundamental group is the same abstract group at any point of the space. It is obvious, however, that this need not always be the case: for instance, we could take as our topological space the union of the surface of a sphere and the surface of a torus (see Chapter 6, page 95). We are led, there-fore, to ask the following question: under what circumstances is the fundamental group at a point x of a topological space $(X, T : X)$ isomorphic to the fundamental group at $x' \in X$? Consider the intuitive situation in terms of curves. If there is a curve from x' to x (b in the diagram) then any closed curve at x' (a in the diagram) can be made into a closed curve at x by simply traversing the joining curve (b) twice. Thus, in the figure, we would go from x to x' along b, nip smartly round a and come back along b. In exactly the same way any closed curve at x can be made into a closed curve at x'. It would seem that we have here a sufficient condition to answer our question. (It is clearly not a necessary

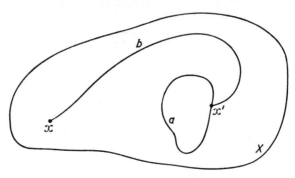

condition; consider the space consisting of the union of two disjoint spheres.) We define a space $(X, T: X)$ to be *path-connected*, if for any two points $x, x' \in X$ there exists a path* f such that $f(0) = x, f(1) = x'$. After the next example, we shall try to prove that in a path-connected space the fundamental groups at any two points are isomorphic. The reader is asked to bear the intuitive discussion in mind.

Example Q. In any topological space $(X, T: X)$ we can say that any point x is related to any point x' if there exists a path f such that $f(0) = x$ and $f(1) = x'$. Show that this relation is an equivalence relation. (In fact, all the results necessary for this occur as trivial details buried in the technicalities of the note at the end of the previous chapter.) It follows that in any path-connected space the whole space is the only equivalence class. It also follows that we can modify our definition of a path-connected space: we need merely require that for any fixed point x_0 and all other points x there exist paths f such that $f(0) = x_0$ and $f(1) = x$.

Let x and x' be any two points in the path-connected space $(X, T: X)$ and let p be a path such that $p(0) = x$ and $p(1) = x'$.

*(Remember that a path is a continuous many-one mapping of $(R_1, T: R_1)$ into $X, T: X$).

Denote by p_1 the path defined by

$$p_1(s) = p(1 - s).$$

Then if $f \in P_x$ (the set of closed paths to x), $p \circ [f \circ p_1] \in P_{x'}$. If we consider the mapping k of P'_x to $P'_{x'}$ defined by

$$k : \{f\} \longrightarrow \{p \circ [f \circ p_1]\}$$

we are immediately in difficulties: we do not even know whether it is justifiable to remove the square brackets: we have not dealt, in general, with anything but the homotopy of closed paths. In fact, however, we need not have imposed this restriction (that the paths be closed) in many of the cases at the end of the last chapter (the exceptions being where combination would otherwise have been undefined) had we not wanted to construct a group. In our attempt to prove that P'_x is isomorphic to $P'_{x'}$ we shall need a number of results about the homotopy of paths with fixed end points (i.e. homotopy relative to x and x'): these results can be obtained with but trivial modifications from those of the previous chapter. We shall leave the details to the reader, indicating by asterisks where the gaps occur.

The mapping k is

$$k : \{f\} \longrightarrow \{p \circ [f \circ p_1]\} = \{p \circ f \circ p_1\}^* = \{p\} \circ \{f\} \circ \{p_1\}^*.$$

In the first place we require that k should not depend on the choice of f, i.e. if $\{f\} = \{g\}$ then we wish to show that

$$\{p\} \circ \{f\} \circ \{p_1\} = \{p\} \circ \{g\} \circ \{p_1\}.$$

Let g_1 be defined for g like p_1 for p above, then consider

$$[\{p\} \circ \{f\} \circ \{p_1\}] \circ [\{p\} \circ \{g_1\} \circ \{p_1\}]$$

$= \{p\} \circ \{f\} \circ \{e_x\} \circ \{g_1\} \circ \{p_1\}$	since $\{p_1\} \circ \{p\} = \{e_x\}^*$,
$= \{p\} \circ \{f\} \circ \{g_1\} \circ \{p_1\}$	since $\{f\} \circ \{e_x\} = \{f\}$,
$= \{p\} \circ \{p_1\}$	since $\{g_1\} = \{f_1\}$,
$= \{e_{x'}\}$	since $\{p\} \circ \{p_1\} = \{e_{x'}\}^*$.

Finally, since $\{p\} \circ \{g_1\} \circ \{p_1\}$ is the inverse of $\{p\} \circ \{g\} \circ \{p_1\}$ we have our result.

Now the rest is quickly disposed of. k is certainly an onto mapping as our intuitive discussion in terms of curves has shown. Further, for any f and g,

$$\begin{aligned} k(\{f\}) \circ k(\{g\}) &= \{p\} \circ \{f\} \circ \{p_1\} \circ \{p\} \circ \{g\} \circ \{p_1\} \\ &= \{p\} \circ \{f\} \circ \{g\} \circ \{p_1\} \\ &= \{p\} \circ \{f \circ g\} \circ \{p_1\} \\ &= k(\{f \circ g\}) \end{aligned}$$

and so k is a homomorphism. The kernel of the homomorphism is the set of all those elements of P'_x which map onto $\{e_{x'}\}$: but if

$$k(\{f\}) = \{p\} \text{ o } \{f\} \text{ o } \{p_1\} = \{e_{x'}\}$$

then $\{f\} = \{p_1\} \text{ o } \{e_{x'}\} \text{ o } \{p\}$ and $\{p_1\} \text{ o } \{e_{x'}\} = \{p_1\}^*$, therefore

$$\{f\} = \{p_1\} \text{ o } \{p\} = \{e_x\}.$$

Thus the kernel contains the identity element only and the homomorphism is an isomorphism. (Note that the last result with an asterisk was in fact proved at the end of the previous chapter before we confined ourselves to closed paths.)

These proofs tend to become very technical and tedious to read: the only amusement to be gained is to construct them oneself, slowly building up the details from the intuitive picture of the corresponding curves. For this reason we shall leave our last important result to the reader as an example with hints.

Example R. If f is a many-one continuous mapping of a topological space $(A, T: A)$ into a topological space $(B, T: B)$, then a closed path to a point $a \in A$ can be mapped into a closed path to the point $f(a) \in B$: i.e. if $p \in P_a$, then $f \square p \in P_{f(a)}$.*

(i) Show that if $p' \sim p$, $p' \in P_a$, then $f \square p' \sim f \square p$. (Hint: if F is a homotopy function for $p' \sim p$, consider $f \square F$.)

(ii) From (i) it follows that we can define a mapping k of P'_a into $P'_{f(a)}$ by

$$k: \{p\} \longrightarrow \{f \square p\}.$$

Show that this mapping is a homomorphic mapping, but note that it is into and not onto. (Hint: if p and $q \in P_a$ then, in fact, $f \square [p \text{ o } q] = [f \square p] \text{ o } [f \square q]$.)

(iii) Show that if f is a homeomorphism then k is onto.

(iv) If f is a homeomorphism, its inverse $\tilde{f}$ is a continuous one-one mapping of $(B, T: B)$ onto $(A, T: A)$ and defines a homomorphism k_1 of $P'_{f(a)}$ onto P'_a given by

$$k_1: \{h\} \longrightarrow \{\tilde{f} \square h\} \qquad h \in P'_{f(a)}.$$

Show that $k_1 \square k$ is the identity mapping of P'_a onto itself, and hence that P'_a is isomorphic to $P'_{f(a)}$.

We append an example on braids (cf. end of Chapter 7, Section (d), p. 118).

Example S. Show that the braids of order n in which A_i is joined to B_i, for all i, form an invariant subgroup of the group of all braids of order n. Consider the group of braids of order 2: describe the factor group derived from the above invariant subgroup.

* We have used $\square$ to denote the combination of the two functions f and p because this is different from the combination of paths. Here we mean the successive application, when we combine paths we do not. In particular the combination of functions under $\square$ is associative, a fact to be used in (iii) and (iv).

CHAPTER 12

GEOMETRY

We tried to express at the end of Chapter 6 the fact that topology is the study of the 'invariants' of topological spaces under the group of transformations whose elements are one-one bi-continuous mappings and whose combination is successive application. It is precisely this approach, the study of invariants under a particular group, which is favoured in geometry today. The first person to make this explicit was Felix Klein in his celebrated 'Erlanger Programm' in 1872. Consequently geometry has become a systematic study at the heart of mathematics and provides interesting applications and illustrations of group theory.

It is impossible in one short chapter to hope to give a systematic study of geometric theories; what we shall attempt to do is illustrate the approach. We can do this in two ways: we can either begin with a geometrical object and find a group of transformations which leave it invariant or we can reverse the order and begin with a given group and discover some of the geometric objects it leaves invariant. We have already given examples of the first type of investigation: the group D_8 of symmetries of the square maps the square into itself, but this is not the only group which has this property. We could chop the square up and rearrange the pieces, or shrink bits of it and stretch other bits to fill the holes, etc., assuming that we can always reverse the process and satisfy the other group conditions. Clearly what we must decide is what we wish to admit as a transformation in any particular case. As far as the symmetry groups, as they are usually called, are concerned, we shall make this precise (see page 205).

This suggests that our second method of investigation would be more reasonable, and we propose to adopt this as the easier alternative. So we shall summarize our view of geometry as the study of the properties of certain spaces which are invariant under chosen groups of transformations: the transformations will always be one-one mappings of the space to itself.

For the time being we will consider transformations of the plane. We have already mentioned rotations and reflections, so let us begin with these. If a particular transformation maps a point P to a point P', then we say that P is an invariant point of that transformation if $P = P'$ (not to be confused with the invariants spoken of above: P would only be an invariant in that sense if $P = P'$ for all transformations of the group: for example, the set of all rotations about a fixed point O form a group* and O is a group invariant). So we see that a significant distinction between a rotation about a point in the plane and a reflection in a line in the plane is that a rotation has only one invariant point, the centre of rotation, whereas a reflection has a line of invariant points, the axis of the reflection. (A translation has no invariant points.) There is, of course, the exceptional case of the identity transformation: all points of the plane are invariant under this transformation.

The set of all rotations about a point P form a group. If R is any other point in the plane then there is a transformation in the group which transforms R into any chosen point R' which lies on the circle of radius PR and centre P. Therefore, if we are looking for invariant figures under this group, we see that they can only be the set of concentric circles centre P. If ϕ is any angle, where

$$\phi = \frac{p\pi}{q} \text{ radians for integral } p \text{ and } q, \text{ then the set of all rotations}$$

through multiples of ϕ forms a group and this group not only leaves the circles centre P invariant but also a set of regular polygons centre P. Thus if $\phi = 100°$, any regular polygon centre P with 18 or a multiple of 18 vertices is invariant.

Reflection in a given line l together with the identity transformation form a group since a reflection in l, followed by a reflection in l, gets you back to where you started. A figure will be invariant under this group if for each point A of the figure distant d from l there is another point A' of the figure such that AA' is perpendicular to l and A' is also distant d from l. Thus examples of invariant figures are shown on the opposite page.

The type of problem we have been considering is really rather special. In the first place the groups have been relatively simple and we have only considered which geometric figures remain invariant, rather than more general geometric concepts, i.e. we have regarded our transformations from the point of view of symmetry

---

* Rotations about a point in the plane form a group, regarded as rotations; however, regarded as transformations of the plane they form a group under combination modulo 2π. In this chapter all combinations of rotations are to be understood as modulo 2π.

BCDEHIKOX

⊲⊢⊢⊣⊢Σ○⊢⊃>≷×≻

invariant figures

operations. It should be made clear that by *invariant* one can mean one of two things:

(i) that a geometric figure is mapped onto itself; this is invariance in the sense we have been using it, e.g. square A is mapped onto square A; or

(ii) that a geometric property is preserved under the group of transformations, e.g. the property of being square, i.e. squares are mapped into squares but square A may be mapped onto square B.

It is invariance in the second sense which we shall now be considering.

Does the set of all rotations about all points in the plane form a group? The only point which may be in some doubt is whether the combination of two rotations is another rotation. If the two rotations are about the same point there is nothing to prove, so suppose that the centres of rotation are distinct, then it is easy to convince oneself by taking a special case that the result is not always a rotation. For instance, let O and O' be the two centres of rotation and AB be any line segment as shown. If we rotate AB

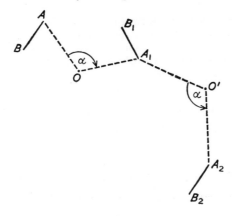

about O through an angle α clockwise and then about O' through an angle α anticlockwise, the final position A_2B_2 of AB is parallel to AB and in the same sense, and so there can be no centre of rotation. In fact, the general result is that the combination of rotations in the same sense (i.e. both clockwise or both anticlockwise about their respective centres) through angles ϕ and ϕ' about centres O and O' is a rotation if $\phi + \phi' \neq 2\pi$, and a translation (as in our example, α clockwise $= 2\pi - \alpha$ anticlockwise) if $\phi + \phi' = 2\pi$.

Example A. Prove this result. (Hint: show first that the combination of two reflections in lines l_1, l_2 intersecting at a point P is a rotation with centre P through twice the angle between l_1 and l_2, the sense depending on the order in which the reflections are performed. Then decompose each of the two rotations ϕ and ϕ' into two reflections, using the line of centres OO' as one of the reflecting lines in each case.)

So in order to obtain a group we must (at least) add to the rotations the translations. Do we now have a group? The answer is yes, because we can now prove that the combination of a rotation and a translation is a rotation and the combination of two translations is a translation. This group is called the *group of displacements*. A very significant invariant is distance: to any pair of points A and B we can associate a real positive number which is the distance between the points, or alternatively, if p denotes the set of all points in the plane, then distance is a mapping of $p \triangledown p$ onto the non-negative real numbers (see Example D). Any transformation which leaves distance invariant is called an *isometry*: the group of displacements is often called the group of *direct isometries*.

Example B. Prove that the combination of a rotation and a translation (and a translation with a rotation) is a rotation. (Hint: using the result of the previous example, express the translation as two rotations. Alternatively one can express the rotation as two reflections in intersecting lines, as above, and the translation as two reflections in a pair of parallel lines. In either case, by careful choice of the reflection lines the result is elegantly proved.)

Example C. The set of all translations form an Abelian group.

Example D. Denote the distance mapping of $p \triangledown p$ onto the non-negative reals by d and write
$$d:(P, P') \longrightarrow d(PP'), \qquad P, P' \in p.$$
Then d has the following characteristic properties:

(i) $d(PP') = 0$ if and only if P is the same point as P',

(ii) $d(PP') + d(P'P'') \geqslant d(PP'')$, for any points P, P', $P'' \in p$,

(iii) $d(PP') = d(P'P)$.

If S is any set and d is a many-one mapping of $S \bigtriangledown S$ into the non-negative reals with the properties (i) to (iii), then d is said to be a *metric* for S. (In fact (iii) can be proved from (i) and (ii) by choosing suitable points.) Are the following mappings metrics?

(a) S is the set V of (free) vectors and d maps any element $(v, v_1) \in V \bigtriangledown V$ onto the inner product $v.v_1$ (see Chapter 3, page 50).

(b) S is the set F of integrable real-valued functions in an interval (a, b) and d maps any element $(f, f_1) \in F \bigtriangledown F$ onto

$$\int_a^b [f(x) - f_1(x)]^2 \, dx.$$

(c) S is any set and d maps any element $(s, s') \in S \bigtriangledown S$ onto 0 if $s = s'$ and onto 1 if $s \neq s'$.

The word 'direct' in direct isometries has the following significance. To any three points we can give a definite sense (usually indicated by the alphabetical order of the letters which are their names): thus the two congruent triangles in the figure have opposite senses. The sense is described by the arrow,

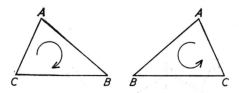

i.e. we walk from A to B to C to A in the first triangle and describe the boundary in a clockwise movement, whereas in the second triangle we walk from A to B to C to A and describe the boundary in an anticlockwise movement. Now both rotations and translations preserve sense, hence the name direct isometries.

Another isometry which we have mentioned is reflection: this is an *indirect isometry*. Thus, whereas neither a rotation about a point in the plane nor a translation can bring the first triangle into coincidence with the second as drawn above, a reflection can. We develop some more results in isometric geometry in the following exercises.

NOTE: We can now eliminate the vagueness on the first page of this chapter. The allowable transformations of the square are to be isometries: in general the symmetry group of a figure is a subgroup of the group of all isometries of the plane.

Exercises

1. There are three possibilities for combining reflections in axes in the plane:

(i) when both axes are in the same line the combination is the identity;

(ii) when the axes are parallel lines l_1 and l_2 the result is a translation through twice the distance between the lines and in a direction perpendicular to them;

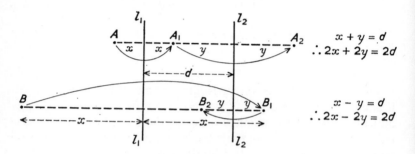

$$x + y = d$$
$$\therefore 2x + 2y = 2d$$

$$x - y = d$$
$$\therefore 2x - 2y = 2d$$

(iii) when the reflections are in axes l_1 and l_2 inclined at an angle α and intersecting at a point O the result is a rotation about O through an angle 2α (or $2\pi - 2\alpha$, depending upon the order of combination).

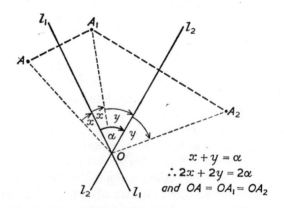

$$x + y = \alpha$$
$$\therefore 2x + 2y = 2\alpha$$
$$\text{and } OA = OA_1 = OA_2$$

(Observe that the combination of reflections is not commutative.) Thus, as remarked in the examples above, we have the following decompositions:

(i) a rotation into two reflections (notice that the combination of two indirect isometries is a direct isometry);

(ii) a translation into two reflections or two rotations.

Using these decompositions many results can be elegantly proved. For instance, investigate the combination of three reflections in the four possible cases (a) lines are parallel, (b) lines intersect in pairs in three points, (c) lines intersect in one point and (d) two lines are parallel and the third intersects them.

2. Are there any more isometries of the plane? The answer to this can be given in two stages:

(i) any two congruent triangles are related by a unique isometry;

(ii) every isometry can be decomposed into at most three reflections.

The first result is based on the fact that any fourth point is entirely determined by its distances from the three points of a given triangle. Thus, if each of two isometries maps A, B and C onto A_1, B_1 and C_1 then any further point D must be so mapped that DA, DB and DC are preserved in length and are mapped onto D_1A_1, D_1B_1, D_1C_1, and there is only one point D_1 which satisfies this condition. This result can either be demonstrated intuitively (which is the way we prefer to regard geometry) or it can be proved from a proper set of axioms (not Euclid's!) (see, for instance, Coxeter*).

To prove the second result we use the first which shows that we need only consider the mappings of congruent triangles, and divide the proof (following Coxeter) into four parts, indicating the reflections necessary to bring ABC into coincidence with $A'B'C'$. (1) When the triangles ABC, $A_1B_1C_1$ coincide we have the identity transformation which (see Exercise 1) can be regarded as a double reflection. Cases (2), (3) and (4) are illustrated in the following diagrams, where each is reduced to a predecessor by a reflection in the line l, where l, in each diagram, is the perpendicular bisector of AA_1.

This result shows that we can get all our isometries by combining reflections and that at most three (case 4(b)) reflections are required. Hence there are no new isometries. Furthermore, as we have seen, rotations and translations can be decomposed into reflections.

3. A reflection is an indirect isometry: rotations and translations are direct isometries. Show that (see also Example B on page 204) the combination of two direct isometries is direct, the combination of a direct and indirect isometry is indirect, and the combination of two indirect isometries is direct. Hence show that the mapping

$$\text{rotations and translations} \longrightarrow +1$$
$$\text{reflections} \longrightarrow -1$$

is a homomorphism of the group of isometries onto the multiplicative group with elements $(+1, -1)$. What is the kernel?

An alternative approach is to show that the direct isometries form a normal†

---

* The references are given in a bibliography on page 225.

† We use the word 'normal' instead of 'invariant' in this chapter to avoid confusion with geometrical invariants.

subgroup of the group of all isometries. To do this one must prove that given a reflection R, then for any direct isometry D we must have

$$R \circ D = D_1 \circ R$$

where D_1 is another direct isometry. We can then realize the factor group. Note: the identity is a direct isometry.

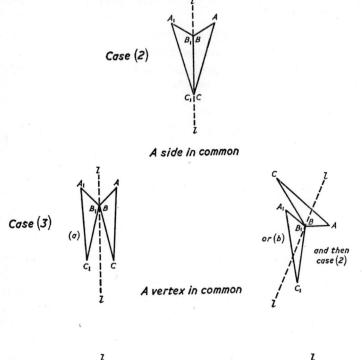

A side in common

A vertex in common

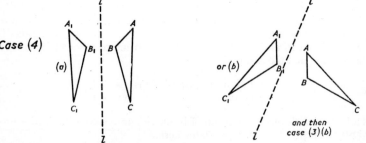

The next two exercises give some interesting applications of this geometric theory: many more can be found in Yaglom.

4. Problem: Small objects in mass production pass through each of two machines. During the process in the first machine the objects travel around a

circle centre O_1 of radius 9 feet. During the process in the second machine the objects travel around a circle centre O_2 of radius 11 feet. O_1 is 30 feet in a direction N.20°E. from O_2. The two circular tracks are to be joined by a straight conveyor belt running precisely North to South and exactly 15 feet long. Draw a plan of the two circles and construct, exactly, the two possible positions of the conveyor belt. (A diagram has not been given, in order to avoid giving the game away to those who prefer to attempt the construction by traditional methods.)

Solution: Translate the circle centre O_1 through 15 feet due South. Let it now cut the circle centre O_2 in A and B. A and B lie on the circle centre O_2; but they have undergone a translation 15 feet due South from the original circle centre O_1: since translations form a group, the inverse of this translation exists and restores A and B to the original circle centre O_1. Let A' be the image of A and B' the image of B under a translation 15 feet due North. Then A' and B' are on the circle centre O_1, A and B are on the circle centre O_2, $A'A = B'B$ = 15 feet and $A'A$ and $B'B$ are both in the direction North to South. Hence $A'A$ and $B'B$ represent the two possible positions of the conveyor belt.

(If one alters the centres or radii of the two circles, are there always two solutions?)

5. If $ABCD$ is a quadrilateral and O_1 is a point outside it so that the angle $AO_1B = 40°$ and $AO_1 = BO_1$ then we call O_1 the 40° node of AB.

Problem: Plot the points $O_1(45, 5)$, $O_2(55, 40)$, $O_3(18, 57)$, $O_4(1,22)$. Construct the quadrilateral $ABCD$ such that O_1 is the 90° node of AB, O_2 is the 90° node of BC, O_3 is the 60° node of CD and O_4 is the 60° node of DA.

Solution: Take an arbitrary point X. Rotate it through 90° about O_1 to X_1, rotate X_1 through 90° about O_2 to X_2, rotate X_2 through 60° about O_3 to X_3, rotate X_3 through 60° about O_4 to X_4. (The rotations to be in the appropriate senses.) Now imagine that the vertex A had been known, and that the line-segment AX had undergone the four rotations. Plainly, as X goes to X_4, A goes back to A via B, C and D. But under rotation the length of line-segments is invariant. Therefore $AX = AX_4$. Hence A lies on the perpendicular bisector of XX_4. Draw this bisector and let it be PQ. Repeat the procedure for another arbitrary point Y and draw RS, the perpendicular bisector of YY_4. Then A is given by the intersection of PQ with RS. B, C and D may then be obtained by rotating A about O_1, O_2 and O_3 in succession. (A, B, C and D are (20, 5), (45, 30), (45, 50) and (25, 30) approximately.)

6. Let us introduce a coordinate system into our plane with fixed origin O. (Note that we are interested in the transformation of points of the plane and not in changing our coordinate system.) Then let (x, y) be the coordinates of a point P and (x', y') be the coordinates of the point P' into which P is transformed by an isometry.

(i) A translation is completely specified by giving the coordinates of the point onto which the origin is transformed. Suppose O is mapped onto O' with coordinates (a, b), then

$$\begin{pmatrix} x' \\ y' \end{pmatrix} = \begin{pmatrix} x \\ y \end{pmatrix} + \begin{pmatrix} a \\ b \end{pmatrix}$$

(ii) A rotation about the origin was discussed in Chapter 8, Exercise 7, page 125. If the rotation is through an angle θ, then

$$\begin{pmatrix} x' \\ y' \end{pmatrix} = \begin{pmatrix} \cos\theta & -\sin\theta \\ \sin\theta & \cos\theta \end{pmatrix}\begin{pmatrix} x \\ y \end{pmatrix}.$$

If the rotation is not about the origin, then we may first translate the origin to the centre of rotation,* then perform the rotation, and then translate back to the original position of the origin, so that in general we have

$$\begin{pmatrix} x' \\ y' \end{pmatrix} = \begin{pmatrix} \cos\theta & -\sin\theta \\ \sin\theta & \cos\theta \end{pmatrix}\left[\begin{pmatrix} x \\ y \end{pmatrix} - \begin{pmatrix} a \\ b \end{pmatrix}\right] + \begin{pmatrix} a \\ b \end{pmatrix},$$

where (a, b) is the centre of rotation.

(iii) We also discussed a reflection in a line passing through the origin in the same exercise. If the line makes an angle θ with the x-axis then

$$\begin{pmatrix} x' \\ y' \end{pmatrix} = \begin{pmatrix} \cos 2\theta & \sin 2\theta \\ \sin 2\theta & -\cos 2\theta \end{pmatrix}\begin{pmatrix} x \\ y \end{pmatrix}.$$

If the line does not pass through the origin we can first translate the origin to some point (a, b) on the line and then perform the reflection and translate back. Thus if the line makes an angle θ with the x-axis, we have

$$\begin{pmatrix} x' \\ y' \end{pmatrix} = \begin{pmatrix} \cos 2\theta & \sin 2\theta \\ \sin 2\theta & -\cos 2\theta \end{pmatrix}\left[\begin{pmatrix} x \\ y \end{pmatrix} - \begin{pmatrix} a \\ b \end{pmatrix}\right] + \begin{pmatrix} a \\ b \end{pmatrix}.$$

We notice that all three cases may be summarized in the equation

$$\begin{pmatrix} x' \\ y' \end{pmatrix} = T\begin{pmatrix} x \\ y \end{pmatrix} + \begin{pmatrix} c \\ d \end{pmatrix},$$

since $\qquad -T\begin{pmatrix} a \\ b \end{pmatrix} + \begin{pmatrix} a \\ b \end{pmatrix} = \begin{pmatrix} c \\ d \end{pmatrix}$ for some c and d,

where $T \in O_2$, i.e. T is an orthogonal matrix. For a translation $T = I$, the unit matrix, for a rotation the determinant of T is $+1$ and for a reflection it is -1. Describe the isometry given by

$$\begin{pmatrix} x' \\ y' \end{pmatrix} = \begin{pmatrix} \frac{\sqrt{3}}{2} & \frac{1}{2} \\ \frac{1}{2} & -\frac{\sqrt{3}}{2} \end{pmatrix}\left[\begin{pmatrix} x \\ y \end{pmatrix} + \begin{pmatrix} 1 \\ 2 \end{pmatrix}\right].$$

We can, of course, prove many of the results in the foregoing exercises using a coordinate system, but here we shall examine a further property of isometries as a last example of this geometry.

The direct isometries are a normal subgroup of the group of all isometries, as we discovered in Exercise 3. Another obvious subgroup is the group of all

---

* We are here changing the coordinate system temporarily and leaving the points of the plane fixed. This is because our transformation matrices are linked to the coordinate system in a special way. When we have performed our transformation of the points of the plane we restore the coordinate system to its original position thus obtaining the coordinates of the transformed point in terms of those of the original point with respect to a fixed coordinate system.

translations. Is it normal? And if so what is the factor group? Writing

$\begin{pmatrix} x \\ y \end{pmatrix} = X$ and $\begin{pmatrix} c \\ d \end{pmatrix} = k$, the general isometric transformation is given by

$$X \to X_1 = TX + k, \qquad T \in O_2$$

and the translations are given by $X_1 = X + k$. Suppose that we follow the general isometry by another general isometry $X_1 \to X_2 = T_1 X_1 + k_1$, then the combination is given by

$$\begin{aligned} X \to X_2 &= T_1 [TX + k] + k_1 \\ &= [T_1 T] X + T_1 k + k_1 \end{aligned} \qquad . \qquad . \qquad . \quad (1)$$

If the second isometry is chosen to undo the first, i.e. is the inverse of the first, we must have $X_2 = X$ which implies

$$T_1 T = I \text{ and } T_1 k + k_1 = \begin{pmatrix} 0 \\ 0 \end{pmatrix},$$

i.e. $\qquad\qquad\qquad T_1 = \tilde{T} = T'$ (the transpose of T, since $T \in O_2$)

and $\qquad\qquad\qquad k_1 = -T_1 k = -T'k$.

Now if the translations are a normal subgroup we must have

$$i \circ t \circ \tilde{\imath} = t_1,$$

where i is any isometry and t, t_1 are translations: therefore, consider

$$\begin{aligned} [X_2 \to X_3 = T'X_2 - T'k] \circ [X_1 \to X_2 = X_1 + k_1] \circ [X \to X_1 = TX + k] \\ = [X_2 \to X_3] \circ [X_1 \to X_2 = TX + k + k_1] \\ = X_2 \to X_3 = T'[TX + k + k_1] - T'k \\ = X_2 \to X_3 = X + T'k_1 \end{aligned}$$

which is a translation. Therefore, the translations are a normal subgroup of the group of all isometries. It remains to realize the factor group. It can be deduced from the above working that every element in any one coset is of the form $X \to X_1 = TX + k$ for varying k and fixed T. Therefore, there is a one-one correspondence between the cosets and the matrices $T \in O_2$: this correspondence can be shown to be an isomorphism and hence the factor group can be realized as the group of all rotations about a point P and reflections in lines passing through P.

The reader might like to consider whether the group of rotations about a fixed point is a normal subgroup of the group of all isometries.

In Exercise 6 we saw that the group of isometries can be represented in terms of coordinates by the transformations

$$X \to X_1 = TX + k \qquad T \in O_2$$

We can use this form to generalize and obtain other geometries. If

$$X \to X_1 = AX + k \quad \text{and} \quad X_1 \to X_2 = BX_1 + k_1$$

are any two transformations, where A and B are 2×2 matrices and k and k_1 are 2×1 matrices, then their combination is

$$X \to X_2 = B[AX + k] + k_1 = [BA]X + Bk + k_1.$$

Thus any set of such transformations will be closed under this combination if A and B are chosen from a closed subset of the multiplicative set of all 2×2 matrices. Further, if the transformations are to form a group, each must have an inverse. The second transformation will be the inverse of the first if

$$BA = I \quad \text{and} \quad Bk + k_1 = \begin{pmatrix} 0 \\ 0 \end{pmatrix}.$$

From $BA = I$ we see that A and B must be *non-singular* (i.e. have multiplicative inverses) and we can always arrange k_1 to satisfy $Bk + k_1 = \begin{pmatrix} 0 \\ 0 \end{pmatrix}$ whatever B and k. It follows that *corresponding to any multiplicative subgroup of the group of non-singular 2×2 matrices we obtain a group of transformations of the plane and hence a geometry.* (By a *geometry* we mean the study of invariants under a group of transformations.) We shall consider two particular cases in the following exercises; these are

(i) the geometry corresponding to the similarity group (see Example I of the last chapter), i.e. the set of matrices satisfying

$$AA' = \lambda I$$

where λ is any positive real number, and

(ii) the geometry corresponding to the whole group M' of all non-singular 2×2 matrices.

Exercises

1. The most important invariant under the group of isometries (hence the name) is the distance between points; what becomes of this invariant under the group of similarities? Remembering that the isometries are a subgroup of the similarity group, we need only consider the distance between two points of which one is at the origin of coordinates. For if we wish to consider the effect of a similarity transformation on the distance between P and Q, we can always first map the plane onto itself in such a way that P is mapped onto the origin by a translation, which does not alter the distance PQ.

Let OP be a line-segment, where O is the origin and P has coordinates (x, y). Then if the length of OP is k

$$k^2 = x^2 + y^2 = (x \ y) \begin{pmatrix} x \\ y \end{pmatrix} = X'X, \text{ where } X = \begin{pmatrix} x \\ y \end{pmatrix} \text{ and } X' \text{ is the transpose of } X.$$

(In general, the [distance]^2 between any two points with *coordinate vectors* X_1 and X_2 is $[X_1 - X_2]'[X_1 - X_2]$.)

Let $X \longrightarrow X_1 = AX + k$ be any similarity transformation, then we can decompose it into two transformations

$$X \longrightarrow X_2 = X + \tilde{A}k, \quad X_2 \longrightarrow X_1 = AX_2$$

of which $X \longrightarrow X_2$ is a translation which does not alter the length and so we need only consider the effect of $X_2 \longrightarrow X_1$ on a line segment OP. This transformation maps

$X_2'X_2$ to $X_1'X_1 = [AX_2]'[AX_2] = X_2'[A'A]X_2 = \lambda X_2'X_2$ for some $\lambda > 0$.

Hence distance is multiplied by a factor λ and is no longer invariant: λ depends on the choice of similarity transformation. (Using the result in brackets above we can derive the result more directly if we wish. The origin is mapped onto O_1 with coordinates given by the vector k under $X \longrightarrow X_1$ and the general point P onto P_1 with coordinates given by the vector X_1. Hence the length d_1 of O_1P_1 is given by

$$d_1{}^2 = [AX + k - k]'[AX + k - k] = [AX]'[AX]$$

as before).

We have lost the most important invariant of distance, but since every distance under any particular similarity is multiplied by the same factor, the ratio of any two distances is invariant. It follows, in particular, that angles are preserved.

It is clear from this exercise that that part of classical Euclidean geometry which deals with similar figures corresponds to the geometry of similarity transformations (hence the name). Similarities are combinations of isometries with uniform dilatations or contractions. Drawing anything to scale is a similarity transformation. Consider the pantograph.

2. We can prove many similarity results 'similar' to those given in the notes on isometries. Corresponding to translation, rotation and reflection we have *dilatation, dilative rotation* (or *spiral similarity*) and *dilative reflection*.

A dilatation preserves direction and maps any line segment into a parallel line segment. Any two parallel line segments are related by a unique dilatation. Algebraically a dilatation is represented by

$$X \longrightarrow X_1 = \alpha X + k \qquad \alpha \text{ a real non-zero number.}$$

The dilatations contain as a subset the translation isometries. Defining direct and indirect similarities analogously to direct and indirect isometries, a dilatation is a direct similarity. There is an important difference between translations and dilatations: whereas a translation has no invariant point, a dilatation which is not a translation has an invariant point. Algebraically a point is invariant if under a transformation $X \longrightarrow X_1$, there is a point for which $X_1 = X$, i.e. any invariant point of a dilatation is given by

$$X = \alpha X + k,$$
whence
$$[1 - \alpha]X = k$$

and since $\alpha \neq 1$ (we have excluded translations) we get the unique point

$$X = \frac{1}{1 - \alpha}k.$$

As an example, consider the two line segments AB, $A'B'$ whose end points are $A(1, 2)$, $B(2, 3)$, $A'(0, -1)$, $B'(3, 2)$. Find the dilatation which maps

$A \longrightarrow A'$ and $B \longrightarrow B'$: find also the invariant point of this transformation and give a general construction for the invariant point.

A spiral similarity is the combination of a non-translative dilatation and a rotation about the invariant point of the dilatation. The invariant point thus remains invariant and is called the centre of the similarity. A spiral similarity is also a direct similarity. If we choose the origin as the centre of the similarity the transformation takes the form

$$X \longrightarrow X_1 = \alpha \begin{pmatrix} \cos \theta & -\sin \theta \\ \sin \theta & \cos \theta \end{pmatrix} X.$$

If the centre is not at the origin then we may proceed as in Exercise 6 above and get

$$X \longrightarrow X_1 = \alpha \begin{pmatrix} \cos \theta & -\sin \theta \\ \sin \theta & \cos \theta \end{pmatrix} [X - k] + k = \alpha TX + k_1,$$

where $k = \begin{pmatrix} a \\ b \end{pmatrix}$ gives the position of the centre.

As an example the reader might like to prove that the combination of two spiral similarities is usually, but not always, another spiral similarity. What is the special case when it is not? Instead of using the pure geometry approach we suggest the algebraic approach, i.e. consider the combination of the two transformations

$$X \longrightarrow X_1 = \alpha TX + k \text{ and } X_1 \longrightarrow X_2 = \alpha_1 T_1 X_1 + k_1,$$

where T and T_1 belong to O_2^+, the subgroup of O_2 with determinant $+1$ which represents the rotations. There are many other similar problems and examples which can be made up by analogy with the isometry examples and exercises given earlier.

Our last similarity is the dilative reflection which is a non-translative dilatation followed by a reflection in an axis through the invariant point of the dilatation. The general transformation of this type is represented by

$$X \longrightarrow X_1 = \alpha TX + k,$$

where $T \in O_2^-$, the subset of O_2 with determinant -1 which represents the reflections. Dilative reflections are indirect similarities.

Once again there are many exercises and problems analogous to the exercises set earlier for isometries. In particular: any two similar triangles are related by a unique similarity. For more information see Coxeter.

3. One now has a large number of subgroups and one can continue to illustrate the algebraic theory by investigating whether the subgroups are normal, and if they are normal one can realize the factor groups. We leave the reader to answer, if he wishes, such questions as 'are the translations still a normal subgroup of the larger group of similarities?'; 'are the dilatations?'; 'what are the factor groups?' etc. . . .

4. We now turn to our second geometry and try to get some idea of its invariants. The general transformation in this geometry is

$$X \longrightarrow X_1 = AX + k,$$

where A is any non-singular 2×2 matrix. We certainly cannot expect length to be an invariant since we have lost that already under the more restricted set of similarity transformations. But have we lost the ratio of lengths? Referring back to Exercise 1 on page 213 we see that

$$X'X \longrightarrow X_1'X_1 = X'A'AX$$

under the transformation $X \longrightarrow X_1 = AX$. But $A'A$ is no longer necessarily of the form λI, so that the lengths of two line-segments and OP and OQ are not altered in the same ratio. Thus angle is not invariant in this geometry.

A line $lx + my + n = 0$ transforms into another line: so we can say that linearity is an invariant. Let us investigate this correspondence exactly: let A be the matrix $\begin{pmatrix} a & b \\ c & d \end{pmatrix}$ and k be the matrix $\begin{pmatrix} e \\ f \end{pmatrix}$ then the line $lx + my + n = 0$ is transformed into

$$l[ax + by + e] + m[cx + dy + f] + n = 0$$

under the mapping $X \longrightarrow AX + k$. Similarly the line $l'x + m'y + n' = 0$ is transformed into

$$l'[ax + by + e] + m'[cx + dy + f] + n' = 0.$$

It follows that if our original lines were parallel, i.e. $l:l' = m:m'$, then the transformed lines will also be parallel since

$$[la + mc]:[l'a + m'c] = [lb + md]:[l'b + m'd] = m:m'.$$

So we have an invariant—parallelism: it is the fundamental invariant of this geometry which is called *affine geometry*.

In both similarity and isometry geometry only special triangles are uniquely related (similar and congruent triangles respectively). What sort of triangles are related in affine geometry? Consider the image of the triangle with vertices $A(0, 1)$, $B(0, 0)$ and $C(1, 0)$ under the transformation $X \longrightarrow AX + k$; the new triangle has co-ordinates $A_1(b + e, d + f)$, $B_1(e, f)$, $C_1(a + e, c + f)$. We are assured that these three points form a proper triangle and are not collinear because our transformation is one-one and maps lines into lines. Now e and f may certainly be chosen arbitrarily and a, b, c, d are only related by the fact that we must have $ad - bc \neq 0$: so it would seem that we can map the given triangle into any triangle whatsoever.

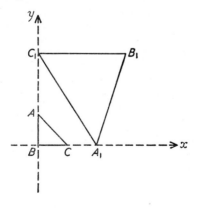

For instance, in the diagram, we have chosen $A_1B_1C_1$ to be $A_1(2, 0)$, $B_1(3, 3)$, $C_1(0, 3)$ then the mapping of ABC to $A_1B_1C_1$ is accomplished with

$$e = 3, f = 3, b = -1, d = -3, a = -3, c = 0,$$

i.e.
$$X \longrightarrow \begin{pmatrix} -3 & -1 \\ 0 & -3 \end{pmatrix} X + \begin{pmatrix} 3 \\ 3 \end{pmatrix}.$$

In general, any two triangles are related by an affine transformation. Is the transformation uniquely defined by giving a pair of corresponding triangles?

5. It is of some interest to consider well-known theorems and the usual geometrical objects and discover to which geometry they really belong, i.e. of the three geometries so far considered, to find the 'largest' (i.e. the most comprehensive), in which the objects are invariant. For instance, a square is not an invariant object of affine geometry: a square can be mapped into an arbitrary parallelogram by an affine transformation (prove this!). A square is always mapped into a square in similarity geometry; so the square belongs to this sub-geometry of affine geometry.

As an example of a theorem which belongs to affine geometry consider the following: the diagonals of a parallelogram bisect each other. A parallelogram $PQRS$ is obviously an affine object, but at first sight it might seem that bi-section has something to do with distance or at least ratio of distance, but if $X \longrightarrow X_1$ and $Y \longrightarrow Y_1$ under an affine transformation then

$$\tfrac{1}{2}[X + Y] \longrightarrow \tfrac{1}{2}[X_1 + Y_1]$$

and so mid-points are transformed to mid-points. (In fact, any linear expression such as $\alpha X + \beta Y$, where α, β are real numbers, is preserved under an affine transformation: we express this by saying that an affine transformation is linear.) So if our stated result is true we should be able to prove it within affine geometry. Let $PQRS$ be the parallelogram: then there is always an affine transformation $X \longrightarrow X_1 = AX + k$ which maps P, Q and R into $P_1(0, 0)$, $Q_1(0, 1)$ and $R_1(1, 0)$. Since the property of being a parallelogram is preserved under $X \longrightarrow X_1$, S_1 will have coordinates $(1, 1)$. The intersection of the diagonals of $P_1Q_1R_1S_1$ is found to be $(\tfrac{1}{2}, \tfrac{1}{2})$ which is the mid-point of these diagonals, hence transferring back under $X_1 \longrightarrow X$ we have that PR and QS bisect each other. Notice that we are getting an affine property of a parallelogram from a property of the square. This is an important aspect of this whole approach to geometry.

As an example the reader might like to prove some such affine result as 'in triangle ABC a line parallel to AB divides AC and BC in the same ratio'.

6. We found that isometries could be represented by combinations of translations, rotations and reflections: we also explained similarities in a similar way. The same can be done for affinities. The essentially new trans-formation is a *shear translation*: under a shear translation there is an invariant line (invariant pointwise in the sense that points on it are invariant, and not merely in the sense that it is mapped into itself) and each other point moves parallel to this line, the distance moved being proportional to its distance from the line.

For instance, if we choose the invariant line as coincident with the x-axis, then $y = 0$ is mapped onto $y = 0$ and any point (x, y) is mapped onto $(x + ky, y)$, where k is a constant. Hence the transformation becomes

$$X \longrightarrow X_1 = \begin{pmatrix} 1 & k \\ 0 & 1 \end{pmatrix} X$$

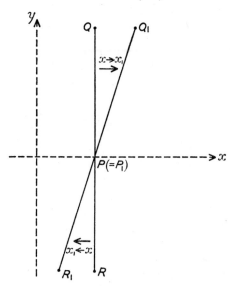

If the invariant line is not coincident with the x-axis we may first rotate the x-axis so that it is parallel to the line, then translate it into coincidence, perform the shear translation to get the compound transformation,

$$X \longrightarrow X_1 = \begin{pmatrix} 1 & k \\ 0 & 1 \end{pmatrix} \left[\begin{pmatrix} \cos \theta & -\sin \theta \\ \sin \theta & \cos \theta \end{pmatrix} \begin{pmatrix} x \\ y \end{pmatrix} - \begin{pmatrix} 0 \\ f \end{pmatrix} \right]$$

and then return to our original coordinate system by the transformation

$$X_1 \longrightarrow X_2 = \begin{pmatrix} \cos \theta & \sin \theta \\ -\sin \theta & \cos \theta \end{pmatrix} \left[X_1 + \begin{pmatrix} 0 \\ f \end{pmatrix} \right].$$

Find a shear translation in which the line $x + y = 1$ is the invariant line. Notice that if we write a shear translation in the form

$$X \longrightarrow AX + k$$

it follows that the determinant of A is $+1$, but this property does not serve to identify a shear translation.

At this stage it would seem that our obvious algebraic generalization of geometries is at an end. But geometrically we may still consider a reasonable further extension: after all, we are still a long

way from the topological group of all bi-continuous one-one transformations. Let us consider the set of all bi-continuous one-one
transformations which map lines into lines. It is not difficult to see
that this set forms a group, so we must have a corresponding
geometry.

An obvious subset of this group is given by

$$x \longrightarrow x_1 = \frac{ax + by + c}{a''x + b''y + c''}$$

$$y \longrightarrow y_1 = \frac{a'x + b'y + c'}{a''x + b''y + c''}$$

with an as yet unstated condition to ensure that the transformation
is reversible (we shall come to this later). The important point is
(see, for instance, Klein) that this set of transformations is in fact
the whole group. The group is usually called the *projective group*.

Example E. The image of the parallel lines
$$x + y + 1 = 0, 2x + 2y + 1 = 0$$
under the transformation given by the equations
$$x = \frac{y_1 + 1}{2x_1 + 1}, y = \frac{2}{2x_1 + 1}$$
is the pair of *non*-parallel lines
$$2x_1 + y_1 + 4 = 0, 2x_1 + 2y_1 + 7 = 0,$$
and the transformation equations belong to the projective group.

From this last example we see that parallelism is no longer an
invariant: we shall also see that 'P lies between A and B', i.e.
'intermediacy' is no longer an invariant (see Exercise 1, page 221).
But in spite of the seeming paucity of natural invariants, projective
geometry is one of the most elegant mathematical systems. We
shall only have time and space to hint at it, but the interested
reader will find plenty to entertain him in such books as those by
Klein and Coxeter. Two elementary and important theorems
which do belong to projective geometry are those known as the
theorems of Pappus and Desargues. We shall prove the latter in
an exercise.

The loss of parallelism is serious: two given lines may meet but
their images under a transformation may not, or vice versa, as we

saw in the above example. While we are listing our problems let us note a few more deficiencies. The transformation equations given above are clumsy: the introduction of the fractional notation has made us lose the convenience of matrices. Further, even in the sub-geometries we have to use both matrix addition and multiplication and, as we noticed in Exercise 6, page 211, finding the inverse of a transformation involves us in two equations. It would be very nice to get rid of all these difficulties at one go.*

We can, in fact, get rid of them all by employing *homogeneous coordinates*: replace the coordinates (x', y') of P by the ratios

$$x' = \frac{x}{z}, y' = \frac{y}{z}, z \neq 0, \text{ and let } P \text{ have the homogeneous coordi-}$$

nates (x, y, z). Then (ax, ay, az) and (x, y, z), where a is any real non-zero number, will represent the same point. In other words, if $R^3 = \triangledown RRR$ is the set of all triples of real numbers (x, y, z), then we say that (x, y, z) is equivalent to (x_1, y_1, z_1) if $x_1 = ax$, $y_1 = ay, z_1 = az$, for some non-zero a. This is a proper equivalence relation and we can identify the equivalence classes one-one with the points of the plane under a more usual coordinate system, with the exception of the classes with elements of the form $(x, y, 0)$. There is no algebraic reason for omitting these classes so we shall enrich our plane and define the *projective plane* which includes points corresponding to the classes in which $z = 0$. We do not, however, include the class $\{(0, 0, 0)\}$.† This means that we have a new set of points $\{(x, y, 0)\}$. Note that the projective plane is more than our normal conception of the plane.

In homogeneous coordinates the equation of a line becomes $lx + my + nz = 0$ and we shall say that any homogeneous linear equation represents a line. It can then be verified that in the projective plane any two distinct points lie on a unique line and any two distinct lines intersect in a unique point.

Example F. Find the line defined by the points $\{(1, 2, 1)\}$ and $\{(3, 0, 1)\}$. Find also the point defined by the lines $x + 2y + z = 0$ and $3x + z = 0$.

* The following discussion is even more sketchy than that preceding and we beg many questions. To establish the system properly would give undue emphasis to what we consider a sideline in this book: we again refer the reader to the books listed on page 225.

† One reason for rejecting $\{(0, 0, 0)\}$ is that our more immediate intuitive ideas of geometry would collapse: for example every line would pass through $\{(0, 0, 0)\}$.

Our last statement implies that distinct parallel lines now also have a point of intersection. Consider

$$lx + my + nz = 0$$
$$lx + my + n'z = 0.$$

Subtracting, we get $[n - n']z = 0$ and since our lines are distinct $n - n' \neq 0$ and so $z = 0$, which means that the point of intersection is one of our new points. All parallel lines meet in the line $z = 0$ (notice that according to our definition any linear equation represents a line). Their point of intersection is given by the class $\{(m, -l, 0)\}$.

So we have got rid of the first difficulty: all lines in the projective plane meet. What about the transformation equations in this new system? It is easily seen that the projective transformation equations can now be written in the form

$$x_1 = ax + by + cz$$
$$y_1 = a'x + b'y + c'z$$
$$z_1 = a''x + b''y + c''z.$$

There is a one-one correspondence between such equations and the 3×3 matrices $\begin{pmatrix} a & b & c \\ a' & b' & c' \\ a'' & b'' & c'' \end{pmatrix}$. Suppose that we have a second transformation $X_1 \to X_2$ and we do the necessary substitutions to obtain (x_2, y_2, z_2) in terms of (x, y, z), then after a tedious manipulation it will be seen that the combination of the two transformations corresponds to multiplying their respective matrices. So if we write $X = \begin{pmatrix} x \\ y \\ z \end{pmatrix}$ we can represent a projective transformation

by $$X \to X_1 = AX,$$

where A is the 3×3 matrix obtained from the transformation equations. It follows that the projective transformations can be represented by the group of all *invertible* 3×3 matrices. The invertibility is the unstated condition on page 218.

NOTE: We have not discussed the invertibility of 3×3 matrices but, basically, it follows the lines described in Chapter 9, Exercise 1, page 141. The algebraic analysis of that exercise becomes a little tedious for a 3×3 matrix and we do not suggest that it be done without a little further development of the general theory, especially of determinants (numerical examples, however, are best done by that method). Note also that we are taking for granted that the product of two invertible matrices is invertible.

The affine transformations form a subgroup of the projective transformations: the subgroup is given by putting $a'' = 0 = b''$, $c'' = 1$, hence in homogeneous coordinates the affine transformations are

$$X \rightarrow X_1 = AX, \text{ where } A = \begin{pmatrix} a & b & c \\ a' & b' & c' \\ 0 & 0 & 1 \end{pmatrix}$$

and $\begin{pmatrix} a & b \\ a' & b' \end{pmatrix}$ is non-singular. The similarity group is given by the same equation but requires $\begin{pmatrix} a & b \\ a' & b' \end{pmatrix} = B$ to satisfy $BB' = \lambda I$, while the isometry group requires $BB' = I$, i.e. $B \in O_2$.

We have achieved all our aims and much more besides as the exercises will show. It is clear that the line $z = 0$ is invariant under the group of affine transformations and this is what one might expect since parallelism is an invariant of affine geometry. The addition of the special points of the line $z = 0$ allows a remarkable simplification in geometry: if we want to get back to the non-homogeneous system it is not difficult to interpret our results. The line $z = 0$ is called either the *line at infinity* or the *vanishing line*: the latter term (although not the more common in the literature) is surely to be preferred. For a topological investigation of the projective plane see Lietzmann: *Visual Topology*, Pt. II, Ch. 4 (Chatto & Windus), 1965. The idea of points at infinity goes back to Kepler.

Exercises

1. To show that 'intermediacy' is no longer invariant consider the non-homogeneous transformation equations given in Example E on page 218 and the three collinear points (x_1, y_1) with coordinates $(-1, -2)$, $(0, -4)$, $(1, -6)$. They correspond to the collinear points (x, y) with coordinates $(1, -2)$, $(-3, 2)$, $(-\frac{5}{3}, \frac{2}{3})$ respectively. Notice that $(-1, -2)$ lies on one side and $(0, -4)$ and $(1, -6)$ on the other side of the point $(-\frac{1}{2}, -3)$ which is the point collinear with the (x_1, y_1) which maps onto the vanishing point on the new line.

2. In the affine plane any triangle is equivalent to any other triangle and so we could give any three non-collinear points the coordinates $(0, 0)$, $(1, 0)$ and $(0, 1)$. In the projective plane any set of four points, no three of which are collinear, is equivalent to any other such set and we can choose any four points, no three of which are collinear, to have homogeneous coordinates

{(1, 0, 0)}, {(0, 1, 0)}, {(0, 0, 1)} and {(1, 1, 1)}. We leave the proof of this to the reader.

3. Not all invertible 3×3 matrices determine distinct projective transformations. If A is one such matrix, then λA, where λ is any real non-zero number, determines the same transformation as A.

4. *Desargues's Theorem.* Let ABC and $A'B'C'$ be two triangles such that the lines joining their corresponding vertices are concurrent in the point P, then the intersections of their corresponding sides are collinear.

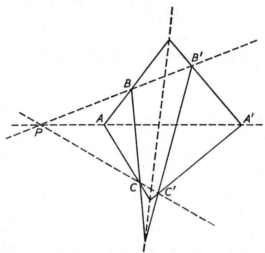

To prove this choose A, B, C, P to have homogeneous coordinates {(1, 0, 0)}, {(0, 1, 0)}, {(0, 0, 1)} and {(1, 1, 1)} respectively. Now if X_1 and X_2 represent any two points* on a line $lx + my + nz = 0$ then $X = \alpha X_1 + \beta X_2$, α and β real numbers (not both zero), is the vector of another point on the same line. (This is most easily seen by writing the equation of the line in the form $L'X = 0$ where $L' = (l\ m\ n)$. (When $\alpha \neq 0$ we can divide through by α and absorb the factor $\frac{1}{\alpha}$ into the vector, then $X = X_1 + \beta' X_2$. For varying β' we can obtain all points on the line except X_2 itself: if we allow the improper value $\beta' = \frac{\beta}{0}$ to deal with this we can represent all the points on the line in this form. It follows that A', B', C' have coordinates {(λ, 1, 1)}, {(1, μ, 1)},

* We represent any point {(x, y, z)} by the vector $\begin{pmatrix} x \\ y \\ z \end{pmatrix}$. This means that $a \begin{pmatrix} x \\ x \\ z \end{pmatrix}$ and $\begin{pmatrix} x \\ y \\ z \end{pmatrix}$, $a \neq 0$, represents the same point. We usually absorb any unnecessary factors into the vector.

$\{(1, 1, \nu)\}$. Consequently using the same method, any points on AB and $A'B'$ are $\{(1, \lambda_1, 0)\}$ and $\{(\lambda + \lambda_2, 1 + \lambda_2\mu, 1 + \lambda_2)\}$. AB and $A'B'$ intersect at the point where these coordinates are the same, for some choice of λ_1 and λ_2. It is easily seen that $\lambda_2 = -1$ and $\lambda_1 = \dfrac{1 - \mu}{\lambda - 1}$ satisfies this condition and so we can write the point of intersection of AB and $A'B'$ as

$$\{(\lambda - 1, 1 - \mu, 0)\}.$$

It can be similarly shown that the intersection of BC and $B'C'$ and AC and $A'C'$ are

$$\{(0, \mu - 1, 1 - \nu)\} \text{ and } \{(1 - \lambda, 0, \nu - 1)\}.$$

We wish to show that these three points are collinear: denote their respective representative vectors by X_1, X_2 and X_3. Then we notice that

$$X_1 + X_2 + X_3 = 0$$

which shows that any one vector can be expressed as a linear combination of the other two and the vectors must therefore represent collinear points.

Our proof has been unnecessarily long because we have developed our techniques as we went along. Given that $X = X_1 + \alpha X_2$ represents any point on the join of X_1 and X_2 and in consequence three points represented by X_1, X_2 and X_3 are collinear if there exist α, β and γ, not all zero, such that

$$\alpha X_1 + \beta X_2 + \gamma X_3 = 0,$$

then the proof is a relatively simple matter. We could further improve matters by adopting some simpler notational conventions.

5. *The Principle of Duality.* We have already noted a remarkable symmetry between points and lines in the projective plane, viz. two distinct points lie on a unique line and two distinct lines intersect in a unique point. Consider the equation $lx + my + nz = 0$. The line is specified by the class of triples $\{(l, m, n)\}$. Instead of thinking of the l, m, n as fixed (except for a multiple) and allowing the x, y, z to vary giving *all the points of the line*, we can reverse the system. Let the x, y, z be fixed (except for a multiple) and allow the l, m, n to vary, then we shall clearly get *all the lines through the point* with homogeneous coordinates $\{(x, y, z)\}$. We call $\{(l, m, n)\}$ *line coordinates* and $\{(x, y, z)\}$ *point coordinates*: we may regard $lx + my + nz = 0$ as the equation of a point or the equation of a line.

It follows that because of this symmetry we can replace points by lines (and vice versa) and make other suitable word changes in the proof of any theorem and we get another theorem: the same algebra will do for both. This principle is known as the principle of duality. (Consider Example F on page 219 again.)

As an example we write out the 'dual' of Desargues's Theorem: Let ABC and $A'B'C'$ be two triangles such that the intersections of their corresponding sides are collinear in a line p, then the joins of their corresponding vertices are concurrent. Note the following 'dual' words illustrated in this theorem:

(i) a triangle is a self-dual figure, defined by three non-collinear points or three non-concurrent lines;

(ii) intersection $\leftrightarrow$ join, vertices $\leftrightarrow$ sides, collinear $\leftrightarrow$ concurrent.

The dual of Desargues's Theorem is what one might usually call the converse: this is not always the case.

6. Another consequence of our improved notation in homogeneous co-ordinates is that we can now invent more geometries in an obvious way. Projective geometry is the study of properties invariant under the transformations of the form

$$X \longrightarrow X_1 = AX,$$

where A is any invertible 3×3 matrix. This group of matrices A has many subgroups besides those which correspond to the affine, similarity and isometry groups. For instance we might consider the geometry corresponding to the transformations

$$X \longrightarrow X_1 = TX$$

where T is an orthogonal 3×3 matrix, i.e. satisfying $TT' = I$. We leave this, like many other things in this chapter particularly, to the interested reader.

7. Finally we suggest a further direction in which we could extend the theory. The points or lines of the projective plane are in one-one correspondence with the set of classes of ordered triples $\{(x, y, z)\}$. Now we need not take the elements of our ordered triples from the reals, we could take our elements from any other field (see the next chapter), and the same axiomatic basis as for the general projective plane will provide a basis for this geometry as well. In particular we could take our elements from a finite field (this is developed in Coxeter) and obtain *finite projective geometries*.

As an example consider the field with elements 0, 1 and addition and multiplication modulo 2. There will only be one triple in each class. The points of this finite projective plane are

$$(0, 0, 1), (0, 1, 0), (1, 0, 0), (1, 1, 0), (1, 0, 1), (0, 1, 1), (1, 1, 1),$$

i.e. seven points. A line will be defined as in any other projective geometry, and if there are seven points, there will be seven lines. Two points P and P' define a unique line and any third point will lie on this line only if it is the sum (modulo 2) of the vectors representing P and P'. Using this fact we obtain the following configuration, where the dotted line is also a line in this finite geometry, even though we cannot represent it so in our diagram.

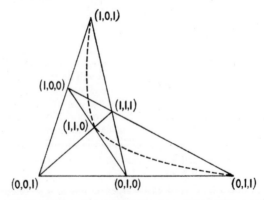

Notice that there are three lines through any point and three points on every line. The reader might like to consider the finite projective plane corresponding to the field with elements 0, 1, 2 under addition and multiplication modulo 3. Find two triangles the joins of whose corresponding points are concurrent and identify the line in which the intersection of corresponding sides are collinear. Note that we need at least ten points for a non-degenerate case of Desargues's Theorem and we have only seven in the case illustrated.

As we have repeatedly said in this chapter, we have only been able to give the barest sketch of geometric theories. Our point was to show that the idea of algebraic structure permeates this subject as well and conversely that we can use geometry to illustrate the algebra: as for the rest we leave the reader to consult such works as those which we cite below.

Yaglom: *Geometric Transformations* (Random House), 1962. This book deals with isometries using pure geometric methods. It contains a large number of interesting examples.

Coxeter: *Introduction to Geometry* (Wiley), 1961. This is a fascinating encyclopaedic book. It covers a vast field and gives a good insight into the range of modern geometry.

Klein: *Geometry: elementary mathematics from an advanced standpoint* (Dover). This is a book written for teachers nearly 60 years ago by a master in the field.

Semple and Kneebone: *Algebraic Projective Geometry* (Oxford). This is a mathematical specialist's book, but the first part 'The origins and development of geometrical knowledge' makes very rewarding reading. It emphasizes the structural aspect of geometry. We quote: 'Mathematics, as conceived today, is fundamentally the study of structure. Thus, although arithmetic is ostensibly about numbers and geometry about points and lines, the real objects of study in these branches of mathematics are the *relations* which exist between numbers and between geometrical entities.'

The next two references are of a completely different sort: they illustrate this geometry in the teaching situation.

Fletcher (ed.): *Some Lessons in Mathematics* (C.U.P.), 1964. One of the lessons in this book is on geometry.

Mansfield and Thompson: *Mathematics: A New Approach*, Book 3 (Chatto and Windus), 1964.

Mansfield and Bruckheimer: *Mathematics: A New Approach*, Books 4 and 5 (Chatto and Windus).

Lastly, the texts now in preparation for the School Mathematics Project and available from the Cambridge University Press contain many useful examples although the reference to the basic algebraic structure is minimal.

*   *   *   *   *

At the beginning of Chapter 13 we consider a set with two binary operations: clearly, in order to obtain something new, interesting and useful, we must have some interaction between the two structures. What is true of algebraic structures is equally true of our present situation where we shall consider a set with a group structure and a topology. If the two structures are unrelated then there is nothing new to say, so we choose some interaction and we shall require that the group operations shall be continuous in the topological space formed by the set and the topology. This statement can be given precision as follows.

Let (G, o) be a group with a topology $T: G$ then we have the product topology defined in $G \triangledown G$. Combination in G can be considered as a many-one mapping c of $G \triangledown G$ onto G defined by

$$c: (g, g') \rightarrow g \circ g' \qquad g, g' \in G.$$

Further, in a group we can form inverses and so we have a mapping i of G onto G defined by

$$i: g \rightarrow \tilde{g}.$$

If the two mappings c and i are continuous then we shall say that $(G, o, T: G)$ is a *topological group*.

Example G. Verify that any group can be given the structure of a topological group by giving the set of elements in G the discrete topology. (Notice that if G has discrete topology so has $G \triangledown G$.)

Example H. Verify that the additive group of real numbers R with the natural topology for R is a topological group. With the same topology, is the multiplicative group of non-zero real numbers a topological group? What happens if it has a different topology as in Chapter 6, Example N, page 97?

Example I. Consider the following group G of order four defined by its combination table

o	a	b	c	d
a	a	b	c	d
b	b	a	d	c
c	c	d	a	b
d	d	c	b	a

In Chapter 2, Example S (ii), page 38 we gave a system of subsets which formed a topology for the set of four elements: this system is

$$G, \emptyset, (a, b, c), (a, b, d), (a, b).$$

The mapping i maps each element onto itself and is, therefore, clearly continuous. In order to decide whether the mapping c is continuous it might seem advisable to discover the open sets of $G \triangledown G$. By definition of the product topology a sub-base is composed of all the sets of the form $U \triangledown G$ and $G \triangledown V$ where U and V are open in $T:G$. So, for example, if we take $U = (a, b)$, we have $U \triangledown G$ as the set whose elements are

$$(a, a), (a, b), (a, c), (a, d), (b, a), (b, b), (b, c), (b, d).$$

In all the sub-base will contain 8 such sets, two of which are $G \triangledown G$ and $\emptyset$. In order to obtain the base for $T:G \triangledown G$ we must consider all intersections of these 8 sets: then, finally, all unions of sets of the base will give the open sets of $T:G \triangledown G$. Not exactly a thought to be relished: the reader might like to try to list all the sets in $T:G \triangledown G$. But, in fact, this is not necessary: consider Example J of Chapter 8 (page 134). The inverse image under the mapping c of the open set $(a, b) \in T:G$ is the set X, where the elements of X are

$$(a, a), (b, b), (c, c), (d, d), (a, b), (b, a), (c, d), (d, c),$$

and, for instance, there are no open sets U, $V \in T:G$, $c \in U$, $c \in V$ such that $U \triangledown V \subset X$. This proves that X is not open in $T:G \triangledown G$ and hence the mapping c is not continuous.

Construct another topology for G, other than the discrete topology, and consider whether the result gives G the structure of a topological group.

Example J. Consider the set M of all 2×2 matrices with real elements. We can introduce a topology into M as follows. M can be put into one-one correspondence with the set $R^4 = \triangledown RRRR$ of all 4-tuples of real numbers: e.g.

$$A = \begin{pmatrix} a & b \\ c & d \end{pmatrix} \longrightarrow (a, b, c, d).$$

Now R^4 can be given a topology by analogy with the product topology. We shall require each of the four projections of R^4 onto R to be continuous (where R has its usual topology) and so obtain a sub-base for $T:R^4$ whose sets are of the form $\triangledown URRR$, $\triangledown RURR$, $\triangledown RRUR$, $\triangledown RRRU$. It is easy enough to form a mental picture of the situation. The resulting topology coincides with the implicit topology of real analysis of functions of four (in general, many) variables. We can now allocate a topology to M in such a way as to make the one-one correspondence with R^4 a homeomorphism.

We can prove, as in Chapter 8, Example K, page 134, that any function f of a topological space $(X, T:X)$ into the generalized product space $(R^4, T:R^4)$ is continuous if, and only if, $p_r \circ f$ $(r = 1, 2, 3, 4)$ is a continuous mapping of $(X, T:X)$ into $(R, T:R)$ where the p_r are projections of R^4 onto R, e.g.

$$p_2 : (a, b, c, d) \longrightarrow b.$$

Using this result the reader should prove the following results.

(i) If A, $B \in M$ and c and i are defined by

$$c : (A, B) \longrightarrow A + B$$

and

$$i : A \longrightarrow -1 . A,$$

show that c and i are continuous. It follows that the additive group of 2×2 matrices is a topological group with the defined topology.

(ii) If A, $B \in M$ and c is defined by

$$c:(A, B) \longrightarrow AB,$$

show that c is continuous. If further $\tilde{A}$ is defined show that

$$i:A \longrightarrow \tilde{A}$$

is continuous. It follows that if we give the set M' of invertible 2×2 matrices subset topology, then M' under multiplication has the structure of a topological group.

As a hint we indicate the proof of the first part of (ii). c is a mapping of the space $(M \triangledown M, T:M \triangledown M)$ homeomorphic to $(R^4 \triangledown R^4, T:R^4 \triangledown R^4)$ into M, and $(M, T:M)$ is homeomorphic to the generalized product space $(R^4, T:R^4)$. Therefore, c can be decomposed into the mappings

$$M \triangledown M \longleftrightarrow R^4 \triangledown R^4 \longrightarrow R^4 \longleftrightarrow M.$$

The first and last mappings in this series are certainly continuous. Consider the middle mapping f, say, then

$$p_1 \circ f:((a, b, c, d), (a', b', c', d')) \longrightarrow aa' + bc'$$

i.e. the image of $p_1 \circ f$ is a polynomial in four 'variables' and every such polynomial is continuous (as proved in real analysis, and we have the same topology as that implicit in real analysis). Similarly $p_2 \circ f$, etc., are continuous, whence f is continuous. Finally, since c is composed of continuous mappings it is itself continuous.

Incidentally, we note that the mapping of an element $A \in M$ onto its determinant is a continuous mapping. Now the set M' maps onto the non-zero real numbers, and this is an open set in $T:R$, hence M' is open in $(M, T:M)$.

Example K. Show that in a topological group the mapping i is a homeomorphism.

We shall continue the development of the elementary properties of topological groups, mainly by way of examples, at the end of Chapter 13.

CHAPTER 13

EXTENSIONS

ALTHOUGH the title of this book restricts us to set and group theory we find ourselves unable to conclude without some reference to some of the 'higher' structures. Of necessity, in a single short chapter, such reference can only be brief and incomplete: much of the theory will be developed in examples with suitable hints: the reader who has worked a fair number of the examples in the earlier chapters of this book should find that he can tackle the problems with some measure of success for the fundamental methods are the same: group concepts are the basis for the development.

Undoubtedly the group is the fundamental structure, but this is not the end of the story. It would be the end if it were true that the higher structures were simply multiple groups, but this is not the case, for a very good reason.

It is perfectly possible for the same set G to possess group structure for each of two or more distinct operations: indeed, we now give an example.

Let $G = (a, b, c, d)$. Let the operation $\oplus$ be defined by the left-hand table and the operation $\otimes$ by the right-hand table.

$\oplus$	a	b	c	d
a	a	b	c	d
b	b	a	d	c
c	c	d	b	a
d	d	c	a	b

$\otimes$	a	b	c	d
a	a	b	c	d
b	b	a	d	c
c	c	d	a	b
d	d	c	b	a

Then G has double group structure. Unfortunately, such a group is almost useless in practice (except, of course, as two single groups), for the two operations are unrelated to each other. In particular, neither is distributive over the other. For example,

$$c \otimes [d \oplus a] = c \otimes d = b,$$

while
$$[c \otimes d] \oplus [c \otimes a] = b \oplus c = d.$$

If we impose, in addition to double group structure, the further requirement that one of the two operations should be distributive over the other, then we meet a contradiction, as we now show. (For convenience, as explained later, we change our notation slightly.)

Let G be a group for $\oplus$, with neutral element $_0g$, and a group for $\otimes$, with neutral element $_1g$. Let $\otimes$ be distributive over $\oplus$. Take any $g \neq {}_1g$. Then

$$g \oplus {}_0g = g,$$

since $_0g$ is neutral for $\oplus$. Hence

$$g \otimes [g \oplus {}_0g] = g \otimes g,$$

i.e. $\qquad\qquad [g \otimes g] \oplus [g \otimes {}_0g] = g \otimes g,$

since $\otimes$ is distributive over $\oplus$. Now $g \otimes g$ and $g \otimes {}_0g$ are elements of G, since G is a group for $\otimes$. Hence the last equation implies that

$$g \otimes {}_0g = {}_0g,$$

for there is only one neutral element for each operation. Now since G is a group for $\otimes$ and $_0g \in G$, $_0g$ has an inverse for $\otimes$. Let it be $_0\tilde{g}$. Then

$$[g \otimes {}_0g] \otimes {}_0\tilde{g} = {}_0g \otimes {}_0\tilde{g},$$

i.e. $\qquad\qquad g \otimes [{}_0g \otimes {}_0\tilde{g}] = {}_1g,$

since $\otimes$ is associative and $_1g$ is the neutral element for $\otimes$. But this gives

$$g \otimes {}_1g = {}_1g,$$

i.e. $\qquad\qquad g = {}_1g,$

which contradicts our assumption for g. Hence it is not possible for the same set to possess group structure for two different operations of which one is distributive over the other.

Since we cannot have what we want we look to see what we *can* have—and the notation in the last proof was chosen to be suggestive. If G is the set of all rational numbers, then we have multiplication distributive over addition, group structure for addition and group structure for multiplication with *one single exception*: the neutral element for addition has no inverse for multiplication. The crucial step in the proof above, the existence of $_0\tilde{g}$, is destroyed and the contradiction disappears.

A set with two combination operations is called a *field* if it forms a commutative group for one operation (usually called addition) and forms a commutative group for another operation (usually called multiplication) which is distributive over the first, with the single exception that the neutral element for addition has no inverse for multiplication. The reader is warned that in some texts one meets statements like 'The non-zero elements from a field form a group for multiplication'. This is a further example of the suggestive, but possibly dangerous, type of notation referred to in Chapter 6, page 89.

The following examples are elementary: they are, however, necessary for a grasp of the field concept. The reader is recommended to work through them.

Example A. Which of the following sets and operations form fields?

(a) The set of all 2×2 matrices with rational elements under addition and multiplication.

(b) The set of all invertible 2×2 matrices with rational elements under the same operations as in (a).

(c) The set $(0, 1)$ under addition and multiplication modulo 2.

(d) The set $(0, 1, 2, 3)$ under addition and multiplication modulo 4.

(e) The set (a, b, c, d) with $\oplus$ and $\otimes$ defined by

$\oplus$	a	b	c	d		$\otimes$	a	b	c	d
a	a	b	c	d		a	a	a	a	a
b	b	a	d	c		b	a	b	c	d
c	c	d	b	a		c	a	c	d	b
d	d	c	a	b		b	a	d	b	c

(f) The complex numbers under addition and multiplication.

(g) The dual numbers under addition and multiplication.

Example B. With the notation above, we have already proved $g \otimes {}_0g = {}_0g$ without invoking commutativity. Prove also that ${}_0g \otimes g = {}_0g$, without using the commutative properties.

From here on we shall use the obvious notation, $+$ and $\times$ for the operations, but shall represent the additive inverse of g by $\tilde{g}$ and the multiplicative inverse of g by $\underset{\sim}{g}$, using ${}_0g$ and ${}_1g$, as above, for the additive and multiplicative neutral elements respectively. (We use ${}_0g$ and ${}_1g$ rather than g_0 and g_1 for the sake of convenience: see, for example, Exercise 2, page 234, where the notation would become awkward if we did not have g_1 available as a general element of the field.)

Example C. In a field, as defined above, the distributivity is from both left and right.

Example D. If g and g' are elements of a field, prove that
$$\tilde{g} \times \tilde{g}' = g \times g'.$$
(This is, of course, the result which corresponds to something like
$$-2 \times -3 = 6$$
in the rational number field. Hint: consider
$$[g \times g'] + [[g \times \tilde{g}'] + [\tilde{g} \times \tilde{g}']] = [[g \times g'] + [g \times \tilde{g}']] + [\tilde{g} \times \tilde{g}']$$
and use distributivity and Example C.)

Example E. In a field, if $g \times g' = {}_0g$ then either $g = {}_0g$ or $g' = {}_0g$. (Hint: assume $g \neq {}_0g$, then $g \times g' = {}_0g = g \times {}_0g$, etc.) To what property in the rational number field does this correspond?

Example F. If g and g' are elements of a field prove:

(a) $\tilde{g} - {}_1\tilde{g} \times g,$

(b) $\tilde{g} \times g' = g \times \tilde{g}' = [\overline{g \times g'}],$

(c) $[\overline{g + g'}] = \tilde{g} + \tilde{g}'.$

To what properties in the rational number field do these results correspond?

Example G. If $[g \times x] + g' = g''$, where $g \neq {}_0g$, prove that
$$x = g \times [g'' + \tilde{g}']$$
is a unique solution.

Exercises

1. From Example G it is evident that if a, b and c ($a \neq {}_0g$) are members of a field then there is in the field a unique x to satisfy $[a \times x] + b = c$. Now the set of natural numbers do not form a field for addition and multiplication, and if a, b and c are members of this set then the solution of $[a \times x] + b = c$ may *not* exist in the set. If we regard the (non-zero) natural numbers as fundamental we must use this set only, in a similar manner to that in Chapter 7, Exercises 7 and 8, page 110 et seq., to create the appropriate elements and operations.

Let a_1, a_2, b_1, b_2, c_1 and c_2 be natural numbers: we require
$$[a_1 \times x_1] + b_1 = c_1$$
to specify a unique x_1. Let x_1 be defined by the triple (a_1, b_1, c_1). Similarly, let $[a_2 \times x_2] + b_2 = c_2$, where x_2 is defined by the triple (a_2, b_2, c_2). Then, in the cases when x_1 and x_2 are natural numbers, we know that
$$a_1a_2x_1x_2 + b_1c_2 + b_2c_1 = b_1b_2 + c_1c_2,$$

where we adopt the more conventional notation and drop the symbol for multiplication. Hence the product, x_1x_2, or $(a_1, b_1, c_1)(a_2, b_2, c_2)$, is specified by the triple $(a_1a_2, b_1c_2 + b_2c_1, b_1b_2 + c_1c_2)$. Similarly, the sum satisfies

$$a_1a_2[x_1 + x_2] + a_1b_2 + a_2b_1 = a_1c_2 + a_2c_1,$$

so that the sum, $x_1 + x_2$, or $(a_1, b_1, c_1) + (a_2, b_2, c_2)$, is specified by the triple $(a_1a_2, a_1b_2 + a_2b_1, a_1c_2 + a_2c_1)$. Lastly, in the case when the same natural number x satisfies the two equations

$$a_1x + b_1 = c_1$$
and
$$a_2x + b_2 = c_2$$
we know that
$$a_2c_1 + a_1b_2 = a_1c_2 + a_2b_1.$$

So we have the relation

$$(a_1, b_1, c_1) \ R \ (a_2, b_2, c_2) \quad \text{if} \quad a_2c_1 + a_1b_2 = a_1c_2 + a_2b_1.$$

The reader might like to verify that this is a proper equivalence relation: he is warned that the verification of the transitive property is very tedious.

If we preserve all the above properties, then the set of all triples of natural numbers has two operations defined as above and an equivalence relation which can be shown to be compatible with the two operations. It remains to verify that the equivalence classes, with these operations, have all the field properties. In particular, one should verify that

(i) the neutral element for addition is $\{(1, 1, 1)\}$,

(ii) the additive inverse of $\{(a, b, c)\}$ is $\{(a, c, b)\}$,

(iii) the neutral element for multiplication is $\{(1, 1, 2)\}$,

(iv) the multiplicative inverse of $\{(a, b, c)\}$ is given by $\{(x, y, z)\}$, where if $b > c$
$$x = b - c, y = a + 1, z = 1,$$
and if $c > b$
$$x = c - b, y = 1, z = a + 1,$$
and if $b = c$ that no multiplicative inverse exists (and hence that $\{(1, 1, 1)\}$ has no such inverse).

(It should be unnecessary to give the reminder that a, b, c, x, y, z are all *non-zero* natural numbers.)

Further, one should specify the sets of classes of triples which are

(v) isomorphic with the natural numbers under addition and multiplication,

(vi) isomorphic with the integers under addition and multiplication,

(vii) isomorphic with the positive rationals under addition and multiplication,

and finally,

(viii) identify the whole set of classes of triples with the set of directed rationals.

One may also, for amusement, show that the square of any triple is a member of the set specified in (vii).

It is very difficult to imagine circumstances under which the above is an appropriate method of *introducing* directed rationals to a class. By contrast, the work suggested in Chapter 7, page 110 et seq., usually proves entirely acceptable. Rather than make one large intuitive leap from that stage to this, some teachers might prefer to break it into smaller jumps. Having already obtained the group operations in the two sets, positive rationals and integers, it is readily possible to derive definitions of the other operation in each case by regarding multiplication by a natural number as equivalent to repeated addition and requiring that multiplication be distributive over addition.

2. The results of Examples E and G together imply that the equation

$$[[g_1 \times x] + g_1] \times [[g_2 \times x] + {}'_2g] \times \ldots \times [[g_n \times x] + g'_n] = {}_0g,$$

where none of the $g_1, g_2, \ldots, g_n$ are equal to ${}_0g$, has n solutions.

(i) The system of residue classes of the integers modulo 5 is a field, and with the obvious interpretations of $+$ and $\times$, the equation

$$2 \times x \times [x + 1] = 0$$

has two solutions. What are they?

(ii) The system of residue classes modulo 6 is *not* a field. Why not? In this system, how many solutions has

$$2 \times x \times [x + 1] = 0?$$

3. Prove that $\sqrt{2}$ is not a rational number and hence prove that the set of all numbers of the form $a + b\sqrt{2}$, where a and b are rationals, is a field.

NOTE: Pupils often find manipulative difficulties in dividing, say, $3 + 4\sqrt{2}$ by $1 + \sqrt{2}$. This offers an opportunity to point out the superiority of using the multiplicative inverse rather than a division process. (The multiplicative inverse of $1 + \sqrt{2}$ is $\dfrac{1}{1 + \sqrt{2}} = \dfrac{1 - \sqrt{2}}{-1} = -1 + \sqrt{2}$. Hence the process is achieved by multiplying $3 + 4\sqrt{2}$ by $-1 + \sqrt{2}$.)

To construct the set of all real numbers would take us considerably further than we wish to go in this book. For the purpose of the exercises which follow we assume that the reals form a field for addition and multiplication. A field may or may not contain subfields: the definition of a subfield of a field is the obvious one, and the reader is left to formulate it for himself.

4. Show that every subfield of the field of real numbers under addition and multiplication contains the field of rationals.

5. Let S be the set of all ordered pairs of real numbers (a, b). Define

$$(a_1, b_1) + (a_2, b_2) = (a_1 + a_2, b_1 + b_2)$$

and $(a_1, b_1) \times (a_2, b_2) = (a_1a_2 - b_1b_2, a_1b_2 + a_2b_1).$

Prove that this structure is a field. Prove also that the subset for which $b = 0$ is a subfield isomorphic to the real numbers. Further prove that for any pair (a, b),

$$(a, b) = (a, 0) + [(0, 1) \times (b, 0)]$$

and lastly, that $(0, 1) \times (0, 1) = (-1, 0).$

(Cf. Chapter 8, Exercise 14, page 130, where we originally discussed this system among others.)

6. A field is a structure as near as we can get to a double group, with distributivity. An intermediate structure, between a group and a field, is a ring. A *ring* is a set which is a commutative group for one operation (usually called addition) and which is closed under another associative operation (usually called multiplication) distributive over addition. (See the next exercise for some examples of rings.)

A fourteen-year-old boy, asked to define a prime number, replied, 'A natural number n such that the ring of residue classes modulo n is a field'. For *every* natural number $n > 1$, does the set of residue classes modulo n form a ring? Is the boy's definition of a prime adequate?

7. If the multiplication operation in a ring is also commutative, the ring is said to be commutative: otherwise it is called non-commutative. If a ring possesses a neutral element for the multiplication operation, it is said to be a 'ring with unity': the absence of such an element is often emphasized by the phrase 'ring without unity'.

The set of all integers forms a ring for addition and multiplication. What sort of ring? The set of all even integers forms a ring for addition and multiplication. What sort of ring? Does the set of all 2×2 matrices with real elements possess any of the above structures for matrix addition and matrix multiplication? If so, which? Does the result $g \times {}_0g = {}_0g$, which we have proved for a field, hold for all rings? Which of the results, proved for fields in Examples D, E, F and G, hold for rings?

8. Take as elements the subsets of some set E. Use two of the operations of union and intersection and symmetric difference to construct a commutative ring with unity. In how many ways can this be done? Construct examples and Venn diagrams of three subsets A, B and C to show that in this structure the solution of

$$[A \square X] \mathrm{o} B = C$$

may be (a) non-existent, (b) unique, (c) existent, but not unique (where o and $\square$ represent the chosen ring operations of 'addition' and 'multiplication' respectively). On the other hand, if B, C and D are given subsets of E and it is known that

(i) $B \triangle C = D$

and (ii) $X \triangle [D \cap B] = D \cap C$,

what can you deduce about X?

Having introduced a field and obtained some familiarity with the definition, we might now proceed by analogy with our discussion of groups and consider isomorphisms and homorphisms of fields. By now we should hardly need to define these terms, but we will do so in order to establish our notation at the same time. A *homomorphism of a field F* onto a field G is a many-one mapping

β of F onto G which preserves structure, i.e. if $f, f' \in F$, then β is such that

$$\beta : f + f' \rightarrow \beta(f + f') = \beta(f) + \beta(f')$$

and
$$\beta : f \times f' \rightarrow \beta(f \times f') = \beta(f) \times \beta(f'),$$

where we denote the operations in F and G by the same symbols $+$ and $\times$. If β is one-one then it is an *isomorphism*. We discuss homomorphisms and isomorphisms of fields in the following examples. The reader might like to reconsider a more unified treatment of the Exercises 4 of Chapter 9 (pages 137 and 144), instead of our discussion there which separated the additive and multiplicative structures.

Example H. If β is a homomorphism of F onto G show that

(i) $\beta(_0f) = {}_0g$ and $\beta(_1f) = {}_1g$,

where $_0f$, $_1f$ are the additive and multiplicative identities of F and, similarly, $_0g$ and $_1g$ for G,

(ii) if $\beta(f) = g$ then

$$\beta(\tilde{f}) = \tilde{g} \quad \text{and} \quad \beta(\underline{f}) = \underset{\sim}{g} \quad (f \neq {}_0f).$$

Note that these results are in fact already proved for groups since β is a homomorphism of the additive group structure and a homomorphism of the multiplicative 'group' structure. (The inverted commas around 'group' are here used to indicate the absence of a multiplicative inverse for the additive neutral element.)

Example I. When we were working with homomorphic groups we discovered that the kernel of the homomorphism played an essential role. We would expect something similar to happen for fields: the only problem is which set of elements do we take as the kernel; all the elements which map onto $_0g$, or all the elements which map onto $_1g$?

(i) We know that $\beta(_0f) = {}_0g$. Suppose that there is some other element $f \neq {}_0f$ such that $\beta(f) = {}_0g$ and show that this leads to a contradiction. (Hint: use part (ii) of the previous example.)

(ii) If, on the other hand, we consider all those elements which map onto $_1g$ we arrive at no immediate contradiction as in part (i), but we do not achieve a subfield either (and this is equally discouraging, remembering that the kernel of a group homomorphism is always a subgroup). For if $\beta(f) = {}_1g$, then

$$\beta(f + {}_1f) = {}_1g + {}_1g \neq {}_1g$$

and so $f + {}_1f$ does not belong to the set.

So analogous considerations to those we used for groups are thoroughly unpromising—or are they? Perhaps we are looking for something which is not there. Consider the implication of part (i): regarding β as a homomorphic mapping of the additive group structure of F onto the additive group structure of G. The kernel is the identity element only: hence the homomorphism (as applied to the additive structures) must be an isomorphism. *Thus a field has no homomorphic images*: two fields are either isomorphic or structurally unrelated.

Example J. A ring is a much more profitable structure from the point of view of homomorphic images.

(i) If β is a homomorphism of a ring R onto a ring R' show that the elements of R which map onto the identity element of the additive group structure of R' form a subring S of R.

(ii) Show further that this subring S possesses the property that if $s \in S$ and r is any element of R, then $r \times s$ and $s \times r$ both belong to S. (Cf. invariant subgroups of a group.)

(iii) Show that any subring S of a ring R with the property (ii) leads to a homomorphism of R onto another ring R'. (Hint: by analogy with groups define an equivalence relation on R by showing that the cosets of the form $\{r + s\}$ for fixed r and $s \in S$, are a partition of R: this equivalence relation is compatible with addition and multiplication, etc.)

The set of all integers J forms a ring and the set of all multiples of 5 forms a subring S with property (ii). Using the same notation as for groups, what is the factor ring J/S? Notice that the factor ring is, in fact, a field. If, however, we take the set of all multiples of 4 the factor ring is not a field. For a general explanation of this situation see Birkhoff and Mac Lane, *A Survey of Modern Algebra* (Macmillan), Chapter 13.

Example K. Returning to our discussion of Example I we shall try to answer the question implicit in the last sentence. Clearly, we can no longer make direct use of the analogy with groups: we must discover some of the special character of a field due to the interaction of the group and 'group' structures and the distinction of the additive identity. But let us not lose sight of the group ideas: we are trying to classify fields in the same way that we began to classify groups in Chapter 11. There we found that the order of an element of a group had the interesting property that it divided the order of the group (if it was finite), and we used this property from time to time. What happens in a field? In the multiplicative 'group' we are unlikely to get anything new: the multiplicative order of any element will have the same property as before, i.e. if the field is finite of order n, say, the order of the element will be a factor of $n - 1$. But what of the additive order? $_0f$ is our special element. Define the additive order of $f \in F$ to be the least positive integer s such that the sum $f + f + f + \ldots$, containing s terms, is $_0f$. Denote by ^rf the sum of r terms each equal to f, then the following results are a simple consequence of our notation and the distributivity of $\times$ over $+$.

$$[^rf] \times f' = f \times [^rf'] = {}^r[f \times f']$$

Hence show that if s is the additive order of f it is also the additive order of any other element $f' \in F$, where neither f nor f' is $_0f$ (remember Example E.) It follows that all elements of a field other than $_0f$ have the same additive order which is called the *characteristic* of the field.

(i) Show that the characteristic, s, of a field is either infinite or a prime number. (Hint: if s is finite but not prime suppose $s = ab$, then

$$_1^sf = {}_1^{ab}f = {}_1^af \times {}_1^bf$$

(where $_1f$ is the multiplicative identity) and use Example E.)

(ii) Show that if the characteristic is a prime integer r that $_1f$ generates an additive subgroup G of the additive structure of F and that G is a subfield of F isomorphic to the field of residue classes of integers modulo r. (One has to show that $^a_1f \longrightarrow \{a\}$ is an isomorphism.)

(iii) We extend our notation slightly before considering the corresponding result for a field with infinite characteristic. Let a be any integer, then we *define*

$$^af = {}^af, \text{ if } a > 0, \, ^af = -{}^a\tilde{f}, \text{ if } a < 0, \, ^af = {}_0f, \text{ if } a = 0.$$

Further we shall denote the multiplicative inverse of ^af by $^a\underset{\sim}{f}, a \neq 0$.

If F is a field with infinite characteristic show that the elements of the form $^a_1f \times {}^b_1\underset{\sim}{f}, b \neq 0$, form a subfield isomorphic with the field of rational numbers.

(Hint: show that $^a_1f \times {}^b_1\underset{\sim}{f} \longrightarrow \dfrac{a}{b}$ is an isomorphism. Notice that if we proceed

by analogy with (ii) above and form the additive subgroup generated by $_1f$ then we do not get a subfield. What do we get? Does it help if we form the additive group generated by $_1f$ and $_1\tilde{f}$?)

Thus we see that every field contains a subfield isomorphic to the rationals or to the residue classes to some modulus. It would seem that at this stage we could justifiably simplify our notation and write

$$_0f = 0, \, _1f = 1, \, ^af = af, \, \tilde{f} = -f, \text{ etc.}$$

We are now in a position where the unjustified suggestiveness of the notation does not provide the results, but the results suggest the notation. Since we shall not pursue the technical details we shall not modify our notation.

It is not difficult to show that if r is the characteristic of any finite field, that F has r^n elements for some integer n. Further, although perhaps not quite so elementary, it can be shown that for any prime r and any integer $n > 0$ there exists a field with r^n elements. The reader who would like to continue these investigations, which have considerable consequences, should consult the reference at the end of Example J. There it is shown that any two finite fields of the same order are isomorphic, which finally answers the classification problem for finite fields. We choose, however, to put our feet back firmly on the ground and consider the more elementary notions of other structures.

Clearly a field is not the most general structure of which we have examples. Consider, for instance, the additive group M of all 2×2 matrices with real elements together with the field R of real numbers (under addition and multiplication), where the interaction between the two sets is defined as scalar multiplication, i.e. if

$k \in R$ and $\begin{pmatrix} a & b \\ c & d \end{pmatrix} = A \in M$, then kA is defined as $\begin{pmatrix} ka & kb \\ kc & kd \end{pmatrix}$. (Note

that we have chosen to ignore at least one further operation in M which gives it ring structure.) The reader should bear this example in mind and reformulate the abstract concepts in the following paragraphs in terms of it.

Group structure and field structure are 'practical' in the sense that they guarantee the explicit solution of particular types of problem (specifically $a \circ x = b$ and $[a \circ x] \,\square\, b = c$ respectively). They also arise frequently in practice, largely for this very reason. The next structure we have selected to discuss is a vector space, which may be regarded as a combination of a group and a field. Vector space structure offers no further guarantees as to solvability in the elementary sense: its importance rests, in the first place, on its extremely wide occurrence, and the economy of effort with which results true for the abstract structure may be applied to particular instances. At a more sophisticated level vector spaces acquire an ever-increasing importance.

We define a vector space as a set V whose elements form a commutative group for an operation represented by $\circ$, together with a set F whose elements form a field for the operations which we shall denote by $+$ and $\times$ as usual, with the additional requirements that

(i) any element $v \in V$ can be combined with any element $f \in F$ by a further operation $\square$ so that for all v and f, $f \,\square\, v \in V$,

(ii) $[f + f'] \,\square\, v = [f \,\square\, v] \circ [f' \,\square\, v]$,

(iii) $f \,\square\, [v \circ v'] = [f \,\square\, v] \circ [f \,\square\, v']$,

(iv) $f \,\square\, [f' \,\square\, v] = [f \times f'] \,\square\, v$,

(v) $_1f \,\square\, v = v$,

where $_1f$ is the multiplicative neutral element of F and f, f' are any elements of F and v, v' any elements of V. When these conditions are met V is said to be a *vector space over the field F*. We reserve v_0 for the neutral element in the group structure of V, $_0f$ for the additive neutral element of F, $_1f$ for the multiplicative neutral element of F and $\tilde{f}$ and $\bar{f}$ for the additive and multiplicative inverses of f respectively. The reader who wishes to do so, may well use the simplified notation of the previous page.

The definition is excessively complicated and the reader should try to obtain some appreciation of the details by considering the significance of each condition in terms of our example above. For instance, that our example satisfies the second condition arises from the fact that multiplication is distributive over addition in the field of real numbers. In fact, this condition and the third can be regarded as distributive conditions, although technically, since we change the operation $+$ to o in (ii) this stretches the meaning of distributivity considerably. Similarly, condition (i) corresponds to what we would call a closure condition, (iv) to an associative condition and (v) to the existence of an identity.

We should also remark that, as usual, we ought to motivate the choice of defining conditions: given enough space we might possibly do this although it seems doubtful whether it can be done as effectively as, for instance, for groups. It is not, in general, sufficient to say that this is what mathematicians call a vector space: given a sophisticated enough audience they might well be willing to wait to see what we can get out of our definition, but it is doubtful whether this is pedagogically sound even then. Since this is effectively a summary chapter we shall be satisfied with pointing out the omission.

Example L. Prove the following consequences of our definition.

(a) $_0f \square v = v_0$, for all v. (Hint: use (ii) with $f = f' = {_0}f$.)

(b) $f \square v_0 = v_0$, for all f. (Hint: use (iii).)

(c) $v \text{ o } [_1\tilde{f} \square v] = v_0$, for all v. (Hint: use (ii), with $f = {_1}f$ and $f' = {_1}\tilde{f}$, and (a).)

(d) $[f \square v] \text{ o } [\tilde{f} \square v] = v_0$, for all f and v.

Example M. Defining a *subspace* of V as a subset of V which is a vector space over F for the same operation o as V, prove that a subset S is a subspace if and only if

$$[s' \text{ o } s] \in S, \text{ for all } s', s \text{ in } S,$$

and

$$[f \square s] \in S, \text{ for all } s \text{ in } S \text{ and all } f \text{ in } F.$$

Example N. If $v_1, v_2, v_3, \ldots, v_n$ are any fixed members of V, prove that the set of all elements of the form

$$[f_1 \square v_1] \text{ o } [f_2 \square v_2] \text{ o } \ldots \text{ o } [f_n \square v_n],$$

where the $f_1, f_2, \ldots, f_n$ take all values in F, is a subspace of V.

Elements of this form are called *linear combinations* of $v_1, v_2, \ldots, v_n$, and the subspace which all linear combinations of $v_1, v_2, \ldots, v_n$ generate is said to be *spanned* by $v_1, v_2, \ldots, v_n$.

If $v = (f_1 \square v_1) \text{ o } \ldots \text{ o } [f_n \square v_n]$ what is $[\tilde{f}_1 \square v_1] \text{ o } \ldots \text{ o } [\tilde{f}_n \square v_n]$? (Hint: it might be advisable to start with one or two terms on the right-hand side and then to consider the general case.)

Exercises

1. Which of the following structures are vector spaces? In the case of structures which are vector spaces specify the elements v_0, $_0f$ and $_1f$.

(a) V_a = set of all localized vectors (see Chapter 3, page 48) in a plane, combined by vector addition (see Chapter 9, Exercise 6, page 147), F = set of real numbers under addition and multiplication, $f \square v$ = scalar multiple of v by f (ibid).

(b) V_b = set of all free vectors in a plane, combination of vectors and F and $f \square v$ as in (a).

(c) V_c = subset of V_b consisting of all free vectors whose direction is parallel to a fixed straight line, combination of vectors and F and $f \square v$ as in (b).

(d) V_d = set of all triples of real numbers (x, y, z), combined by

$$(x, y, z) \circ (x', y', z') = (x + x', y + y', z + z').$$

F = set of real numbers under addition and multiplication,

$$f \square (x, y, z) = (fx, fy, fz).$$

(e) V_e = set of all n-tuples (for fixed n) of real numbers combined by analogy with (d). F = set of real numbers under addition and multiplication, $f \square v$ defined by analogy with (d).

(f) V_f = subset of V_e consisting of all n-tuples of integers combined as in (e), F and $\square$ as in (e).

(g) V_g = set of all triples of symbols 0 and 1 (so that typical members of V_g are $(0, 1, 0)$, $(1, 1, 0)$, $(0, 0, 1)$, etc.), combined by addition of corresponding members modulo 2, e.g. $(0, 1, 0) \circ (1, 1, 0) = (1, 0, 0)$. F is the set $(0, 1)$ with addition and multiplication modulo 2, $f \square v$ corresponding to multiplication modulo 2 of each member of v by f.

(h) V_h = set of all n-tuples (for fixed n) of symbols 0 and 1: otherwise defined by analogy with (g).

(i) V_i = set of all real valued functions of x which are defined on $0 \leqslant x \leqslant 1$. Two members of V_i are combined by algebraic addition, i.e. if $v, v' \in V_i$ then $v \circ v' : x \longrightarrow v(x) + v''(x)$. F is the set of real numbers under addition and multiplication, and if $f \in F$ and $v \in V_i$ then $f \square v$ is defined to be the function v' which is such that $v'(x) = f.v(x)$.

(j) V_j = subset of V_i consisting of all continuous functions, F and $\square$ as in (i).

(k) V_k = set of all polynomials of degree three with real coefficients, combination being algebraic addition. F = set of real numbers under addition and multiplication, and if

$$v = ax^3 + bx^2 + cx + d, f \square v = fax^3 + fbx^2 + fcx + fd.$$

(l) V_l = set of all polynomials of degree not more than five. Otherwise as in (k).

(m) V_m = subset of V_i consisting of all functions whose images are positive. Otherwise as in (i).

There are many other examples of vector spaces, e.g. sets of matrices as on page 238; we leave the reader to find or make up more if he wishes.

2. If pupils named A, B, C, D, E take examinations in subjects called a, b, c, . . ., and obtain non-negative percentage marks as in the table below

	a	b	c	.	.	.
A	x_{Aa}	x_{Ab}	x_{Ac}	.	.	.
B	x_{Ba}	x_{Bb}	x_{Bc}	.	.	.
C	.	.	.	.	.	.
D	.	.	.	.	.	.
E	x_{Ea}	x_{Eb}	x_{Ec}	.	.	.

then the columns may be 'added' so that $a \circ b = x_{Aa} + x_{Ab}$

$$x_{Ba} + x_{Bb}$$
$$.\quad .\quad .$$
$$.\quad .\quad .$$
$$x_{Ea} + x_{Eb}.$$

We take the set of all possible columns as V and take F as the set of real numbers under addition and multiplication, and allow that subjects may be 'weighted' by any real numbers, so that, for example, $f \square a = f \times x_{Aa}$

$$f \times x_{Ba}$$
$$.\quad .\quad .$$
$$.\quad .\quad .$$
$$f \times x_{Ea}.$$

The structure is not a vector space. Why not?

The candidates' marks in each subject are converted by the following mapping

$$x_{Rs} \longrightarrow \frac{x_{Rs} - \bar{x}_s}{\sigma_s},$$

where $\bar{x}_s$ is the mean of all the candidates' marks in the subject s and σ_s is the standard deviation of the marks in the subject s. Does the corresponding structure, with F and weighting as before, form a vector space?

3. The set of elements which span a given space is not unique. For instance, the space V_k in Exercise 1 is spanned by the set of four polynomials $(1, x, x^2, x^3)$. It is also spanned by the set $(4, x - 4, 2x^3 + x^2, 2x^3)$, for any polynomial of degree three, $ax^3 + bx^2 + cx + d$, where a, b, c, d are real numbers, can be expressed as

$$\left(\frac{a}{2} - b\right)2x^3 + b[2x^3 + x^2] + c[x - 4] + \left(c + \frac{d}{4}\right)4.$$

Find a set of five polynomials which span the space. Is it possible to find a set of fewer than four polynomials which span this space?

4. Free vectors in three dimensional space, combined by vector addition, with F as the field of real numbers and $\square$ as scalar multiplication of a vector by a real number, is spanned by the set of three vectors represented by the

position vectors of the points $(1, 0, 0)$, $(0, 1, 0)$, $(0, 0, 1)$. Is it true that the same space is spanned by *any* set of three different vectors? If not, give an example of a set of three different vectors which do not span the space. In geometrical terms, what space is spanned by the vectors represented by the position vectors of the two points $(0, 2, 1)$ and $(1, 3, 2)$? In geometrical terms, what space is spanned by the vectors represented by the position vectors of the two points $(0, 2, 1)$ and $(0, 4, 2)$? Can the last space be spanned by less than two vectors?

If $S = (v_1, v_2, \ldots, v_n)$ is a subset of a vector space V over a field F and if elements of $F, f_1, f_2, \ldots, f_n$, can be found, not all of which are equal to $_0f$, so that

$$[f_1 \square v_1] \circ [f_2 \square v_2] \circ \ldots \circ [f_n \square v_n] = v_0 . \qquad . \quad (1)$$

then the vectors $v_1, v_2, \ldots, v_n$ are said to be *linearly dependent*. If the only set of elements of F satisfying equation (1) is $f_1 = f_2 = \ldots = f_n = _0f$, then the vectors of S are said to be *linearly independent*.

Example O. Prove that a set of elements of a vector space is linearly dependent if, and only if, one of them can be expressed as a linear combination of the others.

Example P. Let v be a linear combination of the linearly independent set $(v_1, v_2, \ldots, v_n)$, so that for some $f_1, f_2, \ldots, f_n$

$$v = [f_1 \square v_1] \circ [f_2 \square v_2] \circ \ldots \circ [f_n \square v_n].$$

Prove that there is no other linear combination of these v_i $(i = 1, 2, \ldots, n)$ which is equal to v. (Hint: assume that there is, and obtain a contradiction; the last part of Example N can be used for this.) Prove also that if, instead, the set of v_i $(i = 1, 2, \ldots, n)$ are linearly dependent, then v can be expressed in at least two different ways as a linear combination of the v_i.

Example Q. Let $(v_1, v_2, \ldots, v_n)$ be a set of n elements spanning a space S. Prove that if, from the space S, a set of more than n elements is chosen, then this set is linearly dependent.

The least number of elements which span a space S is called the *dimension* of S, so that this example shows that the dimension of S is less than or equal to n. Further, any set of linearly independent elements which span S is called a *basis* for S, and Example P shows that any vector $v \in S$ can be expressed as a unique linear combination of the elements of a basis.

Show further, that if the v_i are linearly dependent then S is spanned by less than n vectors. Finally, prove that if V is a vector space of dimension n that any set of n linearly independent elements of V is a basis for V.

Example R. Consider the matrix $A = \begin{pmatrix} a_{11} & a_{12} & a_{13} \cdot & & \cdot & a_{1n} \\ a_{21} & a_{22} & a_{23} \cdot & & \cdot & a_{2n} \\ \cdot & \cdot & \cdot & \cdot & \cdot & \cdot \\ \cdot & \cdot & \cdot & \cdot & \cdot & \cdot \\ a_{m1} & a_{m2} & a_{m3} & \cdot & \cdot & a_{mn} \end{pmatrix}$

where the elements are real numbers. Regard each column as an element $v_1, v_2, \ldots, v_n$ of a vector space V over the field F of real numbers, so that the space is similar to V_e of Exercise 1 on page 241. Then the number of linearly independent columns of A is the dimension of the space spanned by the v_i $(i = 1, 2, \ldots, n)$. This quantity is of considerable importance in matrix theory and its applications (e.g. the theory of linear equations) and is called the *rank* of A.

(a) What is the rank of a column matrix (i.e. an $m \times 1$ matrix) not all of whose elements are 0?

(b) What is the rank of a row (i.e. a $1 \times n$ matrix) not all of whose elements are 0?

(c) What is the rank of $\begin{pmatrix} 1 & 0 \\ 0 & 1 \end{pmatrix}$? of $\begin{pmatrix} 1 & 0 & 0 \\ 0 & 1 & 0 \\ 0 & 0 & 1 \end{pmatrix}$?

(d) What is the rank of any invertible 2×2 matrix? Is any matrix of rank 2 necessarily 2×2 and invertible?

(e) What is the highest possible rank of a matrix with m rows and n columns, $m \geqslant n$?

(f) What is the highest possible rank of an $m \times n$ matrix?

Following on from Example Q it is not far to prove that every finite dimensional vector space V over a field F is isomorphic to a unique vector space which is the set of n-tuples of F, where n is the dimension of V. (We have not defined the term 'isomorphism' for a vector space but it is not difficult to imagine what it will be.) We are really then only at the beginning of a vast and intriguing theory with many applications. For instance, we could examine a subspace of a vector space with a view to defining an equivalence relation in the space compatible with the operations, and so leading on to a factor vector space. (In fact, every subspace of a vector space leads to such an equivalence relation and, hence, a factor space. This has led to the remark that the vector space structure is 'simpler' than group structure, but notice that this can be regarded as purely a matter of special definition: we are using an Abelian group in our structure and any subgroup of an Abelian group is invariant.) Beside the extension of the theory in this direction there are many more extensions, e.g. linear operators, dual spaces, Euclidean spaces, etc. Also, we can connect up with the geometrical discussions of the previous chapter by considering the effect of a change of coordinate system (which corresponds to a change of basis in the vector space) on the matrices which represent the transformations. For the interested reader, Birkhoff and Mac Lane (op. cit.) gives much more information.

What then? Are we anywhere near the end? Obviously not: consider the example on page 238 with which we began our note on vector spaces; we ignored another obvious combination operation. We are led on to algebras: an *algebra* is roughly a vector space and a ring structure combined. And not only can we go onwards, we can return to the very beginning and weaken the group conditions to obtain loops, groupoids, semigroups, etc. Whether or not one cares to examine all these structures individually is very much a matter of taste and inclination: the importance lies in the approach to mathematics. As the amount of knowledge increases and as the applications of mathematics grow in number and the complexity and quantity of material needed gets steadily greater, so the need to systematize our thought becomes more and more acute. The structural examination of mathematics not only helps in that direction, but it also seems to have educational value.

*   *   *   *   *

In this final section we continue the note on topological groups begun at the end of Chapter 12. Probably the most important point about a topological group is that many of the properties of the space can be discovered by examining the open sets containing the identity, for there is always a homeomorphism that maps the identity into any other point. It is this aspect of a topological group that we shall try to bring out in the following examples.

Example R. Consider the following two mappings in a topological group:

(i) *left translation* by a fixed element $g_1 \in G$ defined by

$$g \longrightarrow g_1 \circ g$$

for all $g \in G$. We denote this mapping by L_{g_1};

(ii) *right translation* by a fixed element $g_1 \in G$ defined by

$$g \longrightarrow g \circ g_1$$

for all $g \in G$. We denote this mapping by R_{g_1}.

Show that both L_{g_1} and R_{g_1} are homeomorphisms of $(G, T : G)$ onto itself. This result implies that given any two elements $g, g' \in G$ there exists a homeomorphism under which g is mapped onto g', e.g. $L_{[g' \circ \tilde{g}]}(g) = g'$. A topological space (which need not necessarily be a topological group) is called *homogeneous* if given any two points, a homeomorphism exists which maps one point onto the other.

Example S. Show that $L_g = i \,\square\, R_{\tilde{g}} \,\square\, i$ where i is the mapping defined at the end of Chapter 12, page 226 and $\square$ denotes combination of mappings.

Let $(A, T: A)$ and $(B, T: B)$ be two topological spaces and let f be a many-one mapping of A to B. Then we shall say that f is *continuous at a point* $a \in A$ if for every open set $U \in T: B$ which contains $f(a)$, $\tilde{f}(U) \in T: A$. It is clear that a continuous function of $(A, T: A)$ to $(B, T: B)$ is continuous at every point of A, and conversely, that if a function of $(A, T: A)$ to $(B, T: B)$ is continuous at every point of A it is a continuous mapping of $(A, T: A)$ to $(B, T: B)$. An open set of $T: A$ containing a point a we shall call an *open neighbourhood* in $T: A$ of a.

Example T. Let $(G, o, T: G)$ be a topological group and let U in $T: G$ be an open neighbourhood of the identity e. Further, if $g \in G$, let $g \text{ o } U$ be the set of all elements of the form $g \text{ o } g'$ for all $g' \in U$. Show that $g \text{ o } U$ is an open neighbourhood in $T: G$ of g. (Hint: use the result of Example R.) Conversely, if U is an open neighbourhood in $T: G$ of a point $g \in G$ then $\tilde{g} \text{ o } U$ is an open neighbourhood in $T: G$ of e.

Example U. Let (G, o) be a group with a topology $T: G$. Then we can show that $(G, T: G)^*$ is a topological group if and only if

(i) the left and right translations L_g and $R_{g'}$, $g, g' \in G$, are continuous mappings of $(G, T: G)$ onto itself;

(ii) the mapping $c : (g, g') \longrightarrow g \text{ o } g'$ is a continuous mapping of $(G \bigtriangledown G, T: G \bigtriangledown G)$ onto $(G, T: G)$ at the point $(e, e) \in G \bigtriangledown G$;

(iii) the mapping $i : g \longrightarrow \tilde{g}$ is a continuous mapping of $(G, T: G)$ onto itself at the point $e \in G$.

The demonstration of one half of the proposition is fairly clear: if $(G, T: G)$ is a topological group, then (i), (ii) and (iii) follow from the definition of such a structure and Example R. It remains to prove that these three conditions ensure that $(G, T: G)$ is a topological group, i.e. that the mapping c is continuous at any point $(g_1, g_1') \in G \bigtriangledown G$ and that the mapping i is continuous at any point $g \in G$. We leave this to the reader. (Hint: if (g_1, g_1') is any point of $G \bigtriangledown G$ let $g = g_1 \text{ o } u$ and $g' = v \text{ o } g_1'$, where $u, v \in G$, and show, using (i), that

$$(g, g') \longrightarrow (\tilde{g_1} \text{ o } g, g' \text{ o } \tilde{g_1'}) = (u, v)$$

is a continuous mapping of $(G \bigtriangledown G, T: G \bigtriangledown G)$ onto itself, and note that if (g, g') belongs to an open neighbourhood in $T: G \bigtriangledown G$ of (g_1, g_1') then (u, v) belongs to an open neighbourhood in $T: G \bigtriangledown G$ of (e, e). Then consider the mapping c at (g_1, g_1') decomposed in the form

$$(g, g') \longrightarrow (u, v) \longrightarrow u \text{ o } v \longrightarrow [g_1 \text{ o } u] \text{ o } [v \text{ o } g_1'] = g \text{ o } g'.$$

A similar, but simpler analysis will prove the second result as well.)

* Strictly, we should write '$(G, o, T: G)$ is a topological group $\dots$,'

These last two examples begin to show how much of the topology of a topological group is determined by the open neighbourhoods of the identity, and more and stronger results of this nature can be proved. Instead we turn to a different aspect of topological groups which fits in better with the development of the group theory in the earlier chapters of this book.

Example V. Let H be a subgroup of a group G. Show that if $(G, T: G)$ is a topological group then $(H, T: H)$ is also a topological group, where $T: H$ is the subset topology for H considered as a subset of G.

Example W. A many-one mapping f of a topological group $(G, o, T: G)$ onto a topological group $(G', \Box, T: G')$ is a *continuous homomorphism* if it is a continuous mapping of the topological structure of G onto the topological structure of G', and if it is a homomorphism of the group structure of G onto the group structure of G'. The mapping f will be a *continuous isomorphism* if it is one-one. Verify that L_g and R_g are not continuous isomorphisms of $(G, T: G)$ onto itself.

An example of a topological isomorphism of a topological group $(G, T: G)$ onto itself is the mapping $g \longrightarrow \tilde{g}_1 \, o \, g \, o \, g_1$, where g_1 is a fixed element of G. Verify this result: note that the mapping can be written $g \longrightarrow R_{g_1} \Box L_{\tilde{g}_1} (g)$, (where $\Box$ denotes combination of mappings).

Example X. Let H be an invariant subgroup of a group G. Then if $(G, T: G)$ is a topological group, $(H, T: H)$ is an invariant topological subgroup, where $T: H$ is subset topology. We have defined the factor group G/H and the topology $T: G/H$ induced by $T: G$ onto the space G/H of equivalence classes of G. If H is open in $T: G$ show that $T: G/H$ is the discrete topology. (Hint: use Example T.) It follows that $(G/H, T: G/H)$ is a topological group. The natural mapping f of G onto G/H defined by $f: g \longrightarrow gH$ is, of course, a continuous homomorphism.

Now consider the case when H is an invariant subgroup but not necessarily open in $T: G$. (It is, in fact, still the case that $(G/H, T: G/H)$ is a topological group, but the proof is somewhat more complicated.)

Just to emphasize our remarks on page 245 that we are never more than just beginning, we suggest the following final example.

Example Y. Define a topological field and give an example of such a structure. What results can you deduce from your definition?

We would also like to suggest that it might be a good idea for the reader to go back now and see what he can make of the remarks about 'structure' in Chapter 1.

INDEX

Abelian group 91
Addition of cardinal numbers 70
of matrices 137
of vectors 147
Affine geometry 215
Algebra 245
, abstract 19
Alternating group 215
Analytic function 91
Associativity 23, 90

Base 65
Basis 243
Bi-continuous mapping 97
Bilinear mapping 108, 152
Binary operation 37
as a mapping 60
Bi-uniform mapping 107
Brackets, use of 17
Braid 114 et seq.

Cancellation 28, 92
Cardinal numbers 67
, addition of 70
, finite 76
, infinite 76
, multiplication of 81
Cartesian product 37
Cayley's Theorem 194
Centre of a group 190
Character 191
Characteristic of a field 237
Closure 90
Column vector 124, 139
Commutative group 91
ring 235
Commutativity 22
Compatible 49
Complex numbers 130, 137, 144, 187
Congruence relation 45
Conjugacy classes 192
Conjugate elements 188
subgroups 188
Continuity 95

Continuous deformation 154
homomorphism 247
isomorphism 247
mapping 63
Coordinate spaces 133
vectors 212
Coset, left 167
, right 168
Countably infinite 76
Curve 60, 135, 153
Cyclic group 182

Desargues's Theorem 222
Determinant 143
Dihedral group of order 8 184
Dilatation 213
Dilative reflection 213
rotation 213
Dimension of a vector space 243
Dimensions, method of 94
Direct isometries, group of 204
product 37
Directed number 113
Discrete topology 83
Displacements, combination of 34
, group of 204
Distributive from the left 24
from the right 24
Domain 54
Duality, principle of 223
Dual numbers 138, 145
spaces 244

Empty set 24
Equals sign 20
Equivalence class 40
relation 21, 40 et seq.
relation as a set of ordered
pairs 45
, topological 95, 97
Erlanger Programme 201
Euclidean geometry 24
spaces 244

Factor group 167
ring 237
vector space 244
Faithful representation 191
Field 230 et seq.
Finite cardinal number 76
projective geometries 224
Free vector 48
Function 55, 56
, single-valued 55
Fundamental group of a sphere 196
group of a torus 197
homotopy group 173, 179
theorem of arithmetic 34

Generating elements for the group of braids of order n 116
Geometry 212
(for specific geometries see the appropriate parts of the index)
Graph of a mapping 60
Gravitation, Newton's law of 94
Group, Abelian 91
, commutative 91
, cyclic 182
, definition of 88, 90, 93
, finite 88
, infinite 88
(for specific groups see the appropriate parts of the index)
Groupoids 245
Groups, two of order four 122, 183
, two of order six 122, 183

Highest common factor 33
Homeomorphic mapping 97
Homeomorphism 97
Homeomorphisms, group of 99
Homogeneous coordinates 46, 219
space 245
Homomorphic image 61
mapping 60
Homomorphism 60
of fields 235
of groups 158 et seq.
Homotopic 174

Homotopy classes 176
function 177
group 173

Identification topology 52
Identity element 87
Image 53
Inclusion signs, definition of 21
Index 172
Indiscrete topology 97
Induced topology 39, 52
Inequality, solution set of 31
Infinite cardinal number 76
Inner product 50, 149
Integers, derivation of 112
Intersection 24
Interval 64
Invariance 203
Invariant point of a transformation 202
subgroup 171
, topological 98
Inverse 90
element 87
image 54
mapping 54
matrix 143
Isometries, direct 204
, group of 204
, indirect 205
Isometry 204
Isomorphic 60
mapping 60
Isomorphism 60
Isomorphisms of fields 236
of groups 119 et seq.
of vector spaces 244

Kernel 160
Klein, F. 9, 201

Lagrange's Theorem 172
Leading diagonal 191
Left cosets 167
identity 89
inverse 89
translation 245
Line at infinity 221
coordinates 223

Linear combination 240
  dependence 243
  independence 243
  mapping 108
  operators 244
  programming 33
Localized vector 48
Logarithms 62
Loops 245
Lowest common multiple 33

Many-one mapping 54
Mapping 53 et seq.
  as a set of ordered pairs 57
  , bi-continuous 97
  , bilinear 108
  , bi-uniform 107
  , constant 59
  , continuous 63
  , graph of 60
  , into 53
  , inverse 54
  , linear 108
  , many-one 54
  , natural 61
  , one-many 54
  , one-one 55
  , onto 53
Mappings, combination of 59
Mathematics, modern 18
Matrices 123, 136 et seq.
  , equality of 128, 136
Matrix addition 137
  , definition of 136
  multiplication 140
  , multiplicative inverse of 143
  , orthogonal 151
  representation of a group 191
  , scalar multiplication of 149
  , transpose of 151
  , unit 151
Metric 96, 205
Möbius transformation 108
de Moivre's Theorem 47
Multiplication of cardinal numbers 81

Natural mapping 61
  numbers 71

Natural
  topology for the real line 64
  topology for the real plane 133
Necessary and sufficient condi-
  tions 27
Neutral element 87, 90
Normal subgroup 171
Null set 24

One-many mapping 54
One-one correspondence 55
  mapping 55
Open neighbourhood 246
  set 38, 96
Order of a group 172
  of an element 182
Ordered n-tuples 37
  pair 36
  triple 37
Ordering 44
Orthogonal group of 2×2
  matrices 151
  matrix 151

Parallelism 215
Partial fractions 146
Partition 42
Path 174
Path-connected 198
Permutations 193
  , even 195
  , group of 194
  , odd 195
Point at infinity 106, 150
  coordinates 223
Polynomial, group of 196
  , symmetric 196
Position vector 48
Positive rationals, derivation of 110
Power set 24
Principal value 47
Product space 134
  topology 134
Projections 133
Projective group 218
  plane 46, 219

Quaternions 138, 145, 187

Range   54
Rank   244
Rational numbers as a count-
      ably infinite set   78
   numbers, derivation of   232
Real numbers   234
   numbers as a non-countable
      set   80
Reflection   206 et seq.
   , matrix representation of   125
Reflexive property   20
Representation of a group   191, 195
Residue class   46
Riemann surface   55
Right coset   168
   identity   89
   inverse   89
   translation   245
Ring   235 et seq.
   , commutative   235
   with unity   235
Rotation   203 et seq.
   matrix representation of   125

Scalar   multiplication   of   a
      matrix   149
   multiplication of a vector   147
   product   50
Self-conjugate elements   188
Semigroups   245
Sense   205
Set   18 et seq.
   notation   31
   , open   38
   , permissible   33
Shear translation   216
Similarity, direct   213
   group   185, 212
   , indirect   213
Simple group   196
   pendulum   94
Slide-rule   62, 163
Spanned   240
Spiral similarity   213
Spur   191
Structure   10, 93, 247
Sub-base   132
Subfield   234
Subgroup   104

Subgroup, conjugate   188
   , invariant   171
   , normal   171
   , self-conjugate   171
Subring   237
Subset   19
   , improper   22, 24
   , proper   21
   topology   82
Subspace of a vector space   240
Subtraction   113
Sufficient conditions   27
Summation of cardinal num-
      bers   70
Symmetric difference   28
   group of degree n 194
   polynomial   196
   property   20, 85
Symmetry   102
   group   201, 206
   group of equilateral triangle   103

Topological equivalence   95, 97
   field   247
   group   226
   invariant   98
   isomorphism   247
   space   38, 96
Topology   38
   , discrete   83
   for the real line   64
   for three-dimensional space   95
   , indiscrete   97
   , induced   39, 50
   , natural   64, 133
   , product   135
   , subset   82
Torus   98
Trace   191
Transform   124
Transformation   125
Transitive property   20
Translation   204 et seq.
Transpose   151

Union   22
Unit matrix   151
Universal set   40

Vanishing line	221	Vectors, inner product of	50, 149
Vector	48	, scalar product of	50
, free	48	Venn diagrams	25
, localized	48	Venn, J.	25
, multiplication of by a scalar	147		
, position	48	Work	50
space	239		
, zero	148, 149		
Vectors, addition of	147	Zero vector	148, 149